Date Due

8 29 '62		
10 6. '62		
4 26 '63		
12 15 '65		
4 5 '66		

PRINTED | IN U. S. A.

ELECTRONICS
FOR SPECTROSCOPISTS

SCHWARZ MEMORIAL VOLUME

ELECTRONICS
FOR
SPECTROSCOPISTS

BY MEMBERS OF THE PHOTOELECTRIC
SPECTROMETRY GROUP AND OF THE ELECTRONICS
DEPARTMENT OF SOUTHAMPTON UNIVERSITY

edited by

C. G. Cannon

B.Sc., F.Inst. P.

19 60

INTERSCIENCE PUBLISHERS INC.

NEW YORK

PRINTED IN GREAT BRITAIN

TO THE MEMORY

OF

ERNST SCHWARZ

THIS BOOK IS DEDICATED BY

THE PHOTOELECTRIC SPECTROMETRY GROUP

PREFACE

By H. W. Thompson, Ph.D. (Berl.), M.A., D.Sc., F.R.S.

Fellow of St John's College, Oxford, and University Reader in Infra-red Spectroscopy

I CAN claim to belong to that rapidly dwindling band of spectroscopists who once carried out infra-red measurements with moving-magnet galvanometers and spent many hours taking point-by-point readings. Some of the instruments we used then now have a place in our collection of the old, the honoured, and the obsolete.

Without the newer techniques our knowledge of atomic and molecular energy levels and their implications in physics and chemistry would not have been acquired so quickly. Though photography of the visible and the ultra-violet has its advantages, more modern methods provide the speed and quantitative accuracy that are essential for determining radiation intensity. Here, and in infra-red work too, the newer detectors require robust recording systems and different methods of voltage or current amplification. With the adoption of these new methods we have passed into the hands of the electronics technician.

The older spectroscopists amongst us may still question occasionally whether the construction and use of electronic equipment is an art or a science, but however we may feel about this equipment we cannot avoid using it. For this reason alone, the book is welcome. It presents a background framework for those who are concerned with alternating-current theory, and amplifiers of different kinds. It explains the construction of power supplies and the salient principles of negative feedback, and includes a clear account of the over-riding property—noise. Better still, it gives us some tips about fault finding when things go wrong. There are also interesting accounts of semiconducting detectors, photoelectric devices and appropriate optical instruments.

We should thank the contributors for this co-operative effort which will be useful to the host of workers now involved in spectroscopy of one kind or another, and to many others too.

EDITOR'S PREFACE

DURING recent years physicists and chemists have been making an ever increasing use of techniques requiring electronic equipment. This development is particularly marked in the spectroscopic fields where rapid direct recording of results is required. The operator of a modern infrared spectrometer, sitting comfortably before a neat control panel, may find it hard to realize that only fifteen to twenty years ago the spectra his instruments record in fifteen minutes were obtained by many hours of laborious hand plotting of galvanometer deflections.

These advances in instrumentation have brought in their train much increased servicing to keep the spectrometers in efficient operation. When the recorder pen goes 'dead' and the operator looks behind his neat control panel he is faced with a frightening array of valves and other components, the faulty one of which must be located and replaced. How many of us have not felt in such a situation the inadequacy of our knowledge of modern electronics? We may also want to design our own electronic 'gadgets' for research problems. To meet this need for some knowledge of the electronic techniques used in spectroscopy, the Photoelectric Spectrometry Group in collaboration with the staff of the Electronics Department of Southampton University, led by Prof. E. E. Zepler, organized two summer schools in 1949 and 1950. Guest speakers were also invited to lecture on specialized topics. The Group received so many requests for copies of the summer school course that they decided to publish the proceedings in permanent form, and decided that such a book would be a fitting memorial to the late Ernst Schwarz.

The Group is indebted to Dr G. J. Morris for assistance in reading the original manuscripts, to Mr C. T. Rivington for further editing and preparing the typescripts for the printers, to Mr R. Elam for proof reading chapter nine, and to Mr N. J. Goodman and Mr D. B. Tomlinson at Hilger and Watts Ltd for their helpful co-operation in the final publication.

We should like to thank those editors who have given us permission to reproduce figures from their publications.

Research Department   C. G. Cannon
British Nylon Spinners Ltd
Pontypool
November 1959

CONTENTS

Chapter One

ALTERNATING-CURRENT THEORY

By E. E. Zepler

This chapter summarizes a.c. theory and deals with the behaviour of circuit networks subjected to e.m.f.'s of varying magnitude. The letters 'a.c.', which stand for 'alternating current', do not fully cover the conditions considered here. While 'a.c.' indicates a current changing its direction and magnitude sinusoidally with time, the change of direction is not essential for the current to exhibit all the 'a.c. symptoms'. For instance, suppose a sinusoidal current of 1 amp peak flows in an air-cored coil coupled inductively with another similar coil. The e.m.f. induced in the second coil is unaltered if an additional direct current of, say, 2 amp flows through the first. The total primary current is now unidirectional, varying in magnitude between a maximum of 3 amp and a minimum of 1 amp. Later in this chapter it will be shown that the current in the primary coil may be considered as the sum of a direct current and an alternating current—the a.c. effects being in no way changed by the presence of the direct current.

FUNDAMENTAL EQUATIONS

In a.c. theory the circuit components we are concerned with are resistors, inductors (self and mutual), and capacitors. The fundamental laws connecting the instantaneous voltage v and current i at any instant in such components are

$$v_R = iR \tag{1.1}$$

$$v_L = L\frac{di}{dt} \tag{1.2}$$

$$v_C = \frac{q}{C} \tag{1.3}$$

where v_R, v_L and v_C are the voltages across the resistance R, inductance L, and capacitance C respectively, and q is the quantity of charge on the capacitor. Now $i = dq/dt$ and therefore $q = \int i\,dt$, but since

1

the integration involves a constant depending on the initial conditions (at $t = 0$), q is not fully determined. Since we are concerned only with changes in q, i, and v, we need not know the value of this constant.

The values of resistance, inductance, and capacitance are assumed to be independent of the magnitude or direction of the applied voltages, and such components are referred to as linear impedances. A network of such impedances is called a linear network.

Consider a sinusoidal current $i = I \sin \omega t$ flowing through a linear impedance. Voltages across the components R, L and C are found from eqns. (1.1), (1.2) and (1.3). Thus

$$v_R = iR = IR \sin \omega t \tag{1.4}$$

$$v_L = L\frac{di}{dt} = I\omega L \cos \omega t \quad = I\omega L \sin\left(\omega t + \frac{\pi}{2}\right) \tag{1.5}$$

$$v_C = \frac{q}{C} = \frac{1}{C} \int I \sin \omega t \, dt = -\frac{I}{\omega C} \cos \omega t$$

$$= \frac{I}{\omega C} \sin\left(\omega t - \frac{\pi}{2}\right) \tag{1.6}$$

Impedance. We can define the 'effective resistance', or *impedance*, as the ratio of the peak voltage to the peak current, and in particular from eqns. (1.5) and (1.6) ωL is the *reactance*, as it is called, of the inductor and $1/\omega C$ is the reactance of the capacitor. These reactances do not define completely the behaviour of these components. The voltage and current are in phase in a resistance [eqn. (1.4)] but the voltage leads the current by 90° in an inductance [eqn. (1.5)] and lags 90° behind it in a capacitance [eqn. (1.6)]. Very simple expressions which take into account both the magnitudes of voltage and current and their phase relation can be obtained, if we represent sinusoidal currents (or voltages) by rotating two-dimensional vectors and describe such a vector by a complex number.

Since $\exp(j\omega t) = \cos \omega t + j \sin \omega t$, $i = I \exp(j\omega t)$ can be used to represent a current $i = I \cos \omega t$, if by convention we consider only the real part of $\exp(j\omega t)$ when evaluating the magnitude and phase of the current. For example

$$v_L = L\frac{di}{dt} = j\omega LI \exp(j\omega t) = j\omega Li \tag{1.7}$$

But

$$\exp(j\pi/2) = \cos \pi/2 + j \sin \pi/2 = j$$

Therefore

$$v_L = \omega L I \exp(j\pi/2) \cdot \exp(j\omega t) = \omega L I \exp[j(\omega t + \pi/2)] \quad (1.8)$$

Comparing eqns. (1.7) and (1.8) with eqn. (1.5), we can see that the phase advance of $\pi/2$ is mathematically equivalent to multiplying by j, and that the expression $v_L = j\omega Li$ simultaneously expresses the two facts that $|v_L| = \omega L|i|$ and that v_L leads i by $\pi/2$.

Similarly

$$v_C = \frac{1}{C}\int i\, dt = \frac{1}{j\omega c}I\exp(j\omega t) = \frac{1}{\omega C}I\exp[j(\omega t - \pi/2)] \quad (1.9)$$

since

$$1/j = -j = \exp(-j\pi/2) = \cos\pi/2 - j\sin\pi/2$$

Comparing eqn. (1.9) with eqn. (1.6), we see that the factor $-j(=1/j)$ is equivalent to the phase lag of $\pi/2$.

An example demonstrates the simplicity of expressions when using the j operator. The potential difference across a series combination of R and L for a current $i = I\sin\omega t$ is given in real numbers by

$$v = Ri + L\frac{di}{dt} = I(R\sin\omega t + \omega L\cos\omega t)$$

$$= I(R^2 + \omega^2 L^2)^{1/2}\sin(\omega t + \phi)$$

where $\tan\phi = \omega L/R$. Thus the peak p.d. is $I(R^2 + \omega^2 L^2)^{1/2}$ and it leads the current in phase by the angle arc tan $\omega L/R$.

In complex numbers the whole information is implicit in the expression

$$v = iR + ij\omega L = i(R + j\omega L) \quad (1.10)$$

We see that the effective impedance $Z = v/i = R + j\omega L$ is a complex number, whose magnitude $|Z|$ can be immediately seen to be given by $|Z| = (R^2 + \omega^2 L^2)^{1/2}$. Similarly the voltage is a complex number $(iR + j.i\omega L)$, which can be transformed from the form $a + jb$ to the form $r(\cos\phi + j\sin\phi) = r\exp(j\phi)$, where $r^2 = a^2 + b^2$ and $\phi = $ arc tan b/a. Thus

$$v = i(R^2 + \omega^2 L^2)^{1/2}(\cos\phi + j\sin\phi)$$

$$= (R^2 + \omega^2 L^2)^{1/2} I\exp(j\omega t)\cdot\exp(j\phi)$$

where

$$\phi = \text{arc tan } \omega L/R$$

or

$$v = (R^2 + \omega^2 L^2)^{1/2} I\exp[j(\omega t + \phi)]$$

which again shows that the peak p.d. is $I(R^2+\omega^2L^2)^{1/2}$, leading the current in phase by arc tan $\omega L/R$. In the following paragraphs, the letters V and I stand for time functions or for their peak values.

The voltage V and current I may be represented by two-dimensional vectors which, according to convention, rotate anti-clockwise with time (Fig. 1.1). The length of the vectors indicates the peak value of the quantity concerned, while the instantaneous value of the quantity is given by the projection of the vector on the x-axis or on the y-axis. For example consider a vector in the direction of the positive x-axis at the time $t = 0$; let its length be I, its angular velocity be ω, and its projection on the x-axis indicate its instantaneous value. Then the

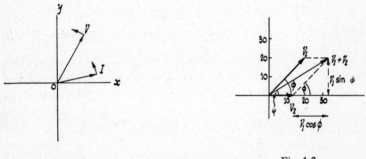

Fig. 1.1   Fig. 1.2

vector expresses the quantity $I \cos \omega t$. If its projection on the y-axis were chosen for its instantaneous value the vector would express the quantity $I \sin \omega t$.

We are concerned in this chapter only with relations between various alternating quantities, so that it is of no interest which projection is considered, as long as we are consistent. For example, in Fig. 1.2 the important facts for us are that the voltage V_1 is twice as large as V_2 and leads V_2 by ϕ.

If V_1 and V_2 are two voltages in series the p.d. V_1+V_2 is found by adding the two voltages vectorially as shown in Fig. 1.2. This is easily proved by writing

$$V_1 \sin(\omega t+\phi)+V_2 \sin \omega t = (V_1 \cos\phi+V_2) \sin \omega t+(V_1 \sin\phi) \cos \omega t$$

$$= [(V_1 \cos\phi+V_2)^2+V_1^2 \sin^2\phi]^{\frac{1}{2}} \sin(\omega t+\psi)$$

where

$$\tan\psi = \frac{V_1 \sin\phi}{V_1 \cos\phi+V_2}$$

From Fig. 1.2 it will be seen that the vector $V_1 + V_2$ in fact represents the expression given.

Vectors can be extremely useful in quickly giving a qualitative conception of phase relations, which is not always so easily obtained by calculation. The value of vector treatment becomes particularly striking when it is realized that vectors can be used to represent all the complex quantities occurring in the a.c. theory of linear networks.

For this purpose let the x-axis be the real, and the y-axis the imaginary axis (Fig. 1.3). Any point in the plane xy has then attached to it a real and an imaginary number. A vector with its origin at zero and its end at this point represents thus a complex quantity $a+jb$, a and b being the projections of the vector on the x- and y-axes respectively. From Fig. 1.3 it can be easily seen that $a+jb = (a^2+b^2)^{\frac{1}{2}}(\cos \phi + j \sin \phi)$, where $\tan \phi = b/a$, as has been proved above.]

A vector of length r, rotating with angular velocity ω, represents the expression $r \exp (j\omega t)$, which is a quantity of peak value r, varying sinusoidally with time at the frequency $\omega/2\pi$.

An arbitary impedance such as $R+j\omega L$ is represented by a fixed vector, while sinusoidal currents or voltages are shown by rotating vectors. Multiplying a rotating vector such as $I \exp (j\omega t)$ by a fixed vector $Z \exp (j\phi)$ advances the current vector by the phase angle ϕ and alters its magnitude by the factor Z. Fig. 1.4 may serve as a

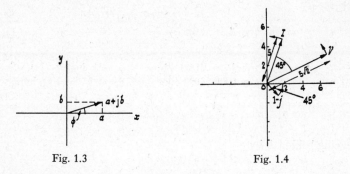

Fig. 1.3   Fig. 1.4

simple example. The vector I indicates a sinusoidal current of magnitude 5 amp and frequency $10^6/2\pi$ c/s, taken at an arbitrary time. The voltage obtained across a series combination of a 1-μF capacitor and a 1-ohm resistor, i.e. across an impedance of $1-j = \sqrt{2} . \exp (-j\pi/4)$ ohms, is given by the vector V shown in the graph. The fixed vector $1-j$, representing the series combination of resistor and capacitor, is also shown.

In Fig. 1.5 the current I_2 is to be found when the electromotive force (e.m.f.) E is given. Without the use of complex numbers even this simple problem would prove to be quite formidable. Using complex

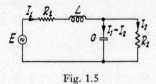

Fig. 1.5

numbers and applying Kirchhoff's laws, we obtain at once the two relations

$$I_1(R_1+j\omega L)+(I_1-I_2)1/j\omega C = E$$

$$(I_2-I_1)/j\omega C+I_2R_2 = 0$$

whence

$$I_2 = \frac{E}{R_1+R_2-\omega^2 LCR_2+j(R_1R_2\omega C+\omega L)}$$

$$= \frac{E}{a+jb} = \frac{E(a-jb)}{a^2+b^2} = \frac{E\exp(-j\phi)\cdot}{(a^2+b^2)^{1/2}}$$

where

$$\tan\phi = \frac{b}{a} = \frac{R_1R_2\,\omega C+\omega L}{R_1+R_2-\omega^2 LCR_2}$$

If $E = 1$ volt, $R_1 = R_2 = 1000$ ohms, $L = 0\cdot1$ henry (H), $C = 1$ microfarad (μF), $\omega = 1000$ rad./s, then $a = 1900$, $b = 1100$; hence

$$I_2 = \frac{1}{\sqrt{(1900^2+1100^2)}} \text{ amp} = 0\cdot45 \text{ milliamp}$$

lagging behind E by

$$\text{arc tan}\frac{11}{19} = 30°$$

Resonance. If a sinusoidal e.m.f. is applied to a series combination of R, L and C as in Fig. 1.6(a), the current I is given by

$$I = \frac{E}{R+j(\omega L-1/\omega C)} \qquad (1.11)$$

The current is a maximum when $\omega L = 1/\omega C$. The frequency $\omega_0/2\pi$

$= 1/[2\pi(LC)^{1/2}]$ at which the current is a maximum is called the *resonant frequency* of the circuit; the ratio $\omega_0 L/R = 1/\omega_0 CR$ is called the *magnification factor* or *Q-factor* of the circuit, because Q gives the ratio of the p.d. across L or C to the applied e.m.f. at the resonant frequency. The larger the Q-factor the sharper the response curve in the neighbourhood of the resonant frequency. Hence such a tuned circuit may be used to admit a certain frequency band while more or less rejecting others. The series tuned circuit of Fig. 1.6(a) represents, to an e.m.f. of the resonant frequency, an impedance which is a minimum and purely ohmic. At much higher frequencies the impedance is

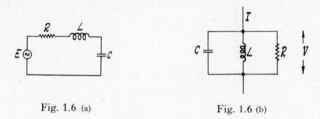

Fig. 1.6 (a)   Fig. 1.6 (b)

essentially inductive and at much lower frequencies essentially capacitive. Q-factors between 50 and 200 are usual for radio-frequency (r.f.) circuits, while at audio frequencies (a.f.) Q-factors of 10–30 are average values. Very much higher Q-factors can be obtained, both for r.f. and a.f. circuits, by careful design of the components.

If a sinusoidal current flows through a parallel combination of R, L and C [Fig. 1.6(b)] the p.d. V across the circuit is given by

$$V = \frac{I}{\dfrac{1}{R} + j\left(\omega C - \dfrac{1}{\omega L}\right)} \qquad (1.12)$$

This equation is analogous to that given for the series tuned circuit [eqn. (1.11)]. Hence we see that the parallel tuned circuit of Fig. 1.6(b) represents to the current an impedance which is resistive and a maximum at the resonant frequency $1/[2\pi(LC)^{1/2}]$. The Q-factor of the parallel circuit is the ratio of the current through L or C at the resonant frequency to the current flowing into the circuit. For the same Q-factor as in Fig. 1.6(a), the variation of V with frequency in Fig. 1.6(b) is similar to that of I with frequency in Fig. 1.6(a). The typical form of the response curve is shown in Fig. 1.7, but the actual proportions vary with the Q-factor. It must, however, be realized that in Fig. 1.6(a) $Q = \omega_0 L/R$, while in Fig. 1.6(b) $Q = R/\omega_0 L$. The condition

B

for a large Q-factor is hence $R \ll \omega_0 L$ in Fig. 1.6(a) and $R \gg \omega_0 L$ in Fig. 1.6(b). Both circuits are to some extent idealized, because there is no inductance without both series and parallel resistance; the former because of copper losses, the latter because of losses in the

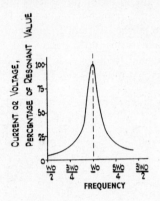

Fig. 1.7

dielectric. It is, however, possible to express all the losses in a circuit by either a parallel or a series resistance. For instance, a parallel combination of R and L may be replaced by a series combination of R' and L', the relation being

$$\frac{R . j\omega L}{R + j\omega L} = R' + j\omega L'$$

Therefore

$$\frac{R . j\omega L (R - j\omega L)}{R^2 + \omega^2 L^2} = R' + j\omega L'$$

Equating real and imaginary terms, we have,

$$R' = \frac{R}{1 + (R/\omega L)^2} \text{ and } L' = \frac{L}{1 + (\omega L/R)^2}$$

When the Q-factor is large, $R \gg \omega L$, in which case

$$L' \sim L \qquad R' \sim \omega^2 L^2 / R$$

The only essential difference between the circuits of Fig. 1.6(a) and Fig. 1.6(b) is that in Fig. 1.6(a) L and C are in series when seen from the generator while in Fig. 1.6(b) they are in parallel. The circuit of

Fig. 1.6(a) would still be called a series tuned circuit if R' were replaced by a large resistance R in parallel with L, and its behaviour would hardly be changed provided that $R/\omega_0 L = \omega_0 L/R'$. Equally the circuit of Fig. 1.6(b) would still be a parallel tuned circuit if R were replaced by a resistance R' in series with L.

A FEW SIMPLE THEOREMS FOR LINEAR NETWORKS

SUPERPOSITION THEOREM

In a linear network containing several generators, the current in any one branch of the network is the sum of all the individual currents that would flow if only one generator were active and the others were left inactive with only their internal impedances in circuit.

The proof of this theorem follows at once from the fact that all mesh equations are linear in I and E. Thus the equation of a particular current I_n is of the form

$$I_n = aE_1 + bE_2 + \ldots$$

where a, b, c, ... are admittances. The individual currents, due to one e.m.f. only, are obtained by equating all e.m.f.'s but one to zero, i.e. $I_1 = aE_1$, $I_2 = bE_2$, etc. Hence the actual current is the sum of the individual currents as stated above. The theorem shows that in a linear network the current caused by one generator is not affected by the existence of other generators. In particular it proves that a unidirectional current varying in magnitude exhibits all the characteristics of an alternating current (p. 1).

THÉVENIN-HELMHOLTZ THEOREM

The current in an impedance Z, connected to two terminals of a linear network containing one or several generators, is the same as if Z were connected to a generator of which the e.m.f. is equal to the open-circuited voltage at the two terminals in question, and of which the impedance is that of the network measured across the terminals, when all sources of e.m.f. are short-circuited but their internal impedances left.

In Fig. 1.8, A and B are the two terminals in question. If the open-circuited p.d. across AB is V, no current will flow in Z, when an e.m.f. V is inserted as shown, since the points B and B' are at the same potential. According to the superposition theorem the zero current in Z

may be considered as the sum of the two currents (a) due to the net-work generators only, and (b) due to the added e.m.f. only. These two currents must be equal, but opposite in sign. The current due to the added e.m.f. is, however, equal to $V/(Z+Z_i)$, Z_i being the network impedance across AB. Hence the theorem is proved.

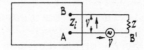

Fig. 1.8

Thévenin's theorem is particularly powerful in simplifying network problems, but it should not be used indiscriminately. An example will show its correct use.

In the circuit of Fig. 1.9, find the p.d. across C_2.

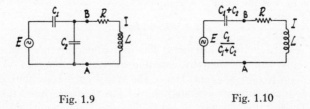

Fig. 1.9   Fig. 1.10

Treating $R+j\omega L$ as the load, we obtain the equivalent circuit of Fig. 1.10; hence

$$I = E\frac{C_1}{C_1+C_2} \times \frac{1}{R+j\omega L+1/j\omega(C_1+C_2)}$$

and the p.d. across C_2 is

$$E\frac{C_1}{C_1+C_2} \times \frac{R+j\omega L}{R+j\omega L+1/j\omega(C_1+C_2)} \qquad (1.13)$$

If C_2 had been treated as the load the equivalent circuit would be shown in Fig. 1.11. It is clear that the application of Thévenin's theorem would then complicate rather than simplify matters. As a general rule, one should preferably apply the theorem in such a way that the e.m.f. of the equivalent generator does not depend on fre-quency, as in Fig. 1.10. Further examples suitable for the use of the theorem may be found in chapter two.

NORTON'S THEOREM

The current in an impedance Z, connected to two terminals of a linear network containing one or several generators, is equal to that obtained from a current generator of which the current is equal to that for $Z = 0$, when the impedance of the network measured across the terminals is connected in parallel with Z.

The theorem follows at once from Thévenin's theorem. Let us assume that a network has been reduced, by the use of Thévenin's theorem, to an e.m.f. E of internal impedance Z_i (Fig. 1.12). Then the current in an external impedance Z is $E/(Z_i+Z)$. For $Z = 0$

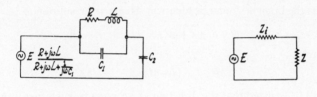

Fig. 1.11	Fig. 1.12

the current is E/Z_i, and hence the equivalent circuit obtained from the application of Norton's theorem is as shown in Fig. 1.13 in which the current through Z is

$$(E/Z_i) \times [Z_i/(Z+Z_i)] = E/(Z+Z_i)$$

which is the same value as obtained from the circuit of Fig. 1.12. An example in which the use of Norton's theorem is preferable to

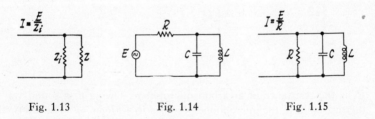

Fig. 1.13	Fig. 1.14	Fig. 1.15

that of Thévenin's theorem is shown in Fig. 1.14. From the equivalent circuit of Fig. 1.15 the potential difference V across the tuned circuit is given by

$$V = \frac{E}{R} \cdot \frac{1}{1/R+1/j\omega L+j\omega C}$$

Fig. 1.15 shows immediately, what is not so obvious from Fig. 1.14, that in the response of the tuned circuit R acts as a parallel damping resistance.

COMPENSATION THEOREM

If the current in an impedance Z is I, and if Z changes by a small amount δZ, the effect on I, and on the currents in other branches of the network, is the same as if an e.m.f. of value $-I\delta Z$ were inserted in series with Z.

This may be shown as follows. In order that the two circuits of Figs. 1.16 and 1.17 shall be equivalent the currents in and the voltages across the branches must be identical. Hence the condition is

$$(I+\delta I)(Z+\delta Z) = (I+\delta I)Z - \delta E$$

Therefore

$$\delta E = -(I+\delta I)\delta Z \sim -I\delta Z$$

It will be realized that the direction of δE must be such that it is equal to the p.d. caused by the insertion of δZ. (If δZ is positive, δI will be negative, hence δE, as an e.m.f., would be negative.)

The compensation theorem, in conjunction with the superposition theorem, sometimes enables one to arrive quickly at a result which otherwise might cause some difficulty. For example, in Fig. 1.18

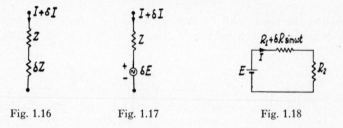

Fig. 1.16   Fig. 1.17   Fig. 1.18

R_1 is the resistance of a carbon microphone. Owing to a sound wave the resistance of the microphone becomes $R_1 + \delta R \sin \omega t$. The alternating voltage across R_2 is to be found. Replacing the change in R_1 by an e.m.f. $-I\delta R \sin \omega t = -[E/(R_1+R_2)]\,\delta R \sin \omega t$, we obtain for the alternating voltage V across R_2 the expression $-[E/(R_1+R_2)]\delta R$ $[R_2/(R_1+R_2)] \sin \omega t$. By differentiation with respect to R_2, it is easily found that the amplitude of V becomes a maximum when $R_2 = R_1$. If, on the other hand, R_2 is coupled to the microphone through a 1/1 transformer, $I = E/R_1$; hence the voltage across R_2 becomes

$$(E/R_1)\delta R[R_2/(R_1+R_2)] \sin \omega t$$

from which it is seen that V is a maximum when $R_2 = \infty$. The difference between the two cases is that in the first the equivalent e.m.f. depends on R_2, while in the second it does not.

SIMPLE TRANSFORMER THEORY

In the following paragraphs only very elementary transformer theory will be given. Transformers will be treated as linear components. If they contain iron cores the effect of hysteresis will be disregarded. Furthermore the transformers will be considered as loss free.

An a.c. generator of internal impedance Z_1 is connected to the primary of a transformer, whilst an impedance Z_2 is connected across the secondary (Fig. 1.19). The current in Z_2 is to be found. The two relevant equations are

$$I_1(Z_1+j\omega L_1)+I_2 j\omega M = E \tag{1.14}$$

$$I_2(Z_2+j\omega L_2)+I_1 j\omega M = 0 \tag{1.15}$$

whence

$$I_1 = E \frac{j\omega L_2+Z_2}{(Z_1+j\omega L_1)(Z_2+j\omega L_2)+\omega^2 M^2}$$

With audio-frequency transformers there is usually almost complete flux linkage between the two transformer windings, i.e. $M \sim (L_1 L_2)^{1/2}$. Then

$$I_1 = E\frac{j\omega L_2+Z_2}{Z_1 Z_2+j\omega L_1 Z_2+j\omega L_2 Z_1} = \frac{E}{Z_1 + \dfrac{j\omega L_1 Z_2}{j\omega L_2+Z_2}}$$

$$= \frac{E}{Z_1 + \dfrac{j\omega L_1\, Z_2 L_1/L_2}{j\omega L_1+Z_2 L_1/L_2}} \tag{1.16}$$

From the last expression it is seen that the generator looks into a parallel combination of an inductance L_1 and an impedance $Z_2 L_1/L_2$ (Fig. 1.20). Because of the complete flux linkage between primary and secondary, $L_1/L_2 = (n_1/n_2)^2$, where n_1 and n_2 are the numbers of turns in primary and secondary respectively. $Z_2(n_1/n_2)^2$ is called the transferred impedance. If L_1 is chosen sufficiently large its effect may be neglected, and the transformer simply serves to transfer in series with the generator a load of a required magnitude.

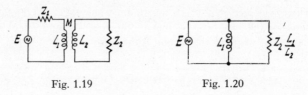

Fig. 1.19   Fig. 1.20

An example may illustrate the use of a transformer. Many types of output valves give the maximum possible power when looking into a load of approximately 10,000 ohms. The actual load is frequently a loudspeaker of resistance 4 ohms. Hence a transformer of turns ratio $(10{,}000/4)^{1/2}$ or 50:1, must be inserted in the anode lead of the valve. It is usually sufficient if at 50 c/s the reactance of the secondary is three to five times the load resistance. Thus in the example the secondary inductance should be of the order of 0·05 henry and the primary inductance 125 henries.

Distortion Due to Non-Linear Impedances

Amplifier valves are among the most usual causes of harmonic distortion, because of their non-linear characteristics. Their behaviour may be understood from the following simple example. It is assumed that the current through a non-linear resistance is given by the relation $I = aV + bV^2$, V being the p.d. across the resistance. When an e.m.f. $E_0 \sin \omega t$ is applied across the resistance, the current is given by

$$I = aE_0 \sin \omega t + bE_0^2 \sin^2 \omega t$$
$$= aE_0 \sin \omega t + bE_0^2/2 - (bE_0^2 \cos 2\omega t)/2 \qquad (1.17)$$

The current obtained contains a sinusoidal term of the frequency of the generator, a sinusoidal term of twice the frequency and a direct current. A sketch of the characteristic of the resistance and of the resultant current is given in Fig. 1.21. The waveform of the current is that of a distorted sine wave, the positive amplitude I_p being larger than the negative I_n. From the expression for I the positive and negative current amplitudes are obtained by equating ωt to $+\pi/2$ and $-\pi/2$ respectively. Hence

$$I_p = aE_0 + \frac{bE_0^2}{2} + \frac{bE_0^2}{2} = aE_0 + bE_0^2$$
$$I_n = aE_0 - bE_0^2$$

If I_1 is the amplitude of fundamental frequency and I_2 that of the second harmonic it follows from the above that

$$I_1 = \frac{I_p + I_n}{2}, \qquad I_2 = \frac{I_p - I_n}{4}$$

Hence

$$\frac{I_2}{I_1} = \frac{1}{2} \frac{I_p - I_n}{I_p + I_n} = \frac{1}{2} \frac{(I_p/I_n) - 1}{(I_p/I_n) + 1}$$

By observing the wave shape of the current, as may be done with the help of a cathode-ray oscilloscope, it is possible to determine the ratio of the second harmonic to the fundamental and thus draw conclusions

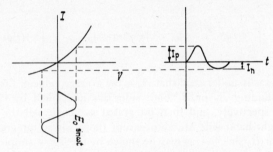

Fig. 1.21

as to the amount of distortion. If the oscilloscope does not respond to direct current the above relation becomes

$$\frac{I_2}{I_1} = \frac{(I_p/I_n) - 1}{(I_p/I_n) + 1}$$

In practice there are other harmonics generated as well by non-linear components, but frequently knowledge of the second gives sufficient information.

Fourier Analysis

From the shape of a periodic waveform it is possible to derive the magnitude of all the harmonics contained with the help of the Fouriers' theorem, which reads as follows:

A periodic, single-valued function which is finite and continuous over the whole of its range may be represented by a series of sinusoidal functions each of whose periods is an integral part of that of the given function.

This relation may be written in the following form:

$$f(t) = A_0 + A_1 \cos \omega t + A_2 \cos 2\omega t + A_3 \cos 3\omega t + \dots$$

$$+ B_1 \sin \omega t + B_2 \sin 2\omega t + B_3 \sin 3\omega t + \dots \quad (1.18)$$

where $\omega = 2\pi/T$, T being the time of a period of $f(t)$. From the shape of $f(t)$ all the coefficients on the right-hand side are determined. It must be remembered that $\int \cos n\omega t\, dt$ and $\int \sin n\omega t\, dt$, taken over an integral number of periods, are zero. Furthermore the value of an integral, taken over one period of an arbitrary periodic function, is independent of the particular limits chosen. In the following, we shall choose as the limits $-\pi/\omega$ and $+\pi/\omega$. We immediately obtain A_0 by integrating both sides:

$$\int\limits_{-\pi/\omega}^{+\pi/\omega} f(t)dt = \frac{2\pi}{\omega}A_0. \quad \text{Therefore } A_0 = \frac{\omega}{2\pi} \int\limits_{-\pi/\omega}^{+\pi/\omega} f(t)dt$$

It will be easily understood that A_0 is the average value of the function $f(t)$. For finding A_n or B_n both sides are multiplied by $\cos n\omega t$ or $\sin n\omega t$ respectively, and then integrated as above. All the integrals on the right-hand side are zero except those whose integrand is $A_n \cos^2 n\omega t$ or $B_n \sin^2 n\omega t$, as may be shown by the use of simple trigonometric functions. Now

$$\int\limits_{-\pi/\omega}^{+\pi/\omega} \cos^2 n\omega t\, dt = \int\limits_{-\pi/\omega}^{+\pi/\omega} \sin^2 n\omega t\, dt = \pi/\omega$$

Hence

$$A_n = \frac{\omega}{\pi} \int\limits_{-\pi/\omega}^{+\pi/\omega} f(t) \cos n\omega t\, dt, \text{ and } B_n = \frac{\omega}{\pi} \int\limits_{-\pi/\omega}^{+/\pi\omega} f(t) \sin n\omega t\, dt$$

In the above analysis we might have introduced the period $T = 1/f = 2\pi/\omega$, as will be done in the later examples.

Fourier's theorem holds not only for regular functions as defined above, but also for functions which are regular in distinct pieces. For instance, pulses—which are functions discontinuous at a finite number of points of a cycle—can also be expressed by a Fourier series.

By a proper arrangement of the time axis it is often possible to simplify the Fourier series of periodic functions so that only sine or cosine terms are existent. For instance, if the periodic function is an even function, i.e. if $f(t) = f(-t)$, then the Fourier series contains only cosine terms. If the function is an odd function, i.e. if $f(t) = -f(-t)$, the Fourier series contains only sine terms. This is found immediately when carrying out the above integration for determining A_n and B_n

Two simple examples may conclude this chapter.

Example 1. The Fourier series of rectangular current pulses of height I, of period 0.01 sec (T) and of duration 1 millisec (τ), is to be found.

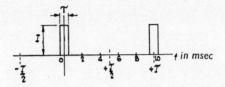

Fig. 1.22

We choose $t = 0$ in the middle of a pulse; then the function is even (Fig. 1.22). Hence

$$f(t) = A_0 + \sum_{n=1}^{\infty} A_n \cos n\omega t$$

where

$$A_0 = \frac{1}{T} \int_{-T/2}^{+T/2} I \, dt = \frac{1}{T} \int_{-\tau/2}^{+\tau/2} I \, dt = I \frac{\tau}{T} = \frac{I}{10}$$

$$A_1 = \frac{2}{T} \int_{-\tau/2}^{+\tau/2} I \cos \left(\frac{2\pi}{T} t \right) dt = \frac{I}{\pi} \left| \sin \frac{2\pi t}{T} \right|_{-\tau/2}^{+\tau/2}$$

$$= \frac{2I}{\pi} \sin \frac{\pi \tau}{T} = \frac{2I}{\pi} \sin \frac{\pi}{10} \sim \frac{I}{5}$$

Generally

$$A_n = \frac{2}{T} \int_{-\tau/2}^{+\tau/2} I \cos \frac{2\pi n t}{T} dt = \frac{I}{n\pi} \left| \sin \frac{2\pi n t}{T} \right|_{-\tau/2}^{+\tau/2} = \frac{2I}{n\pi} \sin \left(n\pi \frac{\tau}{T} \right)$$

$$= 2I \frac{\tau}{T} \frac{\sin (n\pi\tau/T)}{n\pi\tau/T} = \frac{I}{5} \frac{\sin (n\pi/10)}{n\pi/10}$$

The formula shows that the strength of harmonics remains constant, equal to that of the fundamental, as long as $n\pi\tau/T$ is small, so that $\sin(n\pi\tau/T) \sim n\pi\tau/T$. In the particular case of $\tau = T/2$, the function is called a square wave, the fundamental of which is of amplitude $2I/\pi$.

Example 2. A sinusoidal voltage is applied to an ideal rectifier. The Fourier series of the resulting current is to be found.

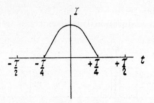

Fig. 1.23

The current waveform during one cycle is seen in Fig. 1.23. We choose $t = 0$ in the middle of a current pulse so that the function is even and $B_n = 0$.

$$A_0 = \frac{1}{T} \int_{-T/4}^{+T/4} I \cos(2\pi t/T)dt = I/2\pi \left| \sin(2\pi t/T) \right|_{-T/4}^{+T/4} = I/\pi$$

$$A_n = \frac{2I}{T} \int_{-T/4}^{+T/4} \cos(2\pi t/T) \cos(2\pi n t/T) \, dt$$

Using the relation

$$\cos\alpha \cos\beta = \frac{\cos(\alpha+\beta)+\cos(\alpha-\beta)}{2}$$

we find

$$A_n = \frac{I}{T} \int_{-T/4}^{+T/4} \left(\cos[(n+1)2\pi t/T] + \cos[(n-1)2\pi t/T] \right) dt$$

$$= \frac{I}{2\pi} \left| \frac{\sin[(n+1)2\pi t/T]}{n+1} + \frac{\sin[(n-1)2\pi t/T]}{n-1} \right|_{-T/4}^{+T/4}$$

$$= \frac{I}{\pi} \left(\frac{\sin[(n+1)\pi/2]}{n+1} + \frac{\sin[(n-1)\pi/2]}{n-1} \right)$$

When n is odd, $\sin[(n+1)\,\pi/2]$ and $\sin[(n-1)\,\pi/2]$ are zero; hence there are no odd harmonics. For $n = 1$, however, the second fraction on the right-hand side becomes $\pi/2$, since $[(n-1)\,\pi/2]_{n\to1} = (n-1)\,\pi/2$. The amplitude of the fundamental is therefore $I/2$. When n is even

$$A_n = \frac{I}{(n^2-1)\pi}\{(n-1)\sin[(n+1)\pi/2]+(n+1)\sin[(n-1)\pi/2]\}$$

For $n = 2, 6, 10, \ldots$, $\sin[(n+1)\,\pi/2] = -1$ and $\sin[(n-1)\,\pi/2] = +1$, while it is the reverse when $n = 4, 8, 12, \ldots$. Hence

$$I(t) = \frac{I}{\pi}\left(1 + \frac{\pi}{2}\cos\frac{2\pi t}{T} + \frac{2}{3}\cos\frac{4\pi t}{T} - \frac{2}{15}\cos\frac{8\pi t}{T} + \ldots\right)$$

Chapter Two

THE RC-COUPLED AMPLIFIER STAGE

By E. E. Zepler

The Triode

The anode current of a triode valve is determined by the p.d. V_g between cathode and grid, and the p.d. V_a between cathode and anode. Fig. 2.1, showing the relation between anode current and grid voltage for various fixed anode voltages, is typical of a triode.

It is seen that the anode current does not vary linearly with V_g, and other curves would show that the same is true for the behaviour of I_a with respect to V_a. However, if we limit our consideration to what is called the linear part of the characteristic, we can treat the valve as a linear device. Then a current change δI_a is proportional to δV_g or δV_a;

$$\delta I_a = g_m \delta V_g \quad (V_a \text{ constant}) \tag{2.1}$$

$$\delta I_a = \frac{1}{r_a} \delta V_a \quad (V_g \text{ constant}) \tag{2.2}$$

and generally

$$\delta I_a = g_m \delta V_g + \frac{1}{r_a} \delta V_a \tag{2.3}$$

where g_m and r_a are constants of proportionality.

In these relationships g_m is called the *mutual conductance* of the valve; its dimension is (resistance)$^{-1}$, and it is usually expressed in milliamperes per volt. Naturally r_a has the dimension of a resistance; it is expressed in ohms and is called the *a.c. resistance* of the valve. Since both g_m and r_a depend on the working condition of the valve they are usually given by the valve manufacturers for a certain anode current and anode voltage.

The effect on the anode current of a voltage applied to the grid is larger than that of an equal voltage applied to the anode, because the grid is nearer to the cathode and also because the grid acts as an electrostatic screen for fields coming from the anode. If the effect of the grid is μ times that of the anode, it follows that $g_m = \mu(1/r_a)$; hence $\mu = g_m r_a$, where μ is called the *amplification factor* of the valve.

20

The mathematical expression $\mu = -\delta v_a / \delta v_g$ (I_a constant) will be easily understood.

GAIN OF A TRIODE

In the following it is assumed that an impedance Z is inserted in the anode lead and that an alternating potential is applied between grid and cathode of a triode valve. We wish to find the alternating anode current and the alternating potential between anode and cathode.

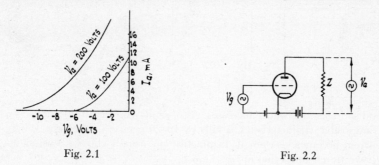

Fig. 2.1   Fig. 2.2

The d.c. values of currents and voltages are of no interest in the following theoretical treatment and the symbols I_a, V_g and V_a represent alternating quantities. Then in Fig. 2.2, as shown above, $I_a = V_g g_m + V_a / r_a$. The alternating anode voltage is caused by the alternating anode current, i.e. $V_a = -I_a Z$, and so

$$I_a = V_g g_m - \frac{I_a Z}{r_a}$$

or

$$I_a = V_g g_m \frac{r_a}{r_a + Z} = \frac{\mu V_g}{r_a + Z} \qquad (2.4)$$

From this we see that, when an alternating voltage V_g is applied between grid and cathode of a valve, the valve acts like a generator of e.m.f. μV_g and internal resistance r_a. The equivalent circuit of the valve is shown in Fig. 2.3. The e.m.f. is given as $-\mu V_g$; this is because the current is conventionally considered positive if flowing clockwise, while in Fig. 2.2 a positive anode current flows anti-clockwise. When Z is resistive, the anode voltage falls as the grid voltage rises, because of the increased voltage drop across the load resistance. The use of the minus sign demonstrates the phase reversal that occurs in a grid-driven one-valve amplifier.

Thus with a purely resistive anode load R the voltage gain from grid

to anode, for either a direct or alternating input voltage, is $\mu R/(r_a+R)$.
It appears from this expression that it would be best to choose R as
large as possible. This deduction is, however, a fallacy. One must bear
in mind that as R is made larger the direct current of the valve decreases,

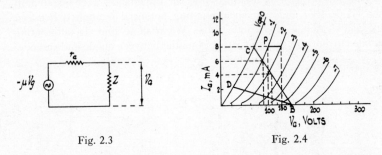

Fig. 2.3   Fig. 2.4

and so its a.c. resistance increases. Also, as may be seen from graphs of
triode valve characteristics, μ falls by 10–20 per cent, when the valve
current becomes very small. In practice one usually chooses a value of
R five to ten times that of r_a.

If we wish to find the behaviour of a valve with resistive load, allowing
for changes in r_a and μ, we must consult the graph giving I_a as a
function of V_a, with V_g as a parameter (Fig. 2.4). Let us first derive
from the graph the valve constants for $I_a = 8$ mA. Changing the
grid voltage by -1 volt, e.g. from -1 volt to -2 volts, and the anode
voltage by 30 volts, e.g. from 100 volts to 130 volts, leaves I_a unchanged
at 8 mA; hence $\mu = 30$. From the slope of the characteristic at P,
where $I_a = 8$mA, $V_g = -1$ volt,

$$\frac{1}{r_a} = \frac{\delta I_a}{\delta V_a} \ (V_g \text{ constant}) = 0\cdot16 \text{ mA/V}$$

Therefore

$$r_a = 6000 \text{ ohms and } g_m = \frac{\mu}{r_a} = 5 \text{ mA/V}$$

The Load Line

We assume that the h.t. supply is 150 volts and the anode load
resistance 10,000 ohms. Suppose we wish to find the grid bias V_g for
which the anode current is 6 mA. This can be found immediately
from the graph given. The voltage drop across the anode load resistance
will be 60 volts, and so V_a will be 90 volts. Thus the required grid
bias is determined from the intersection of the ordinate $V_a = 90$

volts and the abscissa $I_a = 6$ mA; it is approximately -1 volt. Similarly the bias for 4 mA is found to be $-2\cdot3$ volts. All the points obtained in this way lie on a straight line BC, which is called the *load line* of the valve with the given h.t. voltage and for the particular load resistance 10,000 ohms. The slope of the load line dI_a/dV_a is simply $-1/10{,}000$ amp/volt, or $-1/10$ mA/volt. Having drawn the load line BC we can obtain from the graph the anode current and the anode voltage for any given value of V_g, and thus the voltage gain from grid to anode. For example, the gain, for a change in V_g between $-0\cdot6$ volt and $-2\cdot8$ volts, is $50/2\cdot2 = 22\cdot7$.

The load line also enables us to find the distortion caused by the non-linearity of the valve. With a grid bias of -2 volts, a sinusoidal voltage of 2 volts peak applied to the grid produces an alternating anode voltage of which the positive amplitude is about 32 volts and the negative amplitude 34 volts. From elementary Fourier analysis it follows that at the anode the second harmonic of the signal is generated and that the ratio of the amplitudes of the second harmonic and fundamental is given by the expression $\frac{1}{2}(A-1)/(A+1)$, where A is the ratio of the larger to the smaller amplitude (see p. 15). In our case $A = 34/32$, and so the amplitude of the second harmonic is about one-sixtieth of that of the fundamental, i.e. $0\cdot5$ volt. By drawing the load line BD for an anode load of 50,000 ohms, we see at once that the increase in gain compared with an anode load of 10,000 ohms is in the ratio 46:33.

In general the amplifier valve should not pass grid current during any part of the cycle of the alternating input. If it did so it would represent to the input voltage a load of variable resistance, and distortion would result. One must therefore maintain the potential of the grid negative with respect to the cathode. It is inconvenient to incorporate dry batteries in the amplifier for achieving this object, and usually the negative bias required is obtained by the voltage drop across a resistor in the cathode lead (Fig. 2.5). If the resistor is to act as a d.c. battery it must be by-passed by a capacitor whose reactance is negligibly small at the frequencies concerned (see p. 26). The magnitude of the cathode resistance follows from the valve data. If the valve is to work with, say, $2\cdot3$ volts bias, we see from the graph of Fig. 2.4, with the help of the load line, that the anode current will be 4 mA, and thus the correct cathode resistance is clearly 575 ohms.

Usually the alternating anode voltage is to be applied to the grid of another valve for further amplification. To bar the direct voltage from the following grid we use a coupling capacitor, while the grid of the following valve is connected to earth through a resistor (Fig. 2.5). This resistor must not be too small, or it reduces the effective anode load and decreases the stage gain. On the other hand it must not be too

C

large, for the following reason. Even when the grid is negative with respect to the cathode, there usually exists a small grid current due either to traces of gas in the valve or to electronic emission from the grid which is heated by the cathode. A very large grid resistance would

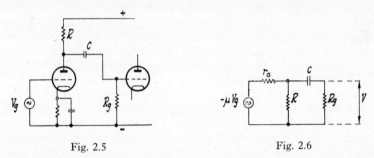

Fig. 2.5   Fig. 2.6

cause a substantial voltage drop, make the grid potential more positive than intended and might lead to the destruction of the valve. The grid resistance given as permissible by the valve makers varies between 0·25 megohm for·powerful valves to several megohms for low-emission valves.

In order to evaluate the gain m of a stage, i.e. the ratio of the voltage at the following grid to that applied to the previous valve, we use Thévenin's theorem after simplifying the circuit of Fig. 2.5 to that of Fig. 2.6. (R is effectively connected between the anode of the valve and the h.t. negative line for audio frequencies since there will be a large capacitor connected across the h.t. supply.)

Putting

$$\frac{Rr_a}{R+r_a} = R'$$

we obtain at once

$$m = \frac{V}{V_g} = \frac{-\mu R}{r_a+R} \cdot \frac{R_g}{R'+R_g+1/j\omega C} = -g_m R' \frac{R_g}{R'+R_g+1/j\omega C} \quad (2.5)$$

For a triode, $R' \ll R_g$, and so approximately

$$|m| = \frac{\mu R}{r_a+R} \cdot \frac{1}{\left[1+\left(\dfrac{1}{\omega C R_g}\right)^2\right]^{1/2}} \quad (2.6)$$

If ϕ is the angle by which V leads V_g, $\phi = \pi + \text{arc tan } 1/\omega C R_g$.

A drop in stage gain in the ratio $\sqrt{2}:1$ occurs when $1/\omega C = R'+R_g$

$\sim R_g$. For a given value of R_g, the magnitude of C is determined by the low-frequency response required. C should not be much larger than necessary, for otherwise an undesired sudden pulse might cause grid current to flow, thus backing the valve off and, owing to the large time-constant, desensitizing the valve for a considerable time. The correct choice of C may be illustrated by a simple example.

A drop in gain of 10 per cent per stage is considered permissible at 30 c/s; R_g is 0·5 megohm. Find the best value of the coupling capacitor C. From the above it follows that

$$\left[1+\left(\frac{1}{2\pi \times 30 \times C \times 0·5 \times 10^6}\right)^2\right]^{1/2} = \frac{1}{0·9}$$

Thus $C = 0·02\ \mu F$.

At high frequencies the stage gain drops off because of the stray capacitance C_s of the stage. By this is meant the sum of the capacitance between anode and cathode of the amplifier valve, the capacitance between grid and cathode of the following valve, and the capacitances to earth of R, C, R_g and of the connecting leads. At the high frequencies where the stray capacitance plays a part, the reactance of C is very small and may be neglected. Hence the equivalent circuit of the stage may be represented as shown in Fig. 2.7. Using Thévenin's

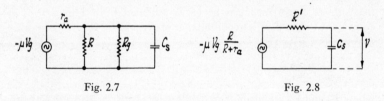

Fig. 2.7   Fig. 2.8

theorem as before, putting $r_a R/(r_a+R) = R'$ and neglecting the influence of R_g we obtain the circuit of Fig. 2.8, from which

$$V = -\mu V_g \frac{R}{r_a+R}\frac{1}{1+j\omega C_s R'}$$

Therefore

$$|m| = \frac{\mu R}{R+r_a}\frac{1}{[1+(\omega C_s R')^2]^{1/2}} = g_m R'\frac{1}{[1+(\omega C_s R')^2]^{1/2}} \qquad (2.7)$$

Here the effect of the grid-anode capacitance of the following valve should also be taken into account. If this valve has a resistive anode load and if its stage again is m, the current through the grid-anode capacitor C_{ga} is $V(m+1)j\omega C_{ga}$. This shows that the input capacitance, due to C_{ga}, is $(m+1)C_{ga}$. With pentodes this effect is negligible.

Numerical implications may be seen from the following example of a triode amplifier stage:

Given $r_a = 10,000$ ohms, $\mu = 20$, $R = 50,000$ ohms, $R_g = 0\cdot5$ megohm, $C = 0\cdot001\ \mu\text{F}$, $C_s = 50$ pF, find the stage gain in the mid-frequency range, and the two frequencies at which the stage gain drops in the ratio $\sqrt{2}:1$. What is the phase relation between V and V_g at each of these two frequencies?

We have $|m|$ (at mid-frequencies) $= 20 \times \frac{5}{6} = 16\cdot6$, assuming $R_g \gg R'$.

If R_g is taken into account, $|m|$ (at mid-frequencies) $= 16\cdot4$.

The low frequency at which $m = 16\cdot4/\sqrt{2}$ is 31c/s, with V leading V_g by 225°.

The high frequency at which $m = 16\cdot4/\sqrt{2}$ is 0·38 Mc/s, V leading V_g by 135°.

From this example we see that there is no difficulty in designing an audio-frequency amplifier stage so that the gain remains constant at the high-frequency end. In video-frequency amplifiers, where the highest frequency is of the order of a few megacycles per second, the stray capacitance is of vital importance, and special measures are required to make the gain constant over the whole frequency band (see p. 51).

EFFECT OF THE CATHODE IMPEDANCE

In the above calculations the impedance in the cathode lead has been disregarded. Although this is permissible over a large part of the frequency range, it is not so at very low frequencies. The influence of the cathode impedance can be easily calculated. In Fig. 2.9 Z_k is equivalent to the parallel combination of R_k and C_k.

As before

$$I_a = g_m V_g + \frac{V_a}{r_a}$$

where V_g and V_a are the potential differences between grid and cathode, and between anode and cathode respectively. Now if an alternating voltage E is applied between grid and the h.t. negative line,

$$V_g = E - I_a Z_k \text{ and } V_a = -I_a(Z_k + R)$$

Hence

$$I_a = g_m(E - I_a Z_k) - \frac{I_a}{r_a}(Z_k + R)$$

Rearranging and putting

$$g_m = \frac{\mu}{r_a}$$

we obtain

$$I_a = \frac{\mu E}{r_a + R + (\mu + 1)Z_k} \tag{2.8}$$

The effect of the finite impedance in the cathode lead is the same as if $(\mu+1)$ times the impedance were connected between the anode and the anode load. If we apply this result to the circuit of Figs. 2.5 and 2.6 and assume $R_g \gg R$, we obtain

$$V = -\mu E \frac{R}{r_a+R+(\mu+1)Z_k} \times \frac{R_g}{R_g-j/\omega C}$$

Putting

$$Z_k = \frac{R_k}{1+j\omega C_k R_k}$$

and rationalizing gives

$$V = -\mu E \frac{R}{r_a+R+\dfrac{(\mu+1)R_k}{1+(R_k\omega C_k)^2}-\dfrac{j(\mu+1)R_k^2\omega C_k}{1+(R_k\omega C_k)^2}} \times \frac{1}{1-\dfrac{j}{\omega C R_g}} \quad (2.9)$$

The denominator of the first fraction on the right gives a clear indication of the influence of the cathode impedance. The reduction in gain is largest at very low frequencies, when the cathode impedance becomes equal to R_k, the reduction being in the ratio $[r_a+R+(\mu+1)R_k]$ to (r_a+R). The influence of the cathode impedance on the phase of V disappears at high frequencies when the cathode impedance is zero, and at very low frequencies when the cathode impedance is resistive.

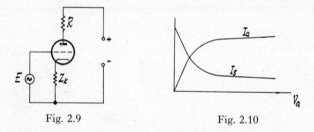

Fig. 2.9   Fig. 2.10

The phase of V is of importance in considering feedback over one or several stages (see chapter three). Differentiating the ratio of imaginary to real terms in the denominator of the first fraction in eqn. (2.9) with respect to ω shows that the phase displacement of V due to the cathode impedance becomes largest when

$$\omega^2 = \frac{r_a+R+(\mu+1)R_k}{(r_a+R)R_k^2 C_k^2}$$

At this frequency V is advanced by an angle equal to

$$\arc\tan \frac{(\mu+1)R_k}{2(r_a+R)} \times \frac{1}{\left[1+\frac{(\mu+1)R_k}{r_a+R}\right]^{1/2}}$$

Example. Let $r_a = 10{,}000$ ohms, $\mu = 20$, $R = 50{,}000$ ohms, $R_k = 1000$ ohms, $C_k = 20\ \mu\text{F}$. We find that the influence of the cathode impedance on the phase of the anode current is largest at 10 c/s and advances it by approximately 9°.

THE PENTODE AMPLIFIER

In contrast to the triode, the anode current of a pentode is, for a large part of its characteristic, almost independent of the potential at the anode. The emission is determined by the potentials of the signal grid and screen grid, and only when the anode potential is very low does the anode current fall rapidly with decreasing anode potential. This is due not to a change in emission but to the fact that the electrons are deflected to the screen grid (Fig. 2.10). In the linear part of the $I_a V_a$ characteristic the a.c. resistance of the pentode is very large, and it is impracticable to use an anode load large compared with r_a. The anode load is usually considerably smaller than r_a and hence the gain is approximately $g_m R$. Average values are $R = 0 \cdot 1 – 0 \cdot 2$ megohm, $r_a = 1$ megohm. To obtain a large gain it is essential that the valve works with a reasonably large anode current, since otherwise g_m will be small. Owing to

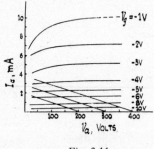

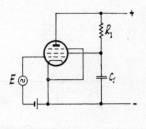

Fig. 2.11   Fig. 2.12

the potential drop across the large anode load resistance, the anode voltage tends to be lower than is desirable for a satisfactory working. For this reason it is essential that the h.t. voltage should be fairly large. The increase in gain with increasing h.t. voltage is very pronounced with a pentode, in contrast to a triode. Conditions may be studied with the help of Fig. 2.11. With an anode load of 100,000 ohms and an h.t. voltage of 200 volts, the gain obtainable is approximately 30; with an h.t. voltage of 300 volts, the gain is 70; and with an h.t. voltage of 400 volts, the gain rises to about 90. From the appropriate load lines it will be seen that little is gained by choosing an anode load of 200,000 ohms, unless a very high h.t. voltage is used.

Varying Screen-Grid Voltage

The screen-grid voltage has so far been considered constant. Owing to the finite magnitude of the screen capacitance C_s (Fig. 2.12), this is not so in practice. To find the influence of the screen impedance, we assume that the following data are known: $\mu_1 = -\partial V_s/\partial V_g$ (I_a constant), $r_s = dV_s/dI_s$, where V_s and I_s are screen voltage and screen current respectively. We assume that I_s is independent of V_a; hence $I_a = g_m V_g + V_s g_m/\mu_1$. If an e.m.f. E is applied between signal grid and cathode,

$$V_s = -\mu_1 E \frac{R_1}{R_1 + r_s} \cdot \frac{1}{1 + j\omega C_s R'}$$

where

$$R' = \frac{R_1 r_s}{R_1 + r_s}$$

Hence

$$I_a = E g_m \left(1 - \frac{R_1}{R_1 + r_s} \cdot \frac{1}{1 + j\omega C_s R'}\right)$$

$$= E g_m \left[1 - \frac{R_1}{R_1 + r_s} \cdot \frac{1}{1 + (\omega C_s R')^2} + j \frac{R_1}{R_1 + r_s} \cdot \frac{\omega C_s R'}{1 + (\omega C_s R')^2}\right]$$

$$= \frac{E g_m}{(R_1 + r_s)[1 + (\omega C_s R')^2]} \times [r_s + (R_1 + r_s)(\omega C_s R')^2 + j R_1 R' \omega C_s] \quad (2.10)$$

The phase displacement ϕ of the anode current due to the screen impedance is given by

$$\tan \phi = \frac{R_1}{(R_1 + r_s)\omega C_s R' + (r_s/\omega C_s R')}$$

Differentiation of the denominator with respect to ω shows that $\tan \phi$ is a maximum when

$$\omega C_s R' = \left(\frac{r_s}{R_1+r_s}\right)^{1/2}, \tan\phi \text{ being } \frac{R_1}{2[r_s(R_1+r_s)]^{1/2}}$$

We put $R_1 = ar_s$, then $\tan\phi$ is a maximum when

$$\omega C_s r_s = \frac{(1+a)^{1/2}}{a}, \tan\phi \text{ being } \frac{a}{2(1+a)^{1/2}}$$

With maximum $\tan\phi$ the anode current becomes

$$I_a = Eg_m\left(1 - \frac{a}{1+a}\times\frac{1}{1+j(1/1+a)^{1/2}}\right) = Eg_m\frac{1+j(1+a)^{1/2}}{1+a+j(1+a)^{1/2}}$$

whence

$$|I_a| = Eg_m\left(\frac{1+1+a}{1+2a+a^2+1+a}\right)^{1/2} = \frac{Eg_m}{(1+a)^{1/2}} \qquad (2.11)$$

When the potential of the screen is obtained by means of a series resistance from a large h.t. voltage, the ratio $a = R_1/r_s$ may easily be about 10, so that the maximum phase displacement of the anode current caused by the screen voltage will be 50–60°. Then the anode current, through the effect of the screen, is reduced to about one-third of its value at higher frequencies. The effect of the screen on the phase of the anode current may easily prove to be very important when feedback over several stages is to be taken into account. It can be kept small by using a low-resistance potentiometer for the screen. The value R_1 in the above calculation is then the parallel combination of the two potentiometer resistances.

Chapter Three

NEGATIVE FEEDBACK

By S. W. Punnett

Introduction

Owing to advances in vacuum tube development and amplifier technique it is now possible to secure any desired amplification over a very great range of frequencies down to and including zero frequency (direct-current amplification). The upper limit of the maximum usable gain is set by the inherent noise generated within the amplifier (see chapter seven).

Often it is desirable that the gain of an amplifier shall be as far as possible independent of variations of valve and circuit parameters. Since the valve parameters are functions of the supply voltages, variations in these must be taken into account. The desirability of stabilizing the supply voltages and methods of achieving this are dealt with in chapter six. Constancy of gain is obviously required where the amplifier is to be used as a means of raising the level of a small signal, to be measured accurately, sufficiently for the signal to actuate an indicating device. Where an accurate absolute measurement is not required, the operation of the amplifier itself may still demand high stability. For example, the bandwidth of the selective amplifiers considered in chapter four depends directly on the magnitude of the gain. Thus variation of the gain results in a variation of the bandwidth of the amplifier. Furthermore, although the modern valve has remarkably linear properties, variations in the valve parameters with the amplitude of signal do occur. The anode current of any valve may be expressed in a power series as follows,

$$I_a = a_0 + a_1(\mu V_g + V_a) + a_2(\mu V_g + V_a)^2 + \dots \qquad (3.1)$$

where a_0, a_1, a_2, etc., are constants depending on the valve geometry, μ is the amplification factor, and V_g and V_a are the alternating voltages applied to the control grid and anode respectively. Thus, if the signal applied to the grid consists of a single-frequency sinusoidal voltage, the output from the anode contains harmonics of the applied signal in addition to the fundamental output. Furthermore, if the applied signal contains voltages of more than one frequency, intermodulation will occur and new frequencies other than harmonics appear. For

31

example, if the applied signal contains voltages of frequency 100 c/s and 150 c/s, the output contains such combination frequencies as 50 c/s, 250 c/s, 350 c/s, and so on.

It is found that considerable improvements in the performance of amplifiers can be achieved by the use of *negative feedback*. Suppose an amplifier is constructed with a gain which is made deliberately 100 times higher (40 dB) than is necessary and then a sufficient proportion of the output is connected to the input to reduce the effective gain to the value necessary for the purpose of the amplifier. A remarkable improvement is then effected in the constancy of the gain. Also, the harmonic and intermodulation voltages generated by the amplifier are reduced in amplitude. Sometimes the noise output is reduced as well; this depends on the point at which the noise is introduced into the amplifier chain. There are also changes in the input and output impedances of the amplifier. Moreover it is possible to arrange for the gain of the amplifier to vary with the frequency of the applied signal in practically any desired manner. In particular the gain may be made small except over a narrow band of frequencies, which thus produces a selective amplifier. A detailed consideration of these changes will next be made.

GENERAL

The generalized feedback amplifier is shown in Fig. 3.1. This consists of two main branches or circuits. The upper, or m branch, contains the active elements, i.e. the amplifying devices. The amplifier has an

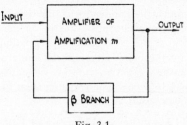

Fig. 3.1

amplification m which is in general complex and may be written $|m|\exp j(\theta)$ where $|m|$ is the magnitude of the amplification and θ is the phase shift introduced by this branch. The lower branch is the feedback or β circuit, and this is usually, but not necessarily, a passive circuit. If a voltage V is applied to this circuit the output is βV. As with m the quantity β is in general complex and may be written $|\beta|\exp j(\phi)$. The manner in which a voltage of unit size is modified after once traversing each circuit is thus denoted by m and β respectively. The product $m\beta$, known as the *feedback factor*, shows the way in which unit voltage is changed after making a single journey round amplifier and feedback branches. Both of the complex quantities m and β are functions of frequency, and in the generalized concept each may be greater or less in absolute value than unity.

The case when there is no feedback (β equal to zero) is used as a reference state. If a signal V_i is applied, the output consists of an amplified signal V_0 equal to mV_i and the components which are not wanted, namely noise and distortion. The noise N_0 and distortion D_0 are both assumed to be generated within the amplifier. It is further assumed that the noise is independent of the signal; noise which is contained in V_i is regarded as part of the input. The distortion D_0 is regarded as being a function of the signal output only; thus D_0 is equal to a function of V_0, say $F(V_0)$. The total output from the amplifier is therefore $(V_0+N_0+D_0)$ and must be given by

$$V_0+N_0+D_0 = mV_i+N_0+F(V_0) \tag{3.2}$$

We now consider the case when β is finite. Let the output voltage then be $(V+N+D)$. A voltage is fed back to the input terminals, and the total signal applied to the upper or m branch is $V_i+(V+N+D)\beta$. In consequence the total output from the amplifier must be m times this voltage plus the components due to noise and distortion. The total output thus equals

$$m[V_i+\beta(V+N+D)]+N_0+F(V)$$

The last term is the distortion and must be a function of the desired signal output V. But the total output must be the assumed output $(V+N+D)$, and therefore

$$(V+N+D) = m[V_i+\beta(V+N+D)]+N_0+F(V)$$

This may be rearranged to give

$$(V+N+D) = \frac{mV_i}{1-m\beta} + \frac{N_0}{1-m\beta} + \frac{F(V)}{1-m\beta} \tag{3.3}$$

This equation gives the total output from the amplifier and may be compared with that for the case when β equals zero. We now consider the three components of this equation separately.

GAIN AND PHASE SHIFT OF THE FEEDBACK AMPLIFIER

The amplification of the signal voltage V_i with feedback equals that without feedback divided by the factor $(1-m\beta)$. The feedback is referred to as positive or negative according as the absolute value of $1/(1-m\beta)$ is greater or less than unity. If $m\beta$ is real and negative the feedback is negative and the amplification is decreased. If $m\beta$ is real, positive and less than unity, the feedback is positive and the amplification is increased. In the special case when $m\beta$ is equal to unity, the amplification is infinite, i.e. the system is no longer stable and self-oscillation occurs. Thus an output is obtained with no applied signal.

A simple example will now be considered. Let the amplifier introduce no phase shift, so that the amplification is $m \exp j (0)$ and let the feedback β be equal to $-n$ where n is a real number. If the effective gain is designated by m_f, then

$$m_f = \frac{m}{1+nm} \tag{3.4}$$

If this expression is differentiated with respect to m at constant n, and then with respect to n at constant m, the following expressions are obtained

$$\left[\frac{\Delta m_f}{m_f} \right]_n = \frac{\Delta m/m}{1+nm} \tag{3.5}$$

and

$$\left[\frac{\Delta m_f}{m_f} \right]_m = -\frac{\Delta n}{n} \cdot \frac{nm}{1+nm} \tag{3.6}$$

These expressions permit a determination of the gain stability for small variations Δm and Δn in the amplifier and feedback branches respectively. It can be seen from eqn. (3.5) that the fractional change in effective gain for a variation Δm is reduced by an amount corresponding to the reduction in amplification. When $m\beta$ is large the effect of introducing a gain or loss in the m branch is to produce no appreciable change in the effective gain of the system. From eqn. (3.6) the stability of effective gain, as affected by variations in the β branch, is almost the same as the stability of gain in the β branch itself. Hence the feedback circuits must be very stable. When $m\beta$ is very large compared with unity, we have from eqn. (3.5)

$$\left[\frac{\Delta m_f}{m_f} \right]_n = \frac{1}{nm} \cdot \frac{\Delta m}{m} \tag{3.7}$$

From this latter equation, or from the accurate equation (3.5), it is possible to calculate the value of the amplification m required with a given value of β to secure a desired constancy of gain.

Examples

1. Suppose the gain of an amplifier is to be made constant to within ± 1 per cent, and the feedback coefficient β equals $-1/500$. Find the necessary value of the amplification. The variations in the circuit parameters, valves and supply voltages are such that variations of ± 20 per cent occur in the value of m.

From eqn. (3.7),

$$0 \cdot 01 = \frac{1}{nm} \times 0 \cdot 2$$

Therefore

$$m = 10{,}000$$

2. Suppose the gain of an amplifier is to be made constant to within ± 1 per cent of the value 100. Find the necessary amplification and feedback coefficient. Simultaneous solution of the two equations (3.4) and (3.5) yields the required values of m and n. Thus

$$100 = \frac{m}{1+nm} \quad \text{and} \quad 0 \cdot 01 = \frac{1}{1+nm} \times 0 \cdot 2$$

Hence $m = 2000$, and $n = 0 \cdot 0095$. The loss in gain of 26 dB (the gain is reduced from 2000 to 100) is amply repaid by the twenty-fold improvement in the stability of the feedback amplifier.

In any real amplifier m and β are complex and the product $m\beta$ can be written $|m\beta| \exp j(\alpha)$. The gain of the feedback amplifier is given by

$$m_f = \frac{m}{1 - |m\beta| \exp j(\alpha)} \tag{3.8}$$

The quantity which is usually of greatest interest is the magnitude of the gain $|m_f|$. We have

$$|m_f| = \frac{|m|}{(1 - 2|m\beta| \cos \alpha + |m\beta|^2)^{1/2}} \tag{3.9}$$

From this expression the following equations, which show the improvement in the stability, may be obtained by differentiation:

$$\left[\frac{\Delta|m_f|}{|m_f|} \right]_{\beta,\,\alpha} = \frac{1 - |m\beta| \cos \alpha}{(1 - |m\beta|)^2} \cdot \frac{\Delta|m|}{|m|} \tag{3.10}$$

$$\left[\frac{\Delta|m_f|}{|m_f|} \right]_{m,\,\alpha} = \frac{|m\beta|}{1 - |m\beta|} \cdot \frac{\cos \alpha - |m\beta|}{1 - |m\beta|} \cdot \frac{\Delta|\beta|}{|\beta|} \tag{3.11}$$

Only eqn. (3.10) is of any great use. Over most of the useful range of a feedback amplifier, α is approximately equal to π, and hence eqn. (3.10) becomes:

$$\frac{\Delta|m_f|}{|m_f|} \sim \frac{1}{1+|m\beta|} \cdot \frac{\Delta|m|}{|m|} \qquad (3.12)$$

If $m\beta$ is very large compared with unity,

$$\frac{\Delta|m_f|}{|m_f|} \sim \frac{1}{|m\beta|} \cdot \frac{\Delta|m|}{|m|} \qquad (3.13)$$

This is the same as eqn. (3.7) deduced in the simple case. Negative feedback, it can be shown, always improves the stability by an amount at least as great as corresponds to the reduction in gain. It should be noted that if $m\beta$ is very large compared with unity, $(1-m\beta)$ tends to $-m\beta$ and thus the effective gain approaches the value of $-1/\beta$. Then the amplifier frequency-gain characteristic is determined solely by the frequency-loss characteristic of the β circuit. This is the principle underlying the audio-frequency amplifiers discussed in Chapter Four.

The effect of feedback on the phase shift introduced by the amplifier is best shown by considering a simple case. Let the amplification of the amplifier branch be $|m|\exp j(\pi+\phi)$ and let the feedback be $n \exp j(0)$ where n is a real number. This holds for a simple resistance-loaded stage

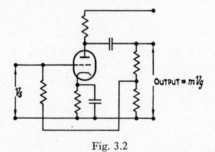

Fig. 3.2

with pure resistance networks for the feedback circuit, as shown in Fig. 3.2. The phase shift deviates from the value π owing to stray capacitances at high frequencies and to the coupling at low frequencies.

Now

$$m_f = \frac{m}{1-m\beta}$$

Hence

$$m_f = \frac{|m|\exp j(\pi+\phi)}{1-n|m|\exp j(\pi+\phi)} \qquad (3.14)$$

Thus

$$m_f = \frac{1 \exp j(\pi+\phi)}{(1/|m|+n \cos\phi)+jn \sin\phi} \tag{3.15}$$

This may be written

$$m_f = \frac{1 \exp j(\pi+\phi)}{n' \exp j(\theta)} \tag{3.16}$$

where

$$n' = [(1/|m| + n \cos\phi)^2+(n \sin\phi)^2]^{1/2}$$

and

$$\tan\theta = \frac{n \sin\phi}{(1/|m|)+n \cos\phi}$$

Therefore n' is greater than n and θ is less than ϕ. The gain with feedback is thus given by

$$m_f = (1/n')/\exp j(\pi+\phi-\theta) \tag{3.17}$$

The phase shift is made more nearly equal to π. If the value of ϕ is small the following is approximately true.

$$\theta = \frac{n\phi}{(1/|m|)+n} = \frac{|m|n\phi}{1+|m|n} \tag{3.18}$$

Hence the value of the new deviation $(\phi-\theta)$, in the phase shift from the value π is

$$\phi - \frac{|m|n\phi}{1+|m|n} = \frac{\phi}{1+|m|n} = \phi' \tag{3.19}$$

Thus the new phase shift is, for small deviations from π, equal to the original value multiplied by the factor $1/(1-m\beta)$.

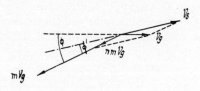

Fig. 3.3

This effect is very clearly demonstrated by the vector diagram of Fig. 3.3. The voltage V_g between grid and cathode of the valve gives rise to the output mV_g, which is $(\pi + \phi)$ out of phase with V_g. The feedback voltage is thus nmV_g. Now V_g is the sum of the feedback voltage and the signal voltage V_s. Hence V_s is as shown; this voltage is only $(\pi + \phi')$ out of phase with mV_g, where ϕ' is less than ϕ.

In the general case, with β equal to $n \exp j(\theta)$ and with $|m\beta|$ large compared with unity, the following holds:

$$m_f = \frac{m}{1 - m\beta} \sim -1/\beta$$

Thus

$$m_f = -\frac{1}{n \exp j(\theta)} = \left(\frac{1}{n}\right) \exp j(\pi + \theta) \qquad (3.20)$$

In general the application of negative feedback to an amplifier is such as to cause the amplifier phase shift to approach that of the feedback circuit plus π.

DISTORTION

To determine the effect of feedback upon the distortion produced in the amplifier it is necessary to assume that the output of the desired signal is made to have the same value for the amplifier operating both with and without feedback. If this is not so, no fair comparison can be made between the two output signals produced with and without feedback. With equal outputs all the valves in the amplifier are operating over the same parts of their characteristics under both feedback and non-feedback conditions.

For the feedback amplifier the output, from eqn. (3.3), is given by

$$V + D = \frac{mV_i}{1 - m\beta} + \frac{F(V)}{1 - m\beta} \qquad (3.21)$$

The noise components are ignored here.

To give the same output V_0 as with no feedback, the input must be increased from V_i to $(1 - m\beta)V_i$. Then the distortion $F(V)$ generated within the amplifier assumes its value without feedback, that is $F(V_0)$. Consequently the resulting distortion D with feedback is given by

$$D = \frac{F(V_0)}{1 - m\beta} = \frac{D_0}{1 - m\beta} \qquad (3.22)$$

From this simple derivation it is seen that the distortion is reduced in the same ratio as the gain is reduced. But this relationship is only approximate. The input without feedback is free from distortion and with feedback it is not. Hence the assumption that the generated distortion is a function of the signal output only is not necessarily justified. Further, it has been assumed that the value of m is constant; when the amplitude characteristic of the amplifier is non-linear this cannot be the case. The value of m varies over the cycle. To take an extreme case, suppose the input valve is biased to cut-off as shown in Fig. 3.4. The output will consist of half-cycles, and no amount of

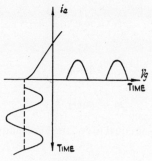

Fig. 3.4

feedback can alter this. The simple formula derived above is however obeyed quite well provided the distortion is not too great.

NOISE

The last term in the expression [eqn. (3.3)] for the total output from the feedback amplifier is now considered. This is the noise output given by

$$N = \frac{N_0}{1 - m\beta} \tag{3.23}$$

Little information can be obtained from this. It is not possible, for example, to determine directly from it whether it implies any improvement in the signal/noise ratio through feedback, since this depends on

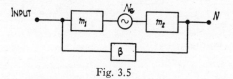

Fig. 3.5

where the noise signals are generated in the amplifier. To examine this question the amplifier branch is split into two sections with amplifications m_1 and m_2, as shown in the block diagram of Fig. (3.5).

D

A noise generator of e.m.f. N_G is inserted between the two sections, and this results in a noise output N. The e.m.f. N_G may be due to such factors as power supply hum, bad contacts, etc. As a result of the feedback path the noise voltage appearing at the output terminals of the m_1 amplifier is $N\beta m_1$. Hence the total input to the m_2 amplifier is $(N_G+\beta m_1 N)$, and the output is therefore $m_2(N_G+\beta m_1 N)$. This must equal N.

Thus

$$N = m_2(N_G+\beta m_1 N)$$

and

$$N = \frac{N_G m_2}{1-m\beta}$$

where

$$m = m_1 m_2$$

Since the output $m_2 N_G$ is equal to N_0, the noise output with no feedback, we have

$$N = \frac{N_0}{1-m\beta} \tag{3.24}$$

which agrees with eqn. (3.23).

Now consider Fig. 3.6(a); the feedback amplifier is split into two sections of amplifications $(1-m\beta)$ and $m/(1-m\beta)$. A signal V_i is applied which results in an output V. A noise voltage N_G is injected at the junction of the two sections as in Fig. 3.5. Fig. 3.6(b) shows an amplifier of amplification $m/(1-m\beta)$ without feedback. This is to be compared with the section having the same amplification in the feedback amplifier of Fig. 3.6(a). A signal voltage V_i and a noise voltage N_G are also applied to the input of this second amplifier. The output voltage is therefore also V. Thus the signal level in the amplifier of Fig. 3.6(b) is the

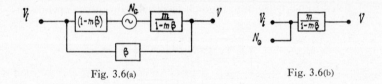

Fig. 3.6(a)   Fig. 3.6(b)

same at every point as in the section of amplification $m/(1-m\beta)$ in the feedback amplifier of Fig. 3.6(a). Hence the conditions in these two are identical and a fair comparison may be made.

The total outputs, including noise, are:

For Fig. 3.6(a) $\quad V_i \cdot \dfrac{m}{1-m\beta} + \dfrac{N_G}{1-m\beta} \cdot \dfrac{m}{1-m\beta}$, from eqn. (3.23)

For Fig. 3.6(b) $\quad V_i \cdot \dfrac{m}{1-m\beta} + N_G \cdot \dfrac{m}{1-m\beta}$

Therefore the output signal/noise ratios in the two amplifiers are:

For Fig. 3.6(a) $\qquad \dfrac{V_i(1-m\beta)}{N_G}$

For Fig. 3.6(b) $\qquad \dfrac{V_i}{N_G}$

Thus there is an improvement in the signal/noise ratio. Hence it may be deduced that for noise originating in the section with an amplification $m/(1-m\beta)$, the feedback is effective in improving the signal/ noise ratio. For noise originating in the section with amplification $(1-m\beta)$ the improvement is smaller. For noise originating at the input terminals where both the signal and noise are reduced by the factor $(1-m\beta)$, feedback produces no improvement at all.

Types of Feedback Circuit

In order to determine the effect of feedback on the input and output impedances of feedback amplifiers, it is necessary to specify in greater detail the exact manner in which the circuit is arranged. Feedback amplifiers can be divided into a number of basic types.[1] The three commonest are:

(i) Series-feedback amplifiers
(ii) Shunt-feedback amplifiers
(iii) A combination of (i) and (ii)

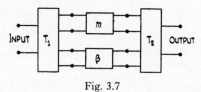

Fig. 3.7

The general arrangement of any feedback amplifier is shown in Fig. 3.7. The layout of the connections within the two six-terminal connectors T_1 and T_2 determines the type to which the amplifier

42

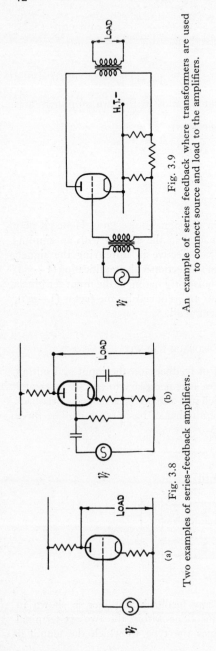

Fig. 3.8

Two examples of series-feedback amplifiers.

Fig. 3.9

An example of series feedback where transformers are used to connect source and load to the amplifiers.

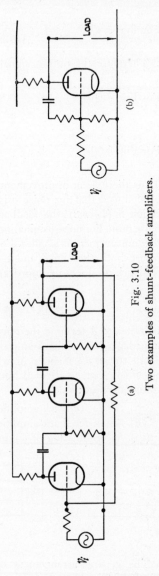

Fig. 3.10

Two examples of shunt-feedback amplifiers.

belongs. Figs. 3.8 to 3.11 show simple examples of the three types dealt with in this chapter. The circuits show clearly the characteristic features of the three types. In the series-feedback amplifiers the m and β circuits, as seen from the signal source or from the load, are in series at each end of the amplifier. In the shunt amplifier the m and β circuits are in parallel as seen from the source and the load. Fig. 3.11

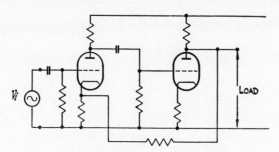

Fig. 3.11
An amplifier which employs both series and shunt feedback.

shows both types of feedback existing in the same circuit. It is also possible to have series connection at the input and shunt connection at the output, and vice versa.

IMPEDANCE CHANGES DUE TO FEEDBACK

It is now proposed to investigate the impedance presented to the signal source and to the load by certain simple feedback amplifiers. In all the following calculations the presence of parasitic elements such as inter-electrode capacitances is ignored unless specifically mentioned. Further it is assumed that biasing and decoupling arrangements are perfect.

The circuit shown in Fig. 3.12 is that of a simple series-type feedback amplifier. In order to find the input impedance between the terminals marked XX it is necessary to find the current I which flows into these terminals on connecting a constant-voltage generator of e.m.f. V_i.

Thus
$$Z_{in} = \frac{V_i}{I}$$

This has two values. One, the passive impedance Z_p, is the value measured when the valve is cold. For the circuit of Fig. 3.12,

$$Z_p = R_g + R_c$$

The other, designated Z_a, is that measured when the valve is functioning normally, and its value is found below. The anode current I_a, due to the applied signal V_i, sets up a voltage $I_a R_c$ across the cathode

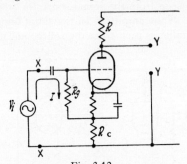

Fig. 3.12

A simple series-feedback amplifier, whose input and output impedances are to be determined.

resistor. Thus the voltage between grid and cathode is not V_i but $(V_i - I_a R_c)$. If use is now made of the formula for the anode current of a valve in terms of the grid and anode voltages the output and gain may be determined.

Thus

$$I_a = g_m V_g + V_a/r_a$$

where g_m and r_a have their usual meanings and I_a, V_i, V_g, and V_a are alternating currents and potentials. The d.c. levels have been assumed to be correctly set and are of no interest here.

Hence

$$I_a = g_m(V_i - I_a R_c) - \frac{I_a(R + R_c)}{r_a}$$

since

$$V_g = (V_i - I_a R_c) \quad \text{and} \quad V_a = -I_a(R + R_c)$$

Thus

$$I_a = \frac{\mu V_i}{r_a + R_c(\mu + 1) + R}$$

The output voltage V_0 and the gain m_f are therefore given by

$$V_0 = -I_a R = -V_i \cdot \frac{\mu R}{r_a + R_c(\mu + 1) + R}$$

$$m_f = -\frac{\mu R}{r_a + \mu R_c + (R + R_c)} \tag{3.25}$$

The voltage across the cathode resistance R_c is also part of the output voltage and this should be included in the calculation of the gain. If allowance is made for this the gain becomes

$$m_f = -\frac{\mu(R+R_c)}{r_a+\mu R_c+(R+R_c)}$$

If the numerator and denominator of this expression are divided by (r_a+R+R_c) the following is obtained:

$$m_f = \frac{-\dfrac{\mu(R+R_c)}{r_a+(R+R_c)}}{1+\dfrac{\mu R_c}{r_a+(R+R_c)}} \tag{3.26}$$

The numerator of this expression is the amplification which would be obtained if R_c were in the anode lead with R, and is the quantity that has been designated m. Therefore the value of the gain can be written

$$m_f = \frac{m}{1-m\cdot\dfrac{R_c}{R+R_c}}$$

The factor $R_c/(R+R_c)$ is β, the feedback. Thus the gain of the feedback amplifier is $m/(1-m\beta)$.

Now the current I which is drawn from the signal source V_i is the voltage V_g divided by R_g, i.e. $I = (V_i-I_aR_c)/R_g$. Insertion of the value of I_a found above gives

$$I = \frac{V_i}{R_g}-\frac{R_c}{R_g}\cdot\frac{\mu V_i}{r_a+\mu R_c+(R+R_c)}$$

Rearrangement of this expression yields

$$Z_a = \frac{V_i}{I} = R_g\cdot\frac{r_a+(R+R_c)+\mu R_c}{r_a+(R+R_c)}$$

Thus

$$Z_a = R_g\left(1+\frac{\mu R_c}{r_a+(R+R_c)}\right) \tag{3.27}$$

As is seen above for the gain the second factor within the bracket is $-m\beta$. Thus the active impedance Z_a is equal to $R_g(1-m\beta)$. One factor has been ignored in this derivation. The current I through R_g also flows through the cathode resistance R_c and modifies the cathode voltage. With the values of R_g and R_c that are normally employed this has only a very small effect on the result. If allowance is made for this, it can be shown that the active impedance becomes

$$Z_a = R_g(1-m\beta)+R_c \cdot \frac{r_a+R}{r_a+R+R_c}$$

The effect of feedback is to multiply the value of the grid resistor by the factor $(1-m\beta)$. Apart from the effect on the term R_c in the value of Z_a, the input impedance is increased by the factor by which the gain is reduced.

The output impedance of this circuit can be found by short-circuiting the terminals XX and connecting the impedanceless generator of e.m.f. V_i to the terminals Y. With no feedback the impedance looking in at these terminals consists of the load R and the valve impedance in parallel. The feedback can be removed for this purpose by the connection of a very large capacitor across the cathode resistor R_c.

Thus
$$Z_p = \frac{Rr_a}{(R+r_a)}$$

or, in terms of admittance, which is the reciprocal of impedance (cf. conductance and resistance),

$$Y_p = 1/R+1/r_a$$

With feedback present the anode current I_a flows through the cathode resistor R_c, and there is therefore a signal between grid and cathode.

Hence
$$I_a = g_m(-I_aR_c)+(V_i-I_aR_c)/r_a \tag{3.28}$$

The grid voltage is $-I_aR_c$ and the anode voltage is $(V_i-I_aR_c)$. Now the generator connected to the terminals YY has no impedance and thus the whole of I_a flows through it. The total current which is drawn from the generator is I_a+V_i/R, this latter current being the current flowing through the anode load resistance.

Thus
$$I = I_a+V_i/R$$

Rearrangement of the expression given above for the anode current I_a yields

$$I_a = \frac{V_i}{(r_a+R_c+\mu R_c)}$$

On insertion of this value in the expression for I the following expression results:

$$I = V_i/R+V_i/(r_a+R_c+\mu R_c)$$

Therefore the active output admittance is

$$Y_a = I/V_i = 1/R + 1/(r_a + R_c + \mu R_c)$$

$$= 1/R + (1/r_a) \times 1/\{1 + R_c(\mu+1)/r_a\}$$

$$= 1/R + \frac{1}{r_a} \cdot \cfrac{1}{1 - m\beta \cdot \dfrac{\mu+1}{\mu} \cdot \dfrac{r_a + R + R_c}{r_a}} \tag{3.29}$$

The internal impedance of the valve is increased by a factor which is greater than the factor $(1 - m\beta)$. The total impedance does not increase by this factor owing to the presence of the anode load resistance R, which is the limiting value of the output impedance. From these and similar results the following general rule may be derived. *The active input and output impedances of a series-type feedback amplifier are $(1 - m\beta)$, or more, times the passive values, except that the change may be masked by the presence of a circuit element not actually participating in the feedback action.* The feedback amplifier considered above exemplifies this latter proviso.

An example of the shunt feedback type is now examined. The circuit is shown in Fig. 3.13; here a pentode valve is used. The amplifier and feedback circuits are in parallel from the point of view of the signal source and of the load. The input impedance which is to be found is that between the terminals XX. As before, the current which flows into these terminals due to the e.m.f. V_i is calculated, and from this the value of the input impedance is found. It is to be noted that this is

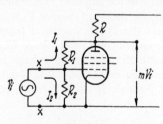

Fig. 3.13
A simple shunt-feedback amplifier whose input and output impedances are to be determined.

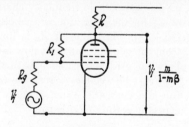

Fig. 3.14
A modification of the circuit of Fig. 3.13.

not the manner in which a signal to be amplified is connected to the circuit. There is no feedback as far as V_i is concerned, and the output is $-g_m R V_i$, the value it has with no feedback circuit. To simplify the calculations, we assume that the load resistance R is very much smaller than r_a, R_1, or R_2. Thus the gain has the value $m = -g_mR$, and β is equal to $R_2/(R_1+R_2)$. The passive input impedance is equal to $R_1R_2/(R_1+R_2)$, the effect of R in series with R_1 being ignored. The value of the active impedance is determined as follows. The voltage at the anode is $-g_mRV_i$, and thus the voltage across R is $[V_i-(-g_mRV_i)]$. The total current which is drawn from the generator is

$$I = I_1+I_2 = V_i/R_2+V_i(1+g_mR)/R_1$$

Therefore the active impedance is

$$Z_a = \frac{V_i}{I_1+I_2} = \frac{R_1R_2}{R_1+R_2-mR_2}$$

where $-g_mR$ has been replaced by the amplification m.
Hence

$$Z_a = \frac{R_1R_2}{(R_1+R_2)-m\cdot\dfrac{R_2}{R_1+R_2}\cdot(R_1+R_2)}$$

$$= \frac{R_1R_2}{R_1+R_2}\cdot\frac{1}{1-m\beta} \tag{3.30}$$

In practice the signal source must be connected to the feedback amplifier as shown in Fig. 3.14. The feedback voltage is developed across the internal impedance R_g of the generator. This impedance can, if necessary, be augmented by the addition of external components to give a desired gain frequency characteristic to the amplifier. The value of Z_p for the generator as a whole is R_1, for the e.m.f. source V_i it is (R_g+R_1). The value of Z_a is found as follows. If a current I flows from the generator it must flow into Z_a, and thus set up a voltage IZ_a between grid and cathode with the result that the anode voltage is $+mIZ_a$. The voltage across the resistance R_1 is therefore $IZ_a(1-m)$. But the current I must actually flow through R_1, and the voltage across it is thus IR_1; hence

$$IR_1 = IZ_a(1-m)$$

and

$$Z_a = \frac{R_1}{1-m}$$

It is to be noted that m is a negative quantity. From the point of view of the generator as a whole the impedance has been decreased by a factor greater than $(1-m\beta)$. An expression involving $(1-m\beta)$ is obtained if the constant-voltage generator is replaced by a constant-current generator having in shunt with it an impedance R_g. This is shown in Fig. 3.15. The feedback voltage is developed across R_g as before. The passive impedance seen by the constant-current generator

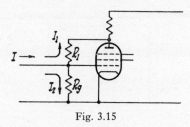

Fig. 3.15

is $R_1R_g/(R_1+R_g)$. In the active state the grid voltage is I_2R_g, where I_2 is the current through the grid resistance. The output is mI_2R_g and thus the voltage across R_1 is $I_2(R_g-mR_g)$. This must equal I_1R_1, where I_1 is the portion of the current from the constant-current generator which flows through R_1.

Thus
$$I_1R_1 = I_2R_g(1-m)$$

The total input current I is the sum of I_1 and I_2, and therefore

$$I = \frac{I_2R_g(1-m)}{R_1} + I_2$$

Hence the current I_2 is given by

$$I_2 = \frac{R_1I}{R_1+R_g-mR_g}$$

The grid voltage V_g must therefore be given by

$$V_g = \frac{R_1R_gI}{(R_1+R_g)-mR_g(R_1+R_g)/(R_1+R_g)} \tag{3.31}$$

On the other hand the grid voltage must also be IZ_a, since, so far as the constant-current generator is concerned, it is working into an impedance Z_a.

Hence
$$Z_a = \frac{R_1R_g}{R_1+R_g} \cdot \frac{1}{1-m\beta}$$

since here β is equal to $R_g/(R_1+R_g)$. The input impedance is thus reduced by a factor at least as great as $(1-m\beta)$.

To determine the values of the output impedances, the generator of e.m.f. V_i and zero internal impedance is connected as shown in Fig. 3.16. This generator drives a current I through the anode load resistance R and a current I_a through the valve. The impedance with no feedback

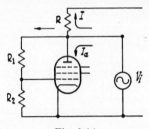

Fig. 3.16

A constant-voltage generator connected to the output of the shuntback amplifier to determine the active output impendance.

is thus R and the anode resistance r_a in parallel; this is approximately R since it is assumed that R is very small compared with r_a. When feedback is applied the active output impedance Z_a is still given by $V_i/(I+I_a)$, but I_a is no longer to be neglected compared with I.

Here
$$I_a = g_m V_g = g_m V_i \cdot \frac{R_2}{R_1 + R_2} = g_m V_i \beta$$

Thus
$$Z_a = \frac{V_i}{V_i/R + g_m V_i \beta} = \frac{R}{1 + g_m R \beta}$$

The amplification m is equal to $-g_m R$, and therefore

$$Z_a = \frac{R}{1 - m\beta}$$

The output impedance is thus reduced by the factor $(1-m\beta)$.

From these and similar calculations the following general rule can be derived. *With shunt feedback the active input and output impedances are equal to the passive values divided by a factor at least as great as* $(1-m\beta)$.

These changes in impedance can be advantageous. This is particularly true of the increase in input impedance with series feedback, and of the decrease in output impedance with shunt feedback. A very high input impedance is most useful when the signal source has itself a high impedance. The loss of signal voltage in the source impedance is then a minimum. The decrease in output impedance is of use when the load is of low impedance. It is particularly useful when employed to damp natural resonances in electro-mechanical devices such as loud-speakers. An extreme example of a low-impedance output is the cathode follower where the whole of the output voltage is used as feedback so that β is unity. Here the output impedance is approximately $1/g_m$ ohms. Since it is possible to have series-type feedback at the input and shunt type at the output, both a high input and a low output impedance are obtainable in the same amplifier.

In certain amplifiers it is desirable that there should be no change in the impedance levels due to the use of feedback. This can be achieved. From the above calculations it can be seen that by the use of equal amounts of series and shunt feedback the impedances should be substantially unchanged. This is in fact the case. It is also possible to arrange the feedback circuits in bridge form. [1] If the balance of the bridge is perfect no change in the impedances will occur.

STABILITY OF THE FEEDBACK AMPLIFIER

The most difficult problem to solve in negative-feedback amplifiers is that of stability. The greater the amount of feedback and the more stages over which it is applied, the greater the problem. The reason for the danger of self-oscillation can be clearly seen from the formula for the gain of a feedback amplifier.

$$G = \frac{m}{1-m\beta}$$

m and β are complex quantities, i.e. they modify voltages in magnitude and phase. They may be written $|m|\exp j(\theta)$ and $|\beta|\exp j(\phi)$ so that the product $m\beta$ is $|m\beta|\exp j(\theta')$ where θ' is equal to $(\theta+\phi)$. Over the useful frequency range of the amplifier, the phase θ' of the loop gain $m\beta$ is π, so that the gain is

$$|G| = \frac{|m|}{1+|m\beta|}$$

The phase of $m\beta$ is however a function of frequency; in general this is due to two factors. At low frequencies, except in the d.c. amplifier, coupling capacitors are used between stages and may also be necessary in the feedback path to block direct voltages. These result in an increased phase angle θ' at low frequencies. At the high-frequency end of the range the stray capacitances, particularly those from the anode to earth of each valve, cause a decreased phase shift. This is illustrated by Figs. 3.17 and 3.18. A simple triode stage is shown with C as the coupling capacitor and C_s as the stray capacitance from anode to earth. The manner in which the phase of m varies from zero frequency upwards is as shown in Fig. 3.18. The phase of m varies from $\pi/2$ to $3\pi/2$ when battery biasing is used and there is no decoupling. When cathode biasing, decoupling and pentodes are employed, these limits can be

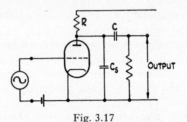

Fig. 3.17

A simple amplifier whose phase-frequency characteristic is sketched in Fig. 3.18.

exceeded. In multistage amplifiers it is possible for the phase of $m\beta$ to change by more than π from its value over the useful range of the amplifier. There will then be two frequencies, one below and one above the useful range, at which the phase of $m\beta$ becomes 0 or 2π

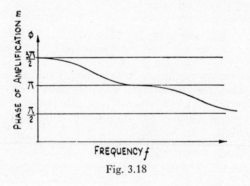

Fig. 3.18

(in general $2n\pi$ where n is any integer). Therefore the gain at these frequencies is given by

$$G = \frac{|m|}{1-|m\beta|}$$

If $|m\beta|$ is equal to unity at one or both of these frequencies, oscillation will occur, i.e. the gain as given by the formula is infinite. In very special circumstances oscillation will not occur, but these need not be considered here. If $|m\beta|$ is only slightly greater than unity, sustained oscillation, approximately sinusoidal, will occur. The amplitude is limited by the curvature of the valve characteristics, the value of $|m|$ being reduced by the curvature until the magnitude of $|m\beta|$ falls to unity.

It is clear that for the feedback amplifier to be stable the magnitude of the loop gain $m\beta$ must fall below unity before its phase has altered by an amount sufficient to cause oscillation. One-stage amplifiers are satisfactory unless they contain a transformer plus a coupling capacitor. The leakage inductance of the transformer may resonate with the capacitor in such a way as to cause a shift of π before $m\beta$ falls to less than unity.[2] Two-stage amplifiers are usually satisfactory when triodes are used unless transformers are present. Thus in the circuit shown in

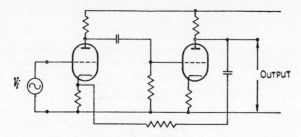

Fig. 3.19
A two-stage feedback amplifier which is stable no matter how
large a value of $m\beta$ is used.

Fig. 3.19 the loop gain will fall below unity in magnitude before the phase changes by π. The phase of the loop gain changes by π when the frequency is zero or infinity and this can cause no trouble. The use of pentodes in this circuit can lead to oscillation at low frequencies if $|m\beta|$ is very large. The chance of oscillation at high frequencies is not increased. The oscillation at low frequencies is due to the effect of the screen decoupling. As explained in chapter four, the presence of the screen capacitor results in the phase shift at low frequencies exceeding the value of $3\pi/2$ per stage. Thus if the feedback is large the magnitude of the loop gain $m\beta$ does not increase below unity before the phase changes by π. Fig. 3.20 shows the input stage of a two-stage amplifier of the type under consideration; the second stage is of identical gain. With an $m\beta$ value of about 100, the feedback amplifier will oscillate at a frequency of a few cycles per second. Increase of the $1\mu F$ screen decoupling capacitor to $4\mu F$ merely results in a decrease of the oscillatory frequency. This trouble can be cured by replacing the screen dropping resistor by a low-resistance potential divider, as shown in Fig. 3.21.

The change in the loop phase shift is now insufficient to produce oscillation until the frequency has fallen to a value such that the loop gain is well below unity in magnitude.

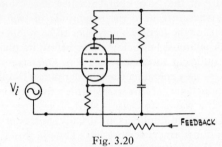

Fig. 3.20

The input stage of the amplifier of Fig. 3.19 when modified for the use of pentodes.

Feedback over three stages presents a much more difficult problem. Unless special steps are taken the maximum value of $m\beta$ that can be used is 8. This is shown by the following calculation. The circuit

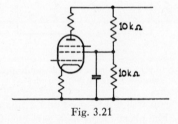

Fig. 3.21

of Fig. 3.22 is considered. Two assumptions are made. First, that the feedback path introduces no phase shift so that β is real, and the second is that r_a is very much larger than any of the load resistors R_1, R_2, and R_3. At the high-frequency end of the amplifier range the presence

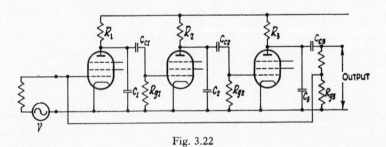

Fig. 3.22

of the coupling capacitors may be ignored and the variation of the gain with frequency is due solely to the stray capacitances C_1, C_2, and C_3. The amplification of the first valve is thus given by

$$m = -g_{m1} \cdot \frac{R_1/j\omega C_1}{R_1 + 1/j\omega C_1} = \frac{-g_{m1}R_1}{1+j\alpha_1}$$

where $\alpha_1 = \omega C_1 R_1$ and g_{m1} is the mutual conductance of the first valve. Thus the overall amplification m when no feedback is applied is given by

$$m = -\frac{g_{m1}g_{m2}g_{m3}R_1R_2R_3}{(1+j\alpha_1)(1+j\alpha_2)(1+j\alpha_3)} \tag{3.32}$$

where $\alpha_2 = \omega C_2 R_2$, and $\alpha_3 = \omega C_3 R_3$. The numerator of this expression is m_0, the amplification over the middle range of frequencies where the effect of the stray capacitances is negligible. Hence the expression can be written

$$m = \frac{m_0}{(1+j\alpha_1)(1+j\alpha_2)(1+j\alpha_3)}$$

$$= \frac{m_0}{1-(\alpha_1\alpha_2+\alpha_2\alpha_3+\alpha_3\alpha_1)+j(\alpha_1+\alpha_2+\alpha_3-\alpha_1\alpha_2\alpha_3)} \tag{3.33}$$

If the time-constants* of the three anode circuits are the same, so that $\alpha_1 = \alpha_2 = \alpha_3 = \alpha$ say, the amplification is given by

$$m = \frac{m_0}{(1-3\alpha^2)+j(3\alpha-\alpha^3)} \tag{3.34}$$

The equality of the time-constants implies that $C_1R_1 = C_2R_2 = C_3R_3$. This does not necessarily mean that the anode load resistances are all equal. As the frequency of the applied signal is raised α increases. When α equals $1/\sqrt{3}$ the amplification is

$$-j\frac{3\sqrt{3}m_0}{8}$$

The phase of $m\beta$ has therefore changed by $\pi/2$ from its value over the useful range of the amplifier since β itself introduces no phase shift. When $(3-\alpha^2)$ is equal to zero, i.e. $\alpha = \sqrt{3}$, the amplification is $-m_0/8$.

---

* Transient currents through a resistance and capacitance (or voltage across capacitance) follow the exponential law $\exp(-t/RC)$ where t=time. The time to the $1/e$ th of the final current (or voltage) is the time constant i.e. $t=RC$.

E

This means that the phase of $m\beta$ has changed by π compared with its value over the middle range of frequencies. Thus the feedback is now positive. When $\alpha = \sqrt{3}$, i.e. the frequency is equal to $\sqrt{3}/(2\pi C_1 R_1)$, the loop gain has decreased in magnitude by a factor of 8 and the phase has changed by π, compared with the values at medium frequencies. Hence if the amplifier is to be stable, the limiting value of $|m\beta|$ that may be employed over the useful range must not exceed 8. The magnitude of $m\beta$ then decreases to a value less than unity before the phase is such that oscillation is possible. Since a safety margin is necessary the usable magnitude of $|m\beta|$ is approximately 4 (12 dB* feedback), giving a safety factor of 2 (6 dB).

Now let one of the anode circuit time-constants be changed so that $\alpha_1 = \alpha_2 = 10\alpha_3 = \alpha$. This can be achieved by making R_3 one tenth of the value of R_1 or R_2. The response of the third stage is then flatter to a much higher frequency than the first two stages; the frequency at which the gain falls by 3 dB is ten times as high for the last stage as for the first two stages. As a result the amplification m is given by the expression

$$m = \frac{m_0}{(1 - 1 \cdot 2\alpha^2) + j(2 \cdot 1\alpha - 0 \cdot 1\alpha^3)} \tag{3.35}$$

The phase of m changes by π with respect to that over the middle range of frequencies when $(2.1\alpha - 0 \cdot 1\alpha^3) = 0$, the solution of this equation being $\alpha = \sqrt{21}$. The frequency at which this occurs is $\sqrt{21}/(2\pi C_1 R_1)$; this frequency is approximately three times as high as with equality of time-constants. The amplification at this frequency is $-m_0/24 \cdot 2$; thus the loop gain decreases by a factor of approximately 24 when the frequency is such that the phase of the loop gain has changed by π. Therefore an $m\beta$ value of 12 (21·6 dB feedback) may be employed with a safety margin of 2 (6 dB). Despite the fact that the value of m_0 in the second example is only one-tenth of that in the first, the second arrangement is to be preferred, since the stability depends on the product $m\beta$ and not on the individual values of m and β.

To determine the optimum conditions, the general case is now considered. Suppose the anode resistances and stray capacitances are such that $\alpha_1 = n\alpha_2 = n'\alpha_3 = \alpha$, and therefore $C_1 R_1 = n C_2 R_2 = n' C_3 R_3$, where n and n' are pure numerics. Since it is not usually advantageous to increase the stray capacitances, these are approximately equal if the same type of valve is used in each stage, and thus $R_1 = n R_2 = n' R_3$.

* The decibel (dB) is the unit of power change expressed as $10.\log_{10}(P_1/P_2)$ for powers P_1 and P_2. As the power is proportional to (volts)^2, a voltage gain is $10.\log_{10}(m_1/m_2)$ dB for gains m_1 and m_2.

In terms of the new variables α, n and n' the overall gain of the three stages becomes

$$m = \frac{-g_{m1}g_{m2}g_{m3}R_1R_2R_3}{I-\alpha^2(1/n+1/n'+1/nn')+j\alpha(1+1/n+1/n'-\alpha^2/nn')} \quad (3.36)$$

The phase of m alters by π when the frequency is such that α^2/nn' is equal to $(1+1/n+1/n')$, that is the variable α is equal to $\sqrt{(n+n'+nn')}$. This occurs when the frequency of the applied signal is $\sqrt{(n+n'+nn')}/2\alpha C_1R_1$; and the overall gain is then

$$m = \frac{m_0}{2+(n+1/n)+(n'+1/n')+(n/n'+n'/n)} \quad (3.37)$$

Clearly the worst possible conditions are those for which n and n' are equal to unity; the three terms in the brackets then have their minimum values. The maximum usable magnitude of $m\beta$ that may be employed is equal to the denominator of the expression for m found above; therefore when it is desired to use large amounts of feedback, n and n' must either be as large, or as small, as possible. Thus the amplifier consists of either (*a*) one narrow-band stage and two wide-band stages; or (b) two narrow-band stages and one wide-band stage. As far as stability against oscillation is concerned, these two arrangements are identical. Other factors determine which is to be used. These are the gain that is required and the frequency range over which the magnitude of the feedback factor $m\beta$ must be maintained approximately constant. The effect of these is shown in the two sections below.

(*a*) *One narrow-band stage.* The magnitude of $m\beta$ is maintained up to the frequency at which the gain of the narrow-band stage begins to fall off owing to stray capacitance. If the feedback is to be maintained up to a frequency f_1 and the first stage is the narrow one, then the value of R_1 is determined by

$$R_1 = \frac{1}{2\pi f_1 C_1} = R, \text{ say}$$

Now $R_1 = nR_2 = n'R_3$, and to simplify calculations (and construction of the amplifier) n and n' may well be equal. Let each be equal to a, where a is greater than unity. Thus stages two and three maintain their gain to a frequency a times as great as the narrow-band stage. The overall amplification over the useful frequency range of the amplifier is

$$m = -\frac{g_{m1}g_{m2}g_{m3}R^3}{a^2} \quad (3.38)$$

The maximum usable magnitude of the feedback factor is

$$|m\beta_{max}| = 4+2(a+1/a) \qquad (3.39)$$

If a safety factor of 2 is used the resulting gain of the feedback amplifier is

$$G = \frac{m}{1-|m\beta_{max}|/2} = \frac{g_{m1}g_{m2}g_{m3}R^3}{a^3+3a^2+a} \qquad (3.40)$$

(b) *Two narrow-band stages.* Here let the second and third stages be the narrow ones and assume that all the stray capacitances are the same size. If the feedback is to be maintained up to the same frequency f_1, the anode resistances are given approximately by

$$R_2 = R_3 = 1/2\pi f_1 C_1 = R$$

This in fact causes a 6 dB drop in the overall gain at this frequency, whereas in (a) there is only a 3 dB drop at a frequency f_1. Thus the two resistances should be a little smaller than R to compensate for this. Now $R_1 = nR_2 = n'R_3$ and R_1 must be in the wide-band stage; thus m and n are less than unity; let them both be equal to $1/a$. Hence the value of $m\beta_{max}$ is the same as before, but the value of the overall amplification over the useful range is

$$m = \frac{g_{m1}g_{m2}g_{m3}R^3}{a} \qquad (3.41)$$

Therefore if a safety factor of 2 is used as in (a) the resulting gain is

$$G = \frac{g_{m1}g_{m2}g_{m3}R^3}{a^2+3a+1} \qquad (3.42)$$

This is a times as large as in (a).

In the design of an amplifier the following factors are specified:

    (i) The overall gain
    (ii) The frequency coverage
    (iii) The necessary feedback factor to secure the required gain stabilization
    (iv) The safety factor to be used

The last two determine the value of $m\beta_{max}$ and hence the value of a that must be employed. The first and third determine the value of m, since

$$G = \frac{m}{1-m\beta}$$

From a knowledge of the mutual conductances of the valves, the stray capacitances and the frequency range the anode load resistances can now be determined. Of course it may be found that the required value of m cannot be obtained with the chosen, or indeed any other, valves. In this case it is necessary either to use a smaller feedback factor, or to employ more valves.

Attention is now turned to the low-frequency end of the amplifier range. If the coupling capacitors are C_{c1}, and C_{c2} and C_{c3}, and the grid leaks R_{g1}, R_{g2} and R_{g3} the following quantities may be defined:

$$\alpha_1 = 2\pi f C_{c1} R_{g1}, \ \alpha_2 = 2\pi f C_{c2} R_{g2} \ \text{and} \ \alpha_3 = 2\pi f C_{c3} R_{g3}$$

In terms of these quantities and the amplification m_0 (this is the value over the useful range of the amplifier) the low-frequency amplification m is given by

$$m = \frac{m_0}{1 - \dfrac{1}{\alpha_1\alpha_2} - \dfrac{1}{\alpha_2\alpha_3} - \dfrac{1}{\alpha_3\alpha_1}} + j\left(\frac{1}{\alpha_1} + \frac{1}{\alpha_2} + \frac{1}{\alpha_3} - \frac{1}{\alpha_1\alpha_2\alpha_3}\right) \quad (3.43)$$

This equation is of exactly the same form as that obtained by a consideration of the effect of the stray capacitances, and the equation can be treated in the same manner as before. Thus if the time-constants of the coupling networks are all the same, so that $\alpha_1 = \alpha_2 = \alpha_3$, the gain is $-m_0/8$ when $\alpha_1 = 1/\sqrt{3}$. This occurs when the frequency is $f = 1/(2\pi\sqrt{3}.C_{c1}R_{g1})$. Therefore the maximum value of $|m\beta|$ that can be employed in the useful range is 8. If now one of the coupling networks is altered so that $\alpha_1 = \alpha_2 = \alpha_3/10$, the same improvement is effected as at the high-frequency end of the amplifier range. This change can be produced by increasing the product $C_{c2}R_{g3}$ ten times, by altering C_{c2}, or R_{g3}, or both. With this change $m = m_0/24 \cdot 2$ at the frequency at which the phase has altered by π from its value over the useful range of the amplifier.

It is obvious that feedback over a number of stages becomes increasingly difficult as the number of stages is raised. With four stages with equality of time-constants the maximum possible value of $|m\beta|$ is 4. The use of large amounts of negative feedback over three or more stages necessitates the use of complex coupling networks between the various stages in order to produce the decrease of $|m\beta|$ to a value below unity before the phase shift round the loop has altered by π. Thus it is essential to control the frequency response of the amplifier well outside the useful range. The frequency range over which this control must be exercised can be deduced from the following considerations.

The networks employed in coupling the stages in a valve amplifier are four-terminal networks, and for all four-terminal networks there is a definite relationship at any frequency between the attenuation and phase shift produced. Further the phase shift is dependent on the rate of change of attenuation with frequency over the whole frequency spectrum from zero to infinity. Thus the phase shift B_c at a frequency f_c is given by the relationship [3]

$$B_c = \frac{\pi}{12} \cdot \left(\frac{dN}{d\mu}\right)_c + \frac{1}{6\pi} \int_{-\infty}^{+\infty} \left[\frac{dN}{d\mu} - \left(\frac{dN}{d\mu}\right)_c\right] \log_e \coth\frac{|\mu|}{2} \cdot d\mu \quad (3.44)$$

where

$$\mu = \log_e (f/f_c)$$

and $dN/d\mu =$ slope of the attenuation curve in dB per octave. If the frequency f_c is reasonably far removed from any abrupt changes in attenuation this approximates to

$$B_c = \frac{\pi}{12}\left(\frac{dN}{d\mu}\right)_c$$

This equation does not apply if the four-terminal network contains a transmission line, or an all-pass section.

The application of the above approximate formula is considered for the simple coupling network of Fig. 3.23. The magnitude of the output voltage from the network is given by

$$V = \frac{V_0}{[1+1/(\omega C R_g)^2]^{1/2}}$$

Thus

$$\log_e \frac{V_0}{V} = \frac{\log_e [1+1/(\omega C R_g)^2]}{2}$$

Therefore the attenuation in nepers* is

$$N = \frac{\log_e [1+1/(\omega C R_g)^2]}{2} \quad (3.45)$$

In order to determine the phase shift it is necessary to find the rate at which this attenuation changes with frequency in dB per octave. This

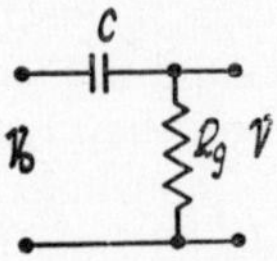

Fig. 3.23

* The *neper* is defined so that two voltages V_1 and V_2 are said to differ by $\log_e (V_1/V_2)$ nepers.

is most easily done by differentiating the expression for N with respect to f. This yields

$$\frac{dN}{df} = \frac{-1}{1+(\omega CR_g)^2} \cdot \frac{1}{f}$$

Hence

$$\frac{dN}{df/f} = \frac{dN}{d(\log_e f/f_c)} = -\frac{1}{1+(\omega CR_g)^2} = \frac{dN}{d\mu}$$

The units for this rate of change of attenuation are nepers per change in frequency equal to a ratio of 2·718 since natural logarithms are used. To convert to decibels per octave this expression must be multiplied by 8·686, the number of decibels per neper, and by $\log_e 2$ since the frequency change is 2 for an octave and not 2·718. Therefore, in the units required,

$$\frac{dN}{d\mu} = \frac{-6}{1+(\omega CR_g)^2}$$

Thus when $\omega = 1/CR_g\sqrt{3}$ the attenuation is changing at the rate of approximately 4 dB per octave. Hence with a three-stage amplifier, containing three networks of this kind, the phase shift from that at mid-frequencies as given by the approximate formula for B_c is π. At this frequency the attenuation per coupling network is 6 dB, and thus the overall gain drops by 18 dB, i.e. by a factor of 8. Therefore the maximum value of $|m\beta|$ that can be employed is 8, which agrees with the previous calculations. In general, simple coupling networks such as that shown attenuate at 6 dB per octave when the frequency is reasonably far removed from $f = 1/2\pi CR$.

The approximate formula for B_c shows that the rate at which the magnitude of the loop gain $m\beta$ is attenuated as the frequency rises or falls outside the useful range must not exceed 12 dB per octave. If at any frequency $dN/d\mu = 12$dB per octave, the phase shift in the amplifier is changed by π, and oscillation at this frequency becomes possible, that is if $|m\beta| \geqslant 1$. Thus the rate of attenuation must be controlled from the edges of the useful band to the frequencies at which $|m\beta|$ falls to unity. To ensure a margin of safety this rate should not exceed 10 dB per octave. Once the magnitude of $m\beta$ falls below unity no further control is necessary and the loop gain may then attenuate in any manner. This implies that the transmission characteristics of the amplifier and the feedback must be controlled over a very much wider range than the useful band; this is the price paid in order to obtain the benefits of negative feedback. The cost is approximately one octave for each 10 dB of useful feedback plus about one or two octaves extra as a margin of

safety and to take care of failure to realize exactly the optimum characteristic. Thus if an amplifier has a useful range from 60 c/s to 10,000
c/s with 30 dB feedback the characteristic of the loop must be carefully
controlled from about 4 c/s to 160,000 c/s.

Provided the above control has been achieved the feedback amplifier
will be stable. The variation of the phases of m and β lead, however,
to other effects which should be considered before the amplifier can be
assumed satisfactory for a given purpose. The uniformity of the gain
within the useful band can lead to very considerable variations in gain
outside this band. This is best shown by means of a definite circuit.

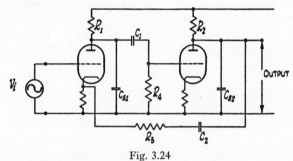

Fig. 3.24

In the feedback amplifier shown in Figure 3.24 the following phase-
turning networks exist.

   (i) LOW FREQUENCIES m branch   One network C_1 and R_4
                             β branch   One network C_2 and R_3
  (ii) HIGH FREQUENCIES m branch   Two networks C_{s1} and R_1
                                                    C_{s2} and R_2
                             β branch   None

The low-frequency gain of the feedback amplifier is therefore

$$m_L = \cfrac{\cfrac{m_0}{1+1/j\omega C_1 R_4}}{1+\cfrac{m_0\beta_0}{\left(1+\cfrac{1}{j\omega C_1 R_4}\right)\left[1+\cfrac{1}{j\omega C_2(R_3+R_5)}\right]}}$$

$$= \frac{m_0(1+1/j\alpha_2)}{\left(1+m_0\beta_0-\cfrac{1}{\alpha_1\alpha_2}\right)-j\left(\cfrac{1}{\alpha_1}+\cfrac{1}{\alpha_2}\right)} \qquad (3.46)$$

where m_0 and β_0 are the values of the amplification and feedback in the useful range, $\alpha_1 = \omega C_1 R_4$, and $\alpha_2 = \omega C_2(R_3 + R_5)$. The manner in which the magnitude of mL varies with frequency is shown in Fig. 3.25 for the cases when $2\alpha_1 = \alpha_2$, $\alpha_1 = 2\alpha_2$, and $\alpha_1 = 10\alpha_2$. The feedback may become positive over certain frequency ranges; it is this fact that leads to the danger of self-oscillation in the three-stage amplifier. It is obvious that if small unwanted signals exist outside the band being

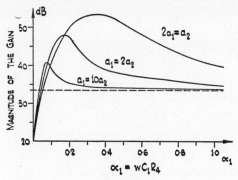

Fig. 3.25

Curves which show the variation of the gain of the feedback amplifier due to the variation of the magnitude and phase of the loop gain at low frequencies.

$m_0 = 1000; \quad \beta_0 = -1/50; \quad G_0 = 33 \cdot 5 \, \text{dB}.$

amplified they are amplified to a much greater extent that those in the desired range. This may be very undesirable; apart from their presence in the output, there is the danger of overloading the amplifier. A similar kind of effect also exists at high frequencies, above the upper frequency end of the useful range. This is not so marked as that at the low-frequency end for the circuit considered. At high frequencies the two phase-turning networks are both associated with m while β is free from phase shift. The high-frequency gain is given by

$$m_H = \cfrac{\cfrac{m_0}{(1+j\omega C_{s1}R_1)(1+j\omega C_{s2}R_2)}}{1 + \cfrac{m_0\beta_0}{(1+j\omega C_{s1}R_1)(1+j\omega C_{s2}R_2)}}$$

$$= \frac{m_0}{(1-\alpha_3\alpha_4+m_0\beta_0)+j(\alpha_3+\alpha_4)} \tag{3.47}$$

where

$$\alpha_3 = \omega C_{S1} R_1 \text{ and } \alpha_4 = \omega C_{S2} R_2$$

The magnitude of the gain as a function of frequency is plotted in Fig. 3.26. Here it is assumed that $\alpha_3 = \alpha_4$. From the curves it can be seen that in general the frequency response of the β circuit should be much flatter than that of the m circuit.

The foregoing sets out briefly the main advantages of the use of

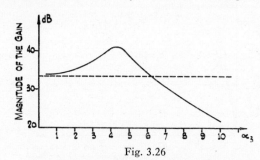

Fig. 3.26

The gain of the feedback amplifier of Fig. 3.22 at the h.f. end of its useful range. The variation is due to the changing magnitude and phase of the loop gain.

$m_0 = 1000; \quad \beta_0 = -1/50; \quad G_0 = 33 \cdot 5 \text{ dB}.$

negative feedback. It also shows in some detail the cost of the improvements obtained. The use of feedback requires the employment of more valves, and with large amounts of feedback over several stages, an increase in the complexity of the coupling networks. Detailed accounts of circuits and the design of such circuits have not been considered. The references given below should be consulted, in particular numbers 1–4, which have been cited earlier in this chapter.

REFERENCES

1. BODE, H. W. *Network Analysis and Feedback Amplifier Design* (Van Nostrand).
2. TERMAN, F. E. *Electronics*, January 1937, p. 12.
3. TERMAN, F. E. *Radio Engineers Handbook* (McGraw-Hill).
4. VALLEY, G. E., and WALLMAN, H. *Vacuum Tube Amplifiers:* M.I.T. Radiation Laboratory Series (McGraw-Hill).

BIBLIOGRAPHY

REICH, H. J. *Theory and Applications of Electron Tubes* (McGraw-Hill).
SANDEMAN, E. K. *Radio Engineering*, Vol. 2 (Chapman and Hall).
ZEPLER, E. E. *Technique of Radio Receiver Design* (Chapman and Hall).

Chapter Four

SELECTIVE AMPLIFIERS

By S. W. Punnett

This chapter is concerned with the behaviour of circuits which will select a desired band of frequencies from the output of a signal source. The process of selection can be performed by the use of tuned circuits or by ordinary LC filters. Such methods are appropriate for frequencies above, say, 100 c/s. Below this frequency the inductors and capacitors required become bulky and the cost may well be prohibitive. Further, the difficulty of the magnetic shielding of large inductors increases as the frequency of operation decreases. Attention is therefore confined to those methods which do not require the use of inductors. When the components of frequency-sensitive networks are limited to resistors and capacitors, the selective effect of a passive four-terminal network is very low. This may be expressed more quantitatively by stating that the Q-factor is less than unity. Consequently it is necessary to employ valves in addition to the passive four-terminal network. This is usually no disadvantage, for amplification of the signal is often required. In Chapter Three it is shown that the gain of an amplifier can be controlled by the feedback or β circuit, the gain with large feedback being approximately $-1/\beta$. Therefore, by the correct choice of the feedback network,

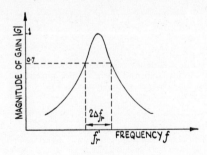

Fig. 4.1

it is possible to give the amplifier a gain-frequency characteristic of the form shown in Fig. 4.1. This can be of almost exactly the same shape as the response of a tuned circuit, and a Q-factor for the circuit as a whole may be shown to be given by the following expression.

$$Q = \frac{f_r}{2\Delta f_r} = \frac{f_r}{B}$$

Here f_r is the frequency at which the response is a maximum, and $B = 2\Delta f_r$ is the bandwidth between the points on the response curve at which the gain has dropped by 3 dB from its maximum value. Any type of gain-frequency response can be obtained by the use of the appropriate β circuit. It should be pointed out that the same response can always be obtained by the use of a circuit having inductors and capacitors only, without valves. Moreover, the β circuit can be given the desired characteristic by the use of resistors and capacitors only, provided it is sufficiently complex. To produce an amplifier with a response curve similar to that shown in Fig. 4.1, by means of negative feedback, requires the β circuit frequency response to be the inverse of that of the required gain characteristic. This is shown approximately in Fig. 4.2. It is to be noted that β is the total feedback applied. The

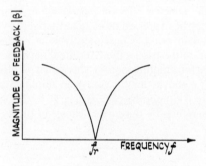

Fig. 4.2

The frequency response of the feedback circuit required to give the amplifier the characteristic shown in Fig. 4.1.

$$\beta = \frac{jy}{3+jy}, \text{ where } y = \frac{f}{f_r} - \frac{f_r}{f}$$

method of multiple-loop feedback can be used so that β is the sum of two or more feedbacks. Fig. 4.3 gives the frequency response of two loops, the resultant total feedback for the amplifier being exactly the same as that of Fig. 4.2. The results are identical as far as the external characteristics of the amplifier are concerned. The advantage of this method lies in the additional freedom that is obtained in the arrangement of the feedback and signal connections.

In this chapter four simple arrangements of resistors and capacitors are considered for the β circuit. The first is a modification of the Wien bridge, in which the frequency-determining network requires four components. The second is the twin-T arrangement requiring six

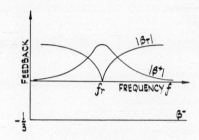

Fig. 4.3

Curves showing the use of multiple-loop feedback to produce the required total feedback.

$$\beta^+ = \frac{1}{3+jy}; \quad \beta^- = \frac{-1}{3}; \quad \beta_T = \frac{-jy}{3(3+jy)};$$

where $y = \dfrac{f}{f_r} - \dfrac{f_r}{f}$, and $\beta_T = \beta^+ + \beta^-$.

components. In both these arrangements β varies both in magnitude and in phase. The third arrangement employs four components, and in this only the phase of β varies; certain advantages arise having β of constant magnitude. Finally circuits are considered which have frequency-loss characteristics similar to those of low-pass and high-pass filters.

SELECTIVE AMPLIFIERS EMPLOYING THE WIEN BRIDGE

A block diagram of the selective amplifier is shown in Fig. 4.4. The output voltage from the amplifier is applied to the β branch, which consists of a Wien bridge. The output from this bridge is the feedback

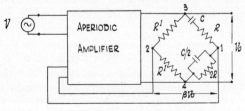

Fig. 4.4

voltage. The value of β as a function of frequency is found as follows:

Voltage at terminal 2 with respect to $4 = V_0/2$.
Voltage at terminal 1 with respect to 4

$$= V_0 \cdot \cfrac{1}{1+(R+\cfrac{1}{j\omega C}) \cdot \cfrac{2(R+1/j\omega C)}{4R/j\omega C}}$$

To simplify this last equation and all other similar ones the following variables are used in this chapter.

The frequency at which $R = 1/\omega C$ is defined as f_0, and hence $\omega CR = \omega/\omega_0$, where $\omega_0 = 2\pi f_0$. The quantity ω/ω_0 is written as α, and finally a variable y is defined by the formula

$$y = \alpha - 1/\alpha$$

Thus the voltage between terminals 1 and 4 can be written as

$$V_0 \cdot \cfrac{1}{1+\cfrac{(1+1/j\alpha)^2}{2/j\alpha}} = \frac{2V_0}{4+j(\alpha-1/\alpha)}$$

Therefore the voltage between terminals 1 and 2 is

$$V = \frac{V_0}{2} - \frac{2V_0}{4+jy} = \frac{V_0}{2} \cdot \frac{jy}{4+jy}$$

This voltage must be βV_0 and therefore

$$\beta = \frac{1}{2} \cdot \frac{jy}{4+jy}$$

Curves which show the variation of the magnitude and phase of β with y, and hence indirectly with frequency, are sketched in Figs. 4.5 and 4.6. The feedback falls to zero at the frequency for which y is zero, this frequency being $f_0 = 1/2\pi CR$. The gain-frequency response curve is therefore of the desired shape. The great disadvantage of this circuit lies in the necessity of using a transformer either at the input or the output of the bridge. The input and the output have no common point, whereas in RC-coupled amplifiers the earth line is usually common to both. When a transformer is used, considerable care is necessary in the design of the intervalve coupling networks if feedback is applied over more than one stage. The magnitude of β becomes very large at both low and high frequencies, and thus the danger of self-oscillation is very great.

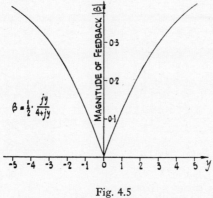

$$\beta = \tfrac{1}{2} \cdot \frac{jy}{4+jy}$$

Fig. 4.5

The apparent solution of the transformer difficulty that is shown in Fig. 4.7 is not satisfactory. The circuit requires both valve outputs to remain very constant; this can be seen from a consideration of the equivalent circuit of Fig. 4.8. If one of the equivalent generator voltages

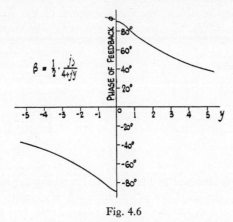

$$\beta = \tfrac{1}{2} \cdot \frac{jy}{4+jy}$$

Fig. 4.6

changes from V to $(1+n)V$ at the band centre frequency f_0, i.e. the frequency at which the bridge is supposedly balanced, the voltage at the output terminals is not zero but $nV/2$. The phase of this voltage is positive or negative depending on the sign of n. Thus the feedback at resonance may be negative, with a consequent reduction in the gain and the Q-factor; or it may be positive, producing an increase in the gain and Q-factor. It may even be large enough to cause self-oscillation.

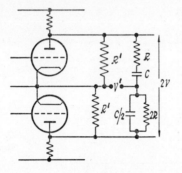

Fig. 4.7 Fig. 4.8

A push-pull valve circuit to replace the transformer supplying the Wien Bridge.

This happens if $mnV/2 = V$, where m is the amplification of the amplifier employed. Thus with a 1 per cent change in one of the outputs oscillation occurs if m is greater than 200. Even if oscillation does not occur the variation in the gain and Q-factor is not acceptable.

One solution which overcomes the need for a transformer makes use of multiple-loop feedback; the block diagram of the arrangement is shown in Fig. 4.9(a). The important frequency determining portion

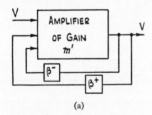
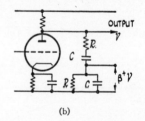

(a) Fig. 4.9 (b)

of the circuit is sketched in Fig. 4.9(b). The heavy negative feedback β^-, applied to the amplifier of amplification m', results in a gain m given by

$$m = \frac{m'}{1 - m'\beta^-}$$

The frequency-sensitive feedback β^+ is such that there is positive feedback for the band of frequencies it is desired to select. The overall

gain G is given by

$$G = \frac{m}{1-m\beta^+}$$

The form of β^+ is found from the equivalent circuit of the final stage of the amplifier, as sketched in Fig. 4.10. Thus

$$\beta^+ = \frac{\dfrac{R}{1+j\omega CR}}{\dfrac{R}{1+j\omega CR}+R+\dfrac{1}{j\omega C}}$$

$$= \frac{1}{1+(1+1/j\alpha)(1+j\alpha)}$$

$$= \frac{1}{3+jy}$$

The variation with frequency of the magnitude and phase of β^+ is

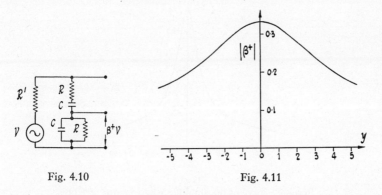

Fig. 4.10   Fig. 4.11

shown in Figs. 4.11 and 4.12 respectively. When the frequency is $f_0 = 1/2\pi CR$, so that y is zero, the value of β^+ is 1/3; the positive feedback is then a maximum. The gain at this frequency is

$$G_0 = \frac{m}{1-m/3}$$

This equation shows that m must be a little less than 3 so that the gain

F

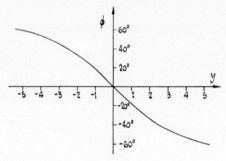

Fig. 4.12

at the resonant frequency f_0 is large. At all other frequencies the gain is given by

$$G = \frac{m}{1 - m/(3 + jy)}$$

Far from resonance when y is large, the gain tends to a value m. The variation of the magnitude of the gain with frequency is shown in Fig.

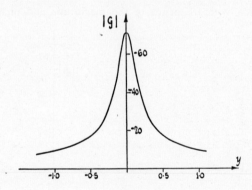

Fig. 4.13

Response curve of the amplifier where gain is given by

$$G = \frac{m}{1 - (m/3 + jy)}, \text{ where } m = 2 \cdot 88; \; G_0 = 72; \text{ and } Q = 8$$

4.13; it has the desired form. Insertion of the value of m from above in the equation for G yields

$$G = \frac{m'}{1 - m'[\beta^- + 1/(3 + jy)]}$$

Since it is not desirable to lower the stability of the amplifier, the value of the total feedback should be negative at all frequencies. The maximum value of β^+ is 1/3 and therefore β^- should be more negative than $-1/3$. If the limiting value of $-1/3$ is taken no decrease in stability occurs and the gain is

$$G = \frac{m'}{1+[jym'/3(3+jy)]}$$

This can be arranged to give

$$G = \frac{m'(1+jy/3)}{1+jy(m'/9+1/3)}$$

For small values of y, that is for frequencies close to the resonant frequency $f_0 = 1/2\pi CR$, this approximates to

$$G = \frac{m'}{1+jy(m'/9)}$$

For a simple tuned circuit the response S for small values of y may be written

$$S = \frac{S_0}{1+jyQ}$$

where S_0 is the response at resonance and Q is the Q-factor. If the form of this response is compared with that of the gain of the selective amplifier it is seen that the effective Q-factor of the latter is $m'/9$. If a more negative value of β^- is employed so that the gain on resonance is G_0 it is found that the Q-factor is $G_0/9$. Thus to obtain a bandwidth at the 70 per cent points of $0 \cdot 1 f_0$ the Q-factor must be 10, and hence G_0 must be about 90. To secure stability of gain, Q-factor, and bandwidth, the value of m' should be much greater than G_0, say of the order of ten times G_0.

Since β^- is of the order of $-1/3$, and since β^+ becomes very small far from resonance, the negative feedback is very large for large y. Hence the design of the amplifier and β^- networks requires careful attention, as discussed in chapter three.

The next question to be considered is the stability of the selective amplifier with reference to variations in the components, and in the amplification m'. Up to this point it has been assumed that the components forming the selective network have exactly their correct values. In a fixed-frequency amplifier the components may be adjusted

to any required accuracy by the use of trimmers and no serious difficulty arises; the components are not the limiting factor except in so
far as they change with age and external conditions. When it is desired
to produce an amplifier whose tuning is continuously variable the
problem is much more serious. It is necessary to gang two of the components and it is not possible for them to be exactly equal at all settings
of the frequency control. To assess the effect of component errors,
let us suppose that one of the components is $(1+k)C$ instead of C,
as shown in Fig. 4.14.

Fig. 4.14

A frequency-sensitive network
with one capacitor $(1+k)$ times
its correct value.

The quantity k is a small positive or negative number. From the
circuit of Fig. 4.14 the new value of β^+ can be found to be

$$\beta^+ = \frac{1}{(3+k)+j(y+k\alpha)}$$

The feedback is pure positive feedback when $(y+k\alpha)$ is zero, and this
occurs when α is approximately $(1-k/2)$. Thus the resonant frequency
f_r is equal to $(1-k/2)f_0$. At this frequency f_r, the value of β^+ is $1/(3+k)$,
and therefore the resonant gain is

$$G_r = \frac{m}{1-m/(3+k)}$$

This equation shows that if $m/(3+k) = 1$, G_r becomes infinite, i.e.
the circuit oscillates. Since m must be a little less than 3 this implies
that for stability k must not be more negative than $(m-3)$. To consider
a definite example; suppose the Q-factor required is 10, so that G_0
(or G_r) is approximately 100. Then m is given by

$$100 = \frac{m}{1-m/3}$$

and therefore

$$m = 2{\cdot}9126$$

Thus k must not be more negative than $-0\cdot09$; an error of ±10 per cent in one of the components causes oscillation, the sign depending on the component concerned. It is negative for the capacitor considered in Fig. 4.14 and positive for the resistor in parallel with it; the reverse holds for the series components. The above discussion is not very important; the real problem is the variation of G_r and Q which result from small changes in the component values such as may occur with age or temperature. If the expression for G_r is differentiated with respect to k, we obtain

$$\frac{dG_r}{dk} = -\frac{1}{(3/G_r + k/G_r)^2}$$

Hence at $k = 0$,

$$\frac{dG_0}{dk} = -\frac{G_0^2}{9}$$

and for small increments

$$\Delta G_0 = -\frac{G_0^2}{9} \cdot \Delta k$$

Thus for a ±5 per cent variation in the gain on resonance, with a Q-factor of 10 so that G_0 is approximately 100, the permitted error in the value of the component considered is $\pm0\cdot45$ per cent. This is not difficult to secure for the moderate value of Q chosen. The tolerance on the components becomes much more stringent if Q-factors of the order of 100 are required; this is especially the case if ganged variable components are employed to tune the amplifier over a range of frequencies. Finally, an examination of the expression for β^+ for the general case when unequal components are used in the bridge shows that three components may be considered to be correct and only one of the wrong value.

Variation of the amplifier gain m is now considered. If the expression for the overall gain at resonance is differentiated with respect to m the result is

$$\frac{dG_0}{dm} = \frac{9}{(3-m)^2}$$

and for small increments

$$\Delta G_0 = \frac{9}{(3-m)^2} \cdot \Delta m$$

Thus, if the amplifier has a Q-factor of 10 and a ±5 per cent variation in G_0 is allowed, the variation in m is

$$\Delta m = \pm0\cdot0042$$

Since m is a little smaller than 3 this represents a variation of approximately ± 0.1 per cent. The gain m is related to the amplification m' by the expression

$$m = \frac{m'}{1+\beta^- m'}$$

and hence

$$\frac{dm}{m} = \frac{dm'}{m'} \cdot \frac{1}{1+\beta^- m'}$$

Now dm/m is ± 0.001 and if the valves and other circuit parameters are assumed to cause a ± 20 per cent variation in m', then $dm'/m' = 0.2$. Therefore $(1+\beta^- m')$ must be at least 200, and since β^- is approximately $1/3$ the value of m' which must be employed is about 600.

A suitable circuit for the selective amplifier is shown in Fig. 4.15.

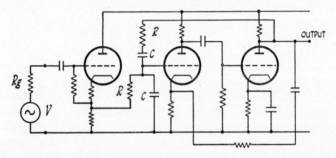

Fig. 4.15

The circuit of a simple selective amplifier employing multiple-loop feedback.

This is only an outline circuit, and it is by no means the best that can be designed. The cathode follower at the input is not essential but its use makes the connection of the signal source much simpler. The output impedance of the cathode follower is very low and thus has little effect on the component R of the frequency-selective network. Figs. 4.16(a) and 4.16(b) show the signal-source connection when the cathode follower is not used, for a low-impedance and a high-impedance source, respectively. In each, allowance must be made for the effect of the source impedance R_g; in Fig. 4.16(a) $R = R_1 + R_g$, and in Fig. 4.16(b) $R = R_2 R_g/(R_2 + R_g)$.

The multiple-loop feedback amplifier considered above can be converted to a single-loop type. Several advantages result, not the least being the change of the Q-factor from $G_0/9$ to $G_0/3$, on the assumption that the same gain is used at resonance in each amplifier. The essential

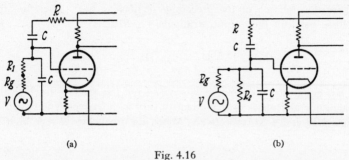

(a)   (b)

Fig. 4.16

Input circuit arrangements for (a) a low-impedance source, and (b) a high-impedance source.

change made in the circuit connections is shown in Fig. 4.17, which gives the arrangement of the frequency-sensitive network. The output V_0 from the amplifier is applied to a triode phase-splitting valve with small anode and cathode resistors; these are of the order of 2–5 kilohms. The frequency-sensitive network is connected between anode and cathode and thus causes some feedback within this stage. However, the impedance of the network is high compared with the impedance at the cathode of the valve, and so to a first approximation this effect can be ignored. Therefore the approximate equivalent circuit is as shown in Fig. 4.18. The resistances R_1 and R_2 are the output impedances at

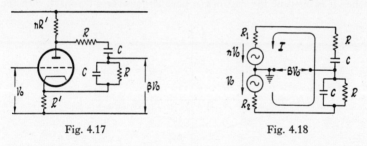

Fig. 4.17   Fig. 4.18

the anode and cathode respectively. R_2 is so small that it can be ignored; R_1, which is of the order of nr, can be allowed for by reduction of the series resistor of the selective network. In actual fact the two voltages are not exactly V_0 and nV_0, but the important factor is that one is n times the other since the valve current flows through both. Further, up to quite high frequencies they are almost exactly in antiphase. The current through the selective network is given by

$$I = V_0 \cdot \frac{(1+n)(1+j\alpha)}{R(3+jy)}$$

where the notation of the preceding sections is used. Therefore the voltage between the output terminals, i.e. βV_0, is

$$\beta V_0 = V_0 - I \cdot \frac{R}{1+j\alpha} = V_0 \cdot \frac{(2-n)+jy}{3+jy}$$

If n is equal to 2 the value of β is $jy/(3+jy)$; the manner in which the magnitude and phase of this quantity vary with frequency is shown in Figs. 4.19 and 4.20 respectively. When the frequency is very high or

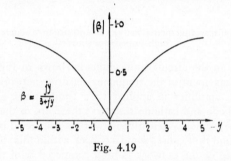

Fig. 4.19

very low the magnitude of β approaches unity and its phase tends to zero. Therefore the feedback connections must be arranged so that when it is off-tune the network applies large inverse feedback with the

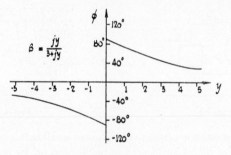

Fig. 4.20

result that the gain of the amplifier falls sharply. If this circuit is employed with an amplifier of gain G_0, the gain G of the whole circuit is

$$G = \frac{G_0}{1+jyG_0/(3+jy)} = \frac{G_0(1+jy/3)}{1+[jy(G_0+1)/3]}$$

This is of the same form as for the previous amplifier but the Q-factor is $(G_0+1)/3$. With the same gain at resonance the Q-factor is increased approximately three times; alternatively, with the same amplifier and increased negative feedback to reduce the gain at resonance, the same Q-factor can be obtained with a greatly improved stability.

A suitable circuit arrangement employing the phase-splitting circuit is shown in Fig. 4.21. A cathode-coupled pair is used so that the signal input voltage and the feedback voltage are isolated from one another.

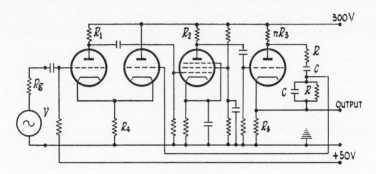

Fig. 4.21

It is important to note that, while at low frequencies there are only two phase-turning networks, at high frequencies there are four, apart from the selective network. There is, therefore, no danger of self-oscillation at low frequencies provided that care is taken in the design of the pentode stage. Oscillation may occur at high frequencies owing to the four phase changes produced by the stray capacitances; those concerned are effectively in parallel with the anode loads R_1 and R_2, and the cathode resistors R_3 and R_4. It is necessary to ensure that the magnitude of the loop gain falls below unity before the frequency is reached at which the phase shift in the amplifier has changed by π from its value over the useful range. Fortunately the phase shifts which occur at the cathodes are not serious except at very high frequencies, when the gain of the two amplifier valves decreases very considerably. This circuit does not contain any special arrangement to provide negative feedback: this is introduced by making the anode resistor of the phase-splitting valve have a value other than twice that of the cathode resistor. The effect of this can be seen by re-examining the expression for β, which is

$$\beta = \frac{(2-n)+jy}{3+jy}$$

If the value of the anode resistor is made a little less than twice the value
of the cathode resistor there will be a small voltage fed back to the first
pair of valves even when y is zero. With the connections shown, this
constitutes negative feedback and results in a reduction of gain even
at resonance. Thus the amplifier is designed to give a gain m' which is
much greater than G_0, and the value of n is adjusted so that at resonance
the gain is reduced to G_0.

The gain of the whole circuit is

$$G = \frac{m'}{1 + \dfrac{m'(2-n+jy)}{3+jy}}$$

$$= \frac{3m'(1+jy/3)}{(3+2m'-nm')+jy(m'+1)}$$

When the amplifier is tuned, so that y is zero,

$$G_0 = \frac{3m'}{(3+2m'-nm')}$$

The required value of n can be calculated from this expression if
m' and G_0 are known. Alternatively, the anode resistor may be made
partially adjustable and the valve set by experiment so that the required
Q-factor is obtained. The effect on the amplifier's other characteristics
of n being other than 2 is very slight. This is shown by rearranging the
expression for G and noting that G_0 is equal to $3m'/(3+2m'-nm')$.
Thus

$$G = \frac{\dfrac{3m'}{3+2m'-nm'} \cdot (1+jy/3)}{1+jy \cdot \dfrac{m'+1}{3+2m'-nm'}}$$

$$= \frac{G_0(1+jy/3)}{1+jy(G_0/3+G_0/3m')}$$

There is only a very slight difference between this expression and that
obtained when n is equal to 2.

The effect of component tolerances is now considered. As before,
let the value of the parallel capacitor be $(1+k)C$ instead of C, so that
the equivalent circuit diagram of Fig. 4.18 changes to that of Fig.

4.22. The value of the feedback can be shown to be approximately equal to

$$\beta = \frac{k+j(y+k\alpha)}{(3+k)+j(y+k\alpha)}$$

β no longer falls to zero at any frequency; it has a minimum value when $(y+k\alpha)$ is zero, i.e. when α is approximately $(1-k/2)$. The resonant

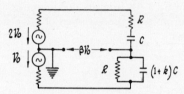

Fig. 4.22

Electrical equivalent of the phase-splitting stage when one capacitor is $(1+k)$ times its correct size.

frequency is no longer f_0 but $f_0(1-k/2)$ and at this frequency the value of β is $k/(3+k)$, so that the gain at resonance is given by

$$G_r = \frac{G_0(3+k)}{3+k(G_0+1)}$$

This shows that oscillation occurs if k is more negative than $-3/(G_0+1)$. The manner in which G_r varies with k can be found by differentiating with respect to k. This variation is

$$\frac{dG_r}{dk} = -\frac{3G_0^2}{[3+k(G_0+1)]^2}$$

and thus when k is zero

$$\left[\frac{dG_r}{dk}\right]_{k=0} = -\frac{G_0^2}{3}$$

or

$$\Delta G_r = -\frac{G_0^2}{3}\cdot\Delta k$$

If the maximum permitted value of the variation of G_0 is ± 5 per cent and the tolerance on the component considered is ± 1 per cent, the maximum value of G_0 that may be employed is 15. This corresponds to a Q-factor of 5. Since the Q-factor for this circuit is $(G_0+1)/3$ the above rates of change may be written

$$\left[\frac{dG_r}{dk}\right]_{k=0} \sim -3Q^2 \quad \text{or} \quad \left[\frac{dQ}{dk}\right]_{k=0} \sim -Q^2$$

The Q-factor is equal to $f_0/\Delta f_0$, where f_0 is the resonant frequency and Δf_0 is the bandwidth between points on the response curve at which the gain has dropped by 3 dB from its maximum value. Thus the last expression gives a formula for the variation of the bandwidth with the component tolerances:

$$\left[\frac{d(\Delta f_0)}{dk}\right]_{k=0} = f_0$$

Up to this point it has been assumed that the resistances employed in the selective network are equal, which necessitates equality of the capacitances. This arrangement is easiest, particularly if it is desired to tune the amplifier continuously over a range of frequencies. The use of unequal components yields higher Q-factors for the same gain at resonance. Consider the circuit of Fig. 4.23(a) and its equivalent

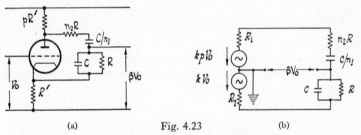

(a) Fig. 4.23 (b)

(a) A generalized frequency-sensitive network and phase-splitting valve.
(b) The equivalent electrical circuit.

circuit of Fig. 4.23(b). The series capacitance is replaced by C/n_1 and the series resistance by $n_2 R$, where n_1 and n_2 are positive numbers. The anode resistance is p times that in the cathode lead, and hence the output voltages are kpV_0 and kV_0, where k is less than unity. The factor k can be considered as part of G_0; a slightly increased amplification m' can compensate this small decrease in the effective value of the gain at resonance. The value of β for this circuit can be shown to be given by

$$\beta = \frac{(n_1+n_2-p)+jy\sqrt{n_1 n_2}}{(1+n_1+n_2)+jy\sqrt{n_1 n_2}}$$

where k is assumed equal to unity. The resonant frequency no longer occurs at $f_0 = 1/2\pi CR$, but at $f_r = f_0\sqrt{n_1}/\sqrt{n_2}$ and the variable y in the expression for β refers to this latter frequency and not to f_0. If $p = (n_1+n_2)$ the feedback is zero at the resonant frequency f_r, if on the other hand p is a little smaller than (n_1+n_2) negative feedback is applied to the amplifier in addition to any other which may be used. Only the case for which $p = (n_1+n_2)$ is dealt with here, and thus

$$\beta = \frac{jy\sqrt{n_1 n_2}}{(1+n_1+n_2)+jy\sqrt{n_1 n_2}}$$

The gain of the selective amplifier is given by

$$G = \frac{G_0(1+n_1+n_2+jy\sqrt{n_1 n_2})}{(1+n_1+n_2)+jy\sqrt{n_1 n_2}(G_0+1)}$$

Therefore the effective Q-factor for small values of y is

$$Q = \frac{(G_0+1)\sqrt{n_1 n_2}}{1+n_1+n_2} = \frac{(G_0+1)}{\sqrt{n_1}/\sqrt{n_2}+\sqrt{n_2}/\sqrt{n_1}+1/\sqrt{n_1 n_2}}$$

To obtain a large Q-factor for a given gain n_1 and n_2 must be equal and as large as possible; the limiting value of Q is $(G_0+1)/2$, when n_1 and n_2 are infinitely large. However, too large values must not be used since p is equal to (n_1+n_2), and large values of p lead to a marked decrease in k. Further the output impedance at the anode of the phase-splitting valve increases as the value of p increases. The formulae developed here assume that the output impedances at the anode and cathode can be ignored.

SELECTIVE AMPLIFIERS EMPLOYING THE TWIN-T NETWORK

The twin-T network is the next frequency-sensitive circuit to be considered. This has been extensively employed [1,2] although it requires six components and is, in consequence, somewhat more difficult to adjust. The symmetrical form of the network which is most often used is shown in Fig. 4.24. The derivation of the expression for β assumes that the network is connected between a generator of zero impedance and a load of infinite impedance. This is approximately true when the network is connected to the output of an amplifier employing heavy negative feedback. The output terminals of the twin-T network are usually connected to the grid and cathode of a valve and thus the load impedance is also large. If the two T networks are converted to their equivalent π networks it is easy to show that the twin-T network is identical with the circuit of Fig. 4.25. [3]

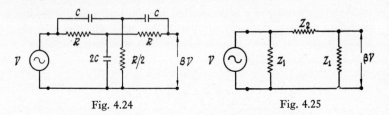

Fig. 4.24   Fig. 4.25

The values of the impedances Z_1 and Z_2 are given by

$$Z_1 = \frac{R(1+1/j\alpha)}{2}, \qquad Z_2 = \frac{2R(1+1/j\alpha)}{j(\alpha-1/\alpha)}$$

The series arm Z_2 becomes infinite at the frequency at which α is equal to unity, and the output from the network is therefore zero at this frequency. This is so whatever the impedance of the generator and load, for the only effect that finite generator and load impedances can have is to reduce the selectivity when the network is used to produce a selective amplifier.

For this network the value of β must be given by

$$\beta = \frac{Z_1}{Z_1+Z_2} = \frac{1}{1+Z_2/Z_1}$$

Hence

$$\beta = \frac{1}{1+[4/j(\alpha-1/\alpha)]}$$

$$= \frac{jy}{4+jy}$$

This value of β is just twice that obtained for the Wien bridge discussed in the previous section. In fact if the Wien bridge is employed with a 1:2 step-up transformer so that the voltage applied to the bridge is $2V_0$ it can be shown that the two arrangements are electrically equivalent. [4] The twin-T network has the important advantage of a terminal common to the input and the output.

When the twin-T network is used with an amplifier of gain G_0 the resulting gain with feedback is

$$G = \frac{G_0(1+jy/4)}{1+jy(G_0+1)/4}$$

This expression is of the same form as those previously obtained and therefore the Q-factor is $(G_0+1)/4$, which is of the same order as is obtained with the amplifiers previously described but it is at the expense of six components in the frequency-sensitive network.

EFFECT OF PHASE SHIFT IN THE AMPLIFIER GAIN

Up to this point it has been assumed that G_0 is real, i.e. the amplifier branch introduces no phase shift. In any real amplifier G_0 is complex, and this can be expressed by writing it as $|G_0|\exp j(\theta)$. The feedback can be expressed in the same form, namely

$$\beta = \frac{1}{(1+16/y^2)^{1/2}} \exp j(\text{arc} \tan 4/y)$$

Hence the value of the feedback factor is

$$m\beta = \frac{G_0}{(1+16/y^2)^{1/2}} \exp j\,(\theta+ \text{arc} \tan 4/y)$$

and this expression must give the stability conditions of the amplifier as a whole. The magnitude of $m\beta$ tends towards G_0 for large y whether positive or negative. Therefore the loop phase must not change by as much as π from its value at the resonant frequency. The term arc tan $4/y$ tends to zero at both high and low frequencies, and thus θ is the determining factor. If the amplifier consists of a single stage, θ cannot alter by more than $\pm\pi/2$ from its value over the useful range, and thus oscillation is impossible. For a two-stage amplifier θ may alter by π from its value over the useful range at zero and at infinite frequency and again oscillation is not possible. If pentodes are employed it is possible for θ to change by π before the frequency reaches zero or infinity and oscillation is a possibility; care must be taken with the coupling networks and with the screen decoupling.

A suitable circuit for the twin-T network with a two-stage amplifier is shown in Fig. 4.26. The articles by Scott and Sturtevant referred to on p. 105 should be consulted. With a three-stage amplifier the coupling networks between the valves must be carefully designed if more than a small fraction of the output of the twin-T network is to be used as feedback. [5] It is, however, unnecessary to use three stages, for sufficient amplification and hence stability can normally be obtained by the use of only two. The component errors become the overriding factor in the stability of the selective amplifier. These are now considered.

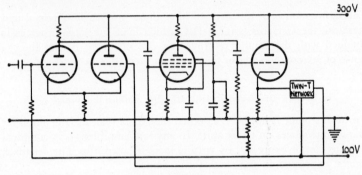

Fig. 4.26

COMPONENT TOLERANCES

Let us assume that one of the resistors is $(1+k)$ times its correct value, as shown in Fig. 4.27. This change leads to the following approximate value for the feedback;

$$\beta = \frac{1}{1+4/X}$$

where X is given by

$$X = j\alpha - \frac{j(1-3k/4)}{\alpha} - \frac{k}{4}$$

Therefore β does not decrease to zero; it is approximately a minimum when $\alpha - (1-3k/4)/\alpha = 0$, which occurs when the frequency is approximately $f_r = (1-3k/8)/2\pi CR = f_0(1-3k/8)$. This minimum value of β is $1/(1-16/k)$, and hence the gain at the new resonant frequency f_r is given by

$$G_r = \frac{G_0(k-16)}{k(G_0+1)-16}$$

This shows clearly that if k is greater than $16/(G_0+1)$ the amplifier oscillates; the greater the gain at resonance, the closer the components must be to the correct values. If the same procedure is adopted here as for the previous circuits the following expressions are found:

$$\left[\frac{dG_r}{dk}\right]_{k=0} = \frac{G_0{}^2}{16}$$

$$\left[\frac{dG_r}{dk}\right]_{k=0} = Q^2$$

$$\left[\frac{dQ}{dk}\right]_{k=0} = \frac{Q^2}{4}$$

If these quantities are compared with those previously obtained the new arrangement appears to be four times as stable. This is not true as can be seen from the following argument. Suppose that it is desired to tune the amplifier from frequency f_1 to frequency f_2, and that the capacitors are all fixed. Further it is assumed that all the components

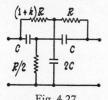

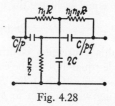

Fig. 4.27

A twin-T network with an error of kR in one of its resistive arms.

Fig. 4.28

have their correct values at frequencies f_1. In order to tune to frequency f_2, at least two of the components must be changed, and thus there are two resistor error factors at the new frequency f_2. Therefore the above variations must be doubled, and thus the circuit is twice as stable as those previously considered.

It is possible to employ an asymmetric twin-T network, although the increase in complexity resulting from the inequality of the components is more than commensurate with the slight improvement in the Q-factor for a given gain. The general twin-T network is shown in Fig. 4.28. The value of β is again easily derived by converting the two T networks to their equivalent π networks; it is

$$\beta = \frac{1}{1 + D/jy}$$

where

$$D = \{2n_1(n_2+1)/q\}^{1/2} + \{2p(q+1)/n_2\}^{1/2}$$

G

Here q is a positive number with the following restriction placed on it and the positive numbers $n_1 n_2$ and p:

$$4n_1n_2pq = (n_2+1)(q+1)$$

The twin-T network is essentially a bridge, and if the above restriction is not obeyed the bridge will not balance at any frequency, and the output voltage will never be zero.

With the asymmetric twin-T network the gain of the selective amplifier is

$$G = \frac{G_0(1+jy/D)}{1+jy(G_0+1)/D}$$

and thus the Q-factor is $(G_0+1)/D$.

It is of interest to determine the minimum value of D, since this gives the maximum Q-factor. If n_2 and q are fixed, and the resonant frequency $f_r = f_0(2p^2q)^{1/2}/\{n_1(n_2+1)\}^{1/2}$ is also fixed, then, since $4n_1n_2pq = (n_2+1)(q+1)$, the product $n_1\,p$ must be constant. Let the product $n_1\,p$ equal k; hence the expression for D can be written

$$D = \{2n_1(n_2+1)/q\}^{1/2} + \{2k(q+1)/n_1n_2\}^{1/2}$$

If this expression is differentiated with respect to n_1 and the result made equal to zero, the condition for a minimum value of D is obtained; this is $n_1 = (q+1)/2n_2$. Similarly, by replacing n_1 by k/p and differentiating with respect to p, it is found that p must equal $(n_2+1)/2q$ for a minimum value of D. When these values of n_1 and p are substituted in the equation for D the result is

$$D = 2\left[\left(1+\frac{1}{n_2}\right)\left(1+\frac{1}{q}\right)\right]^{1/2}$$

This expression shows that n_2 and q should be as large as possible. In the limit when n_2 and q are infinite so that $n_1 = p = 1/2$ the value of D is 2. Thus the maximum Q-factor that can be obtained with this circuit is $(G_0+1)/2$. One other factor prevents too large a value of n_2 and of q from being used, namely the output impedance of the network. Examination of the circuit of Fig. 4.28 shows that as these two factors are increased the output impedance must also increase, and this makes it difficult to fulfil the condition that the load shall have no appreciable influence on the network.

A Selective Amplifier Employing Phase Shift

The final selective amplifier to be considered embodies the circuit

shown in Fig. 4.29, the equivalent circuit being given in Fig. 4.30.
The output impedances at the anode and the cathode are both very
much smaller than R and are therefore ignored to begin with. The
voltages at anode and cathode are in antiphase but equal in magnitude.

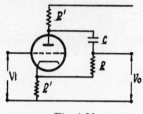

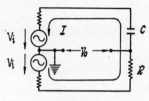

Fig. 4.29   Fig. 4.30

A circuit for which the output is constant
in magnitude but variable in phase.

It is assumed here that this magnitude is V_i, that of the input voltage.
In fact the magnitudes are kV_i where k is less than unity, but this may
be compensated for by an increase in the gain of the main amplifier
which is used with this circuit. The voltage V_0 which appears between
the junction of C and R and the negative rail is therefore given by

$$V_0 = V_i - IR$$

$$= V_i - R \cdot \frac{2V_i}{R + 1/j\omega C}$$

$$= V_i - V_i \cdot \frac{2}{1 + 1/j\alpha}$$

$$= V_i \cdot \frac{1 - j\alpha}{1 + j\alpha}$$

The magnitude of the output is independent of frequency but the
phase changes from zero to π as the frequency varies from zero to
infinity. This can be seen by considering the action of the circuit at
zero and infinite frequency. At zero frequency the capacitor C is
open-circuited, and thus the output voltage must be that at the cathode
which is in phase with V_i. At infinite frequency the capacitor has zero
reactance and the output voltage is that at the anode which is in antiphase with V_i. The constant-magnitude of the output is clearly shown
by the vector diagram of Fig. 4.31. This diagram shows the anode
and cathode voltages, V_a and V_{ca} respectively. The two voltages V_R
and V_{co} across the resistor and capacitor must be at right angles in the

vector diagram, but their vector sum must equal the total voltage between anode and cathode of the valve. Therefore the junction P of V_R and V_{co} must lie on a circle of radius V_i. The output voltage V_o is the vector sum of the cathode voltage V_{ca} and the voltage across the

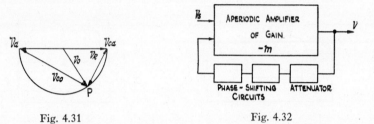

Fig. 4.31   Fig. 4.32

resistor R, and is thus as shown. Whatever the frequency, the output voltage vector V_o always lies along, and is equal in magnitude to, the radius of the circle.

When the frequency is $f_0 = 1/2\pi CR$ so that α is equal to unity, the output lags on the input by $\pi/2$. If two of these circuits are connected in cascade, the final output voltage is

$$V = V_i \frac{(1-j\alpha)^2}{(1+j\alpha)^2} = -V_i \cdot \frac{2-jy}{2+jy}$$

The magnitude is still independent of frequency, while the phase now changes from 0 to 2π as the frequency varies from zero to infinite. When α is equal to unity, $y = 0$ and the output is in antiphase with the input.

To produce a selective amplifier two cascaded phase-shift circuits and an attenuator are used together with an amplifier, as shown in block form in Fig. 4.32. If the output from the attenuator is $1/n$ of its input the feedback is

$$\beta = -\frac{1}{n} \cdot \frac{2-jy}{2+jy}$$

The overall gain of the circuit is therefore

$$G = \frac{-m}{1 - \frac{m}{n} \cdot \frac{2-jy}{2+jy}}$$

$$= \frac{-m(1+jy/2)}{(1-m/n)+jy(1+m/n)/2}$$

The gain at the resonant frequency, $f_0 = 1/2\pi CR$, is found by putting y equal to zero; this gain is

$$G_0 = \frac{-m}{1-m/n}$$

Therefore the gain G can be expressed as

$$G = \frac{G_0(1+jy/2)}{1+jy(G_0/2n+G_0/2m)}$$

This equation is of the same form as those obtained for the previous selective amplifiers, and thus the Q-factor is given by

$$Q = \frac{G_0}{2n} + \frac{G_0}{2m}$$

To obtain a high Q with a moderate value of G_0 the values of m and n must be small. Since this is an example of positive feedback, the voltage fed back at resonance is in phase with the input, and n must be slightly greater than m or oscillation results. For example, if G_0 is to be 100 and m is 4, the value of n required is 4·17. The Q-factor obtained is thus approximately G_0/m; in the example considered $Q = 25$. This circuit possesses certain advantages over the others. Error factors such as appear in the other selective amplifiers do not apply to it. If one of the components is not the correct size the amplifier is merely slightly out of tune; the magnitude of the feedback is not altered and hence the values of G_0 and Q are not altered. Thus the circuit is particularly useful when the frequency to which the amplifier tunes is to be continuously variable. There is, therefore, no difficulty in gauging the two resistors or the two capacitors of the frequency-sensitive network. Equality of the two variable elements is not necessary, for a frequency must exist at which the total phase shift produced by the two phase-shifting circuits is π. This frequency is the resonant one, since, if the phase shift is π, the feedback is real and positive.

The circuit of Fig. 4.33 is one example of the use of the phase-shifting networks to produce a selective amplifier. A single pentode amplifier stage is followed by the cascaded phase-shifting circuits. Negative feedback is applied by means of R_1 and R_2 feeding a fraction of the voltage from the anode of first phase-shifter valve to the cathode of the pentode. The value of m is thus very nearly $(R_1+R_2)/R_1$. A fraction of the output of the second phase-shifting valve is fed back to the pentode grid. This fraction is approximately $R_4/(R_3+R_4)$, although the input impedance of the pentode modifies this to a certain extent.

Furthermore, R_3, R_4 and this input impedance impose a load on the last stage, and therefore these impedances should be large compared with the resistance R in the frequency-determining network. The resistor R_3 determines the amount of positive feedback at resonance

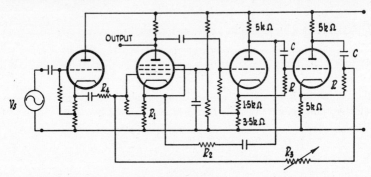

Fig. 4.33
A circuit diagram of the amplifier in Fig. 4.32.

and thus is a very convenient means of adjusting the Q-factor. The cathode-follower input stage is not essential. In this circuit it prevents the source of impedance from forming part of R_4; without its use the factor n in the expression for G depends on the source impedance.

This type of selective amplifier is easy to use at very low frequencies. Circuits can be constructed to tune to frequencies as low as 1 c/min

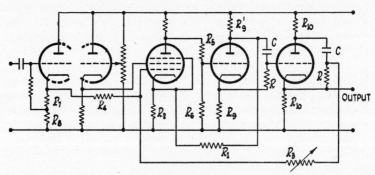

Fig. 4.34

without any trouble. For such frequencies all coupling capacitors are removed from the circuit, as shown in Fig. 4.34. The values of the numbered resistors are determined partly by the required values of m and n, and partly by the d.c. levels which must exist in the circuit.

The gain at resonance, and hence the Q-factor, is determined by the setting of R_3, which thus forms a convenient gain control.

The stability of this type of amplifier with respect to changes in the m branch is essentially the same as that of the other types. Thus, if an amplifier of gain G_0 is used with the twin-T network the gain and Q-factor are given by

$$G = \frac{G_0(1+jy/4)}{1+jy(G_0+1)/4} \quad \text{and} \quad Q = (G_0+1)/4$$

With the same amplifier, but with additional negative feedback to reduce the gain to m, the use of phase-shifting circuits gives

$$G = \frac{G_{01}(1+jy/2)}{1+jy(G_{01}/2n+G_{01}/2m)} \quad \text{and} \quad Q_1 = \frac{G_{01}}{2n}+\frac{G_{01}}{2m}$$

If the two selective amplifiers are to be identical, G_0 must equal G_{01}, and Q must equal Q_1. But G_{01} is equal to $m/(1-m/n)$, and therefore the following must hold,

$$G_0 = \frac{m}{1-m/n} \quad \text{and} \quad \frac{G_0+1}{4} = \frac{G_{01}}{2n}+\frac{G_{01}}{2m}$$

The solution of these two equations yields the condition for equality of gain and Q-factor; it is

$$n = \frac{4G_0m}{G_0(m-2)+m}$$

If this value of n is substituted in the expression for the gain of the phase-shift type of selective amplifier, we obtain

$$G = \frac{G_0(1+jy/2)}{1+jy(G_0+1)/4}$$

This is essentially the same as for the twin-T amplifier. Hence variations in G_0 lead to the same variation in the Q-factor in each type.

In the phase-shift type of amplifier it is seen above that equality of the components forming the frequency-sensitive network is not necessary. This facilitates the construction of tunable amplifiers since costly accurate ganging of the two variable elements is avoided. Certain factors do, however, influence the stability and these are considered now. The phase-shifting circuit is shown in Fig. 4.35 and it is assumed that the anode resistance is n times the cathode resistance. Exact equality of the two resistances is impossible, and further there is necessarily change due to age, etc. The effect of the feedback from anode to cathode is also taken into account; this feedback is caused by the current I_2 flowing through C and R. The equations governing the circuit are

$$V_g = V_i - R'I_1$$

$$I_2 = I_1 - I_a = -\frac{I_1 R'(n+1)}{R+1/j\omega C}$$

and

$$I_a = g_m V_g - \frac{I_1 R'(n+1)}{r_a}$$

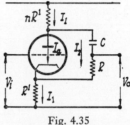

Fig. 4.35

All the currents and voltages appearing in the equations are a.c. quantities. The equations can be solved to give the voltage V_c at the cathode of the valve; this is

$$V_c = V_i \cdot \frac{g_m}{\dfrac{1}{R'} + g_m + \dfrac{n+1}{r_a} + \dfrac{n+1}{R+1/j\omega C}}$$

The feedback current is found to be

$$I_2 = -V_c \cdot \frac{n+1}{R+1/j\omega C}$$

Thus the output voltage V_0 is given by

$$V_0 = V_c + I_2 R = \frac{g_m V_i}{D}\left(1 - \frac{n+1}{R+1/j\omega C}\right)$$

where

$$D = \frac{1}{R'} + g_m + \frac{n+1}{r_a} + \frac{n+1}{R+1/j\omega C}$$

$$= \frac{1}{R'} + g_m + \frac{n+1}{r_a} + \frac{(n+1)}{R(1+1/j\alpha)}$$

since $\alpha = \omega CR$. Thus

$$V_0 = \frac{Vg_m}{D} \cdot \frac{1-jn\alpha}{1+j\alpha}$$

This output voltage can be expressed in the form

$$V_0 = \frac{V_i g_m}{D} \cdot \sqrt{\left(\frac{1+\alpha^2 n^2}{1+\alpha^2}\right)} \exp j(-\text{arc tan}\,\alpha n - \text{arc tan}\,\alpha)$$

The variation with frequency of the factor D is ignored for the moment; the frequency-dependent term in it is small compared with the other terms, e.g. g_m is of the order of 10^{-3}, whereas $(n+1)/R$ is of the order of 10^{-6} for low-frequency amplifiers. We now assume that the second phase-shifting circuit produces exactly a $\pi/2$ phase shift at resonance. Then the circuit under consideration must also produce a phase shift of exactly $\pi/2$ at resonance; thus

$$\text{arc tan}\,\alpha n - \text{arc tan}\,\alpha = \pi/2$$

Hence

$$\alpha^2 = 1/n \text{ or } \alpha = 1/\sqrt{n}$$

Substitution of this value of α in the equation for V_0 gives the value of this voltage at resonance as

$$V_0 = \frac{V_i g_m}{D} \cdot \sqrt{n} \exp j(-\pi/2)$$

Apart from the factor D this is independent of frequency; the fact that n is other than unity has no influence other than the necessary alteration of the feedback control. The magnitude of the feedback is not altered as the amplifier is tuned over its desired range. The significance of the factor $(n+1)/[R(1+1/j\alpha)]$ in the expression for D is now examined. The main influence of the term occurs near resonance, where small changes are of the greatest effect. Hence α may be taken equal to unity. Thus the expression for D reduces to

$$D = \frac{1}{R'} + g_m + \frac{2}{r_a} + \frac{(n+1)}{2R} + \frac{j(n+1)}{2R}$$

for, if $\alpha = 1$,

$$\frac{(n+1)}{R(1+1/j\alpha)} = \frac{(n+1)}{R(1-j)} = \frac{(n+1)(1+j)}{2R}$$

Since α is taken equal to unity $R = 1/j\omega C$ and the expression for D can be written

$$D = \frac{1}{R'} + g_m + \frac{2}{r_a} + \frac{\omega C(n+1)}{2} + \frac{j\omega C(n+1)}{2}$$

Comparison of these two expressions shows that capacitive tuning is preferable since ωC is constant and therefore D is unchanged as the amplifier is tuned. With resistive tuning D varies as the amplifier is tuned; increase of R to decrease the resonant frequency results in a decrease in the magnitude of D and a slight decrease in the phase angle. This results in increased feedback, an increased gain and thus increase of the Q-factor. The above discussion gives only an indication of the influence of the factor concerned; the two stages should be considered together. However the circuit does behave in practice approximately as would be expected from this simple discussion.

FILTER AMPLIFIERS

We now turn to circuits which pass a comparatively wide band of frequencies. Such circuits fall into four groups:

    (a)   Band-pass filters
    (b)   Band-elimination filters
    (c)   Low-pass filters
    (d)   High-pass filters

Those circuits already dealt with are included in group (a). To increase the bandwidth one method, similar to that employed with r.f. amplifiers, can be used. This consists in connecting a number of

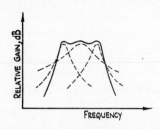

Fig. 4.36

The individual and overall response curves of a three-stage staggered tuned amplifier.

narrow-band amplifiers in cascade, with their resonant frequencies staggered about the band centre. [6] The response curves of the individual stages and of the complete circuit are shown in Fig. 4.36. Reference should be made to the work cited; no further details are given here. The class of filter-designated band-elimination can be produced by the rearrangement of the circuit connections of the amplifiers of the band-pass types. To illustrate this type the circuit shown in Fig. 4.37 is

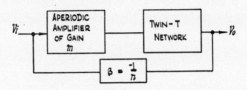

Fig. 4.37

A block diagram of the circuit of a rejection amplifier.

investigated. With the β branch broken the gain from the input V_i to the final output V_0 is $jym/(4+jy)$. The magnitude of this gain is plotted against y in Fig. 4.38, a zero of output occurring when $y = 0$; the corresponding frequency is $f_0 = 1/2\pi CR$ when a symmetrical twin-T network is used. The sharpness of the rejection can be improved

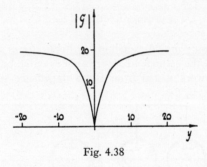

Fig. 4.38

by the aid of negative feedback, which, if large, has the effect of tending to maintain the output constant though a zero of output must still occur. If $\beta = -1/n$ the gain with negative feedback is

$$G = \frac{\dfrac{jym}{4+jy}}{1+\dfrac{jym/n}{4+jy}} = \frac{jym}{4+jy\left(1+\dfrac{m}{n}\right)}$$

For large positive or negative values of y the gain is

$$G = \frac{m}{1 + m/n}$$

The curves of Fig. 4.39 show the increased sharpness of the rejection when heavy negative feedback is applied. The gain is plotted on a decibel scale, the zero of gain being taken as that at frequencies far

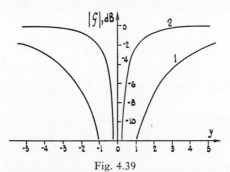

Fig. 4.39

Curves showing the increased sharpness of the rejection brought about by the use of negative feedback. Curve 1 is that of Fig. 4.38 replotted on a decibel scale. Curve 2 is that obtained when large negative feedback is used.

from the rejection point. A sketch of a suitable circuit is shown in Fig. 4.40. The use of the cathode follower is not essential but it ensures that the twin-T network works from a low-impedance source, which is

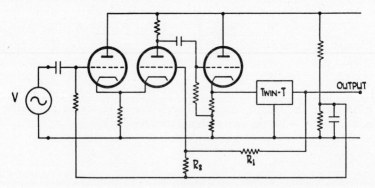

Fig. 4.40

The circuit diagram of a narrow-band rejection amplifier.

necessary if the transmission coefficient is to be $jy/(4+jy)$. The value
of β is determined by R_1 and R_2, and these should be as large as possible.
A number of these circuits can be connected in cascade with staggered
tuning to give a wide-band rejection amplifier. It should be noted that
the gain from the input to the anode of the amplifier valve rises to a
value m at the rejection frequency. This must be so, since the output
from the twin-T network is zero at this frequency and there is therefore
no feedback. Thus the danger of overloading the amplifier must be
assessed by the magnitude of the voltages near the rejection frequency.

The other types of selective network can also be used to produce
rejection amplifiers. Thus the phase-shifting circuits, arranged as shown
in the block diagram of Fig. 4.41, give a rejection amplifier which is

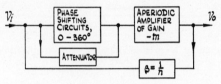

Fig. 4.41

easier to tune than the twin-T arrangement. The input to the amplifier
proper consists of two signals: V_i which is applied direct; and kV_i
$(2-jy)/(2+jy)$ which is applied through the two phase-shifting
circuits. Again k is a factor less than unity. These two signals can be
adjusted to equality of magnitude by means of the attenuator shown.
The resultant voltage applied to the amplifier is then

$$kV_i - kV_i \cdot \frac{2-jy}{2+jy} = kV_i \cdot \frac{2jy}{2+jy}$$

The output from the amplifier is thus $-mkV_i \cdot 2jy/(2+jy)$; this
expression is of similar form to that for the twin-T arrangement when
no feedback is applied. When overall negative feedback is applied the
gain becomes

$$G = \frac{-jym}{1+jy(m/n+1/2)}$$

where $+1/n = \beta$.

Except for the factor $1/2$ in the denominator this value is exactly the
same as that for the twin-T amplifier. The adjustment of the circuit is
very simple. The attenuator controlling the equality of the signals is
set to give zero output at the desired rejection frequency, and then the

amount of negative feedback is adjusted to control the sharpness of the rejection. A sketch of a suitable circuit is shown in Fig. 4.42.

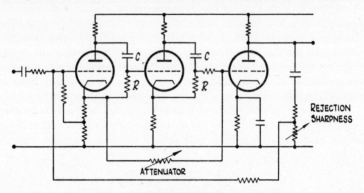

Fig. 4.42

The circuit diagram of a rejection amplifier with variable tuning and rejection sharpness.

A circuit which acts as a quite satisfactory low-pass filter is drawn in Fig. 4.43. The action of this circuit is very simple. Feedback is applied through the ladder network connected to the output from the anode of the amplifier valve. A cathode follower is actually connected between the network and the anode so that the network works from a

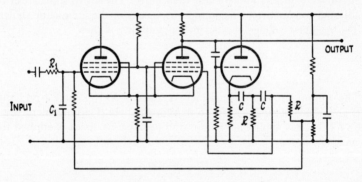

Fig. 4.43

low-impedance source. It is clear that the feedback is large at high frequencies and small at low frequencies, β being zero at zero frequency and rising to approximately unity as the frequency tends to infinity. Thus the gain decreases as the frequency of the applied signal is raised.

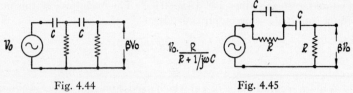

Fig. 4.44   Fig. 4.45

The feedback network incorporated
in the circuit of Fig. 4.43.

The variation of β with frequency is found by considering the circuit of Fig. 4.44. The equivalent of this obtained by use of Thévenin's theorem is shown in Fig. 4.45. The value of β is found to be

$$\beta = \frac{R}{R+\dfrac{1}{j\omega C}} \cdot \frac{R}{R+\dfrac{1}{j\omega C}+\dfrac{R/j\omega C}{R+1/j\omega C}}$$

$$= \frac{1}{1+\dfrac{1}{j\alpha}} \cdot \frac{1}{1+\dfrac{1}{j\alpha}+\dfrac{1}{1+j\alpha}}$$

$$= \frac{j\alpha}{3+jy}$$

Therefore the overall gain of the amplifier is

$$G = \frac{-m}{1+\dfrac{j\alpha m}{3+jy}}$$

$$= \frac{-m(3+jy)}{3+j(y+\alpha m)}$$

When the frequency is very low, α tends to zero and y to minus infinity, and thus G tends to $-m$. Both α and y become large when the frequency is very high and the gain tends to $-m/(m+1)$. At the frequency $f = 1/2\pi CR$, α is equal to unity and y is zero, and the gain is then approximately 3 for large values of m. The curve shown in Fig. 4.46 gives the variation of the magnitude of the gain with α. The peak in the curve occurs approximately at the value of α which makes the denominator of the expression for the gain a minimum, i.e. when

$(y+\alpha m) = 0$ and thus $\alpha = 1/(m+1)^{1/2}$. The magnitude of this maximum gain is therefore approximately

$$G_{max} = \frac{m\sqrt{(m+10)}}{3}$$

A more accurate value of α at which maximum gain occurs is obtained by differentiating the magnitude of G with respect to α and equating the result to zero; this gives $\alpha = 1/(m+4)^{1/2}$ approximately.

This rise in the gain is undesirable and is removed by means of the simple equalizer at the input, formed by the resistor R_1 and the capacitor

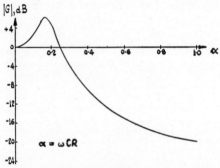

Fig. 4.46

C_1. The actual signal which is applied to the amplifier is therefore $V_i/(1+j\omega C_1 R_1)$. An approximately flat-topped response is obtained if the decrease in signal due to this factor is such as to reduce the effective gain at $\alpha = 1/(m+1)^{1/2}$ to that at zero frequency. Thus the time-constant $C_1 R_1$ is approximately given by

$$\sqrt{(1+\omega^2 C_1{}^2 R_1{}^2)} = \frac{\sqrt{(m+10)}}{3}$$

If the cut-off frequency of the filter is to be continuously variable it is convenient to use a three-gang variable element. Thus with resistive tuning R_1 can be made equal to R; alternatively with capacitive tuning C_1 can be equal to C. The curves of Fig. 4.47 illustrate the gain-frequency response of an actual amplifier with and without the equalizer. That with the equalizer shows that the cut-off frequency of the filter is very nearly that at which maximum gain occurs; thus

$$1/\alpha = 2\pi f_c CR = (m+1)^{1/2}$$

where f_c is the cut-off frequency.

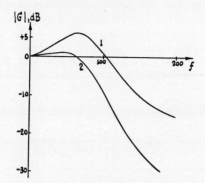

Fig. 4.47

Curve 1 shows the normal gain-frequency
response of a certain simple amplifier; and
curve 2 shows how this response changes
when an equalizer is fitted at the input of
the amplifier.

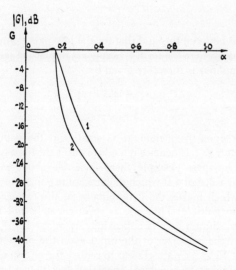

Fig. 4.48

1. Filter amplifier.   2. Constant-k filter.

Finally, in Fig. 4.48 the gain-frequency response of this amplifier is compared with that of a single section of an ordinary LC constant-k filter of the same cut-off frequency.

The high-pass filter can be produced by interchanging the resistors and capacitors, as shown in the circuit of Fig. 4.49. Feedback is now a

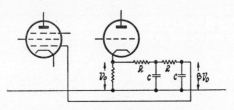

Fig. 4.49

The feedback network required to convert the circuit of Fig. 4.43 to that of a high-pass filter amplifier.

maximum at zero frequency and it falls to zero as the signal frequency tends to infinity. The value of β is determined as in the low-pass example; it may be found from the equivalent circuit of Fig. 4.50. Thus

$$\beta = \frac{1/j\alpha}{3+jy}$$

The difference between this and that for the low-pass example lies only in the numerator where the term $1/j\alpha$ appears in place of $j\alpha$. The overall gain of the amplifier is therefore given by

$$G = \frac{-m(3+jy)}{3+j(y-m/\alpha)}$$

For very low signal frequencies α is small and the gain approaches $-m/(m+1)$; at high frequencies it tends towards the limiting value $-m$. As with the low-pass example there is a rise above m for certain values of α; the value of α at which the maximum gain occurs is approximately that which makes the denominator of the expression for G a minimum in magnitude. Thus α_{max} is approximately $(m+1)^{1/2}$ and the value of the maximum gain is approximately $m(m+10)^{1/2}/3$. This rise is removed by the equalizer at the input as in the previous amplifier. The values of R_1 and C_1 are chosen to reduce the output at the peak to the value at higher frequencies. In actual fact a band-pass filter is produced, since the gain falls at very high frequencies owing to the shunt capacitances present in the circuit.

Two very simple circuits have been considered which provide reasonable cut-off characteristics; should the sharpness of the cut-off not be sufficient it can be improved by employing two filters in cascade. Further if a low-pass and a high-pass filter are connected in cascade a

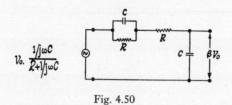

$$V_o. \frac{1/j\omega C}{R+1/j\omega C}$$

Fig. 4.50

wide-band-pass filter can be produced with an easily adjustable bandwidth.

It is possible to produce any desired filter characteristic by the use of valves, resistors and capacitors only. In general the circuits are complicated and the design procedure is beyond the scope of this work. For more information reference (7) in the list below should be consulted.

REFERENCES

1. SCOTT, H. H. 'A New Type of Selective Circuit and some Applications' *Proc. I.R.E.* (1938), **226**, p. 26.
2. STURTEVANT, J. 'A Stable Selective Audio Amplifier'. *Rev. Sc. Instr.*, 1947, **124**, p. 18.
3. PUNNETT, S. W. 'Audio-Frequency Selective Amplifiers'. *J. Brit. I.R.E.* (1950), **39**, p. 51.
4. PUNNETT, S. W. *loc. cit.*, p. 57.
5. PUNNETT, S. W. *loc. cit.*, p. 56.
6. VALLEY, G. E., and WALLMAN, H. 'Vacuum Tube Amplifiers' (M.I.T. Radiation Laboratory Series; McGraw-Hill, 1st Edition), p. 407.
7. SHUMARD, C. C. 'Design of High-Pass, Low-Pass and Band-Pass Filters using R-C Networks and D.C. Amplifiers with Feedback', *R.C.A. Rev.* (1950) **534**, p. 11.

BIBLIOGRAPHY

THIESSEN, G. J. 'R-C. Filter Circuits'. *J. Acoust. Soc. Amer.* (1945), **275** p. 16.
TISDALE, G. E. 'Continuously adjustable Electronic Filter Networks', *Proc. I.R.E.* (1950) **796**, p. 38.

Chapter Five

DIRECT-CURRENT AMPLIFIERS

By E. E. ZEPLER

Sometimes in amplifier technique the variations in signal voltage are
so slow that capacitance or transformer coupling cannot be employed.
Among the various solutions of the problem the direct-current amplifier
plays a prominent part. In a d.c. amplifier the anodes of the amplifier
valves are connected to the grids of the next valves either direct or
through resistive components. The type of amplifier stage that was
employed in the past is shown in Fig. 5.1. The main disadvantage

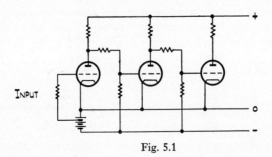

Fig. 5.1

of this type of amplifier is that slow variations in the high-tension
supply, in the negative bias voltage, or in the filament supply cause
such a large output that only input signals well in excess of one milli-
volt can be detected at the output.

Modern development has succeeded in so reducing this output from
slow drift that d.c. amplifiers with large gain and good stability have
now become possible. In describing the methods of doing this, we shall
discuss the sources of slow drift in the order of their importance. (The
treatment is largely for instructional purposes.) We first consider
variations in filament voltage.

In Fig. 5.2, the variation of the anode voltage V_a with the filament
Voltage V_f of a diode is shown, for two values of emission current.
From the graph it is seen that a change of 10 per cent in the filament
voltage is equivalent to a change of approximately 0·1 volt in anode
voltage. This applies generally to oxide-coated unipotential cathodes.

106

In triode valves we can best find the output due to changes in filament voltage by assuming an equivalent e.m.f., namely 0·1 volt for a 10 per cent change in V_f, in series with the cathode lead. This e.m.f. acts both as

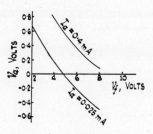

Fig. 5.2

a grid voltage and as an anode voltage, hence its effect is the same as if a voltage of $(1+1/\mu)$ times its value were applied between grid and cathode.

Apart from stabilizing the filament voltage, there are essentially two ways of minimizing the undesired output. The first method may be seen from Fig. 5.3. We assume that both triodes react similarly to a

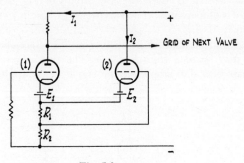

Fig. 5.3

change in filament voltage, so that we may reckon with two e.m.f.'s E_1 and E_2 of the same sense in the two cathode leads. If there is to be no change of I_1 the p.d. caused by I_2 across R_1+R_2 must be equal to E. Now

$$I_2 = (E_2-I_2R_1)g_m + \frac{E_2-I_2(R_1+R_2)}{r_a}$$

where g_m and r_a refer to valve 2. Putting $g_m = \mu/r_a$, we have

$$I_2 = \frac{(\mu+1)E_2}{r_a+R_2+(\mu+1)R_1}$$

This result proves the property noted above, namely that an e.m.f. in the cathode lead is equivalent to $(1+1/\mu)$ times its value applied between grid and cathode [or, of course, $(1+\mu)$ times its value applied in the anode lead]. The effect of the cathode resistance has been discussed on page 26. The condition for $I_1 = 0$ is therefore

$$\frac{(\mu+1)E_2(R_1+R_2)}{r_a+R_2+(\mu+1)R_1} = E_1$$

In the special case when $E_2 = E_1$, the condition becomes $R_2 = r_a/\mu = 1/g_m$.

The circuit of Fig. 5.3 does not provide any compensation for variations in the h.t. supply, another source of slow drift. On the contrary, the valve 2 increases the effect for the following reason. Let us assume that the h.t. voltage increases. This causes the anode voltage of valve 1 to increase, even if valve 2 were not there. On the other hand, the increased anode current of valve 2 applies a negative bias to the grid of valve 1, thus reducing I_1 and further increasing the potential at the anode of valve 1. If, therefore, the circuit of Fig. 5.3 is used, special means of compensation for variations in the h.t. supply must be provided.

The second method for compensating the effect of variable filament voltage may be seen from Fig. 5.4. The two valves shown form the input pair of a d.c. amplifier, the signal being applied between grid

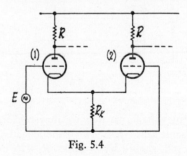

Fig. 5.4

and earth of one of the two valves. Owing to the coupling cathode resistor R_k the signal voltages at the two anodes are in antiphase; they are applied to the grids of the next pair working in push-pull.

Variations in filament or h.t. voltage change the anode voltages of each of the first pair in the same way, provided that the two valves and their loads are identical. If then the following part of the amplifier is symmetrical, there is no p.d. between the two output anodes, i.e. no output from the amplifier. The efficiency of the amplifier will largely depend on the equal behaviour of each valve in a pair working in push-pull, and of the equality of the appropriate components. The more critical stage is the first one, for obvious reasons. It seems likely that the push-pull (or differential) amplifier is the most satisfactory solution of the problem, and therefore the following discussion is confined to this type, and in the main to the input stage. The results derived apply equally to subsequent stages.

The behaviour of a cathode-coupled push-pull stage towards a signal that is not symmetrical with respect to earth will first be studied. We assume the two valves of Fig. 5.4 to be identical. Using the relation $I_a = g_m V_g + V_a/r_a$ (p. 21), we obtain

$$I_1 = [E-(I_1+I_2)R_k]g_m - \frac{(I_1+I_2)R_k+I_1R}{r_a}$$

which, on rearranging, becomes

$$I_1\left(1+R_kg_m+\frac{R_k+R}{r_a}\right)+I_2\left(R_kg_m+\frac{R_k}{r_a}\right) = Eg_m \qquad (5.1)$$

Correspondingly, the equation for I_2 is

$$I_2 = -(I_1+I_2)R_kg_m - \frac{(I_1+I_2)R_k+I_2R}{r_a}$$

which gives

$$I_1\left(R_kg_m+\frac{R_k}{r_a}\right)+I_2\left(1+R_kg_m+\frac{R_k+R}{r_a}\right) = 0 \qquad (5.2)$$

Replacing g_m by μ/r_a, we have

$$I_2 = -I_1\frac{R_k(1+\mu)}{r_a+R+R_k(1+\mu)} \qquad (5.3)$$

From this we see that the two anode voltages are in antiphase; they are of approximately equal magnitude when $R_k(1+\mu) \gg (r_a+R)$.

Subtracting eqn. (5.2) from eqn. (5.1) gives

$$I_1\left(1+\frac{R}{r_a}\right)-I_2\left(1+\frac{R}{r_a}\right) = Eg_m$$

Therefore

$$I_1 - I_2 = E\frac{\mu}{R + r_a}$$

The signal applied to the next stage is

$$V_{a1} - V_{a2} = -(I_1 - I_2)R = -\mu E\frac{R}{R + r_a}$$

Hence, for any value of R_k, the gain of the stage is that of a single valve working without cathode feedback.

In the special case of $R_k(1 + \mu) \gg (r_a + R)$,

$$V_{a1} = -V_{a2} = -(\mu/2)E \cdot R/(R + r_a)$$

The result is at first surprising because one might expect a large decrease in gain due to the cathode feedback. However, so far as the first valve is concerned, the cathode resistance is R_k in parallel with the

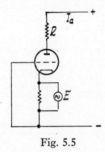

Fig. 5.5

resistance between cathode and earth represented by the second valve. From Fig. 5.5, we have

$$I_a = Eg_m + \frac{E - I_a R}{r_a}$$

whence

$$I_a = \frac{(\mu + 1)E}{r_a + R}$$

and this shows that the resistance represented by the second valve is $(r_a + R)/(\mu + 1)$.

If in the circuit of Fig. 5.4 an additional signal $-E$ is applied between grid and earth of the second valve, the p.d. $(V_{a1} - V_{a2})$ is doubled, as follows at once from the above treatment. Since then the input signal is really 2*E*, applied in push-pull between the two grids, the gain is still the same as that of a single valve with no cathode load. Because of the symmetry, no signal voltage would exist across R_k, a clear indication that there would be no negative feedback.

As follows from the above, it is important that R_k is large, say, 0·2 megohm. In order that the valves work with a reasonable current, a positive voltage ought to be inserted in the two grid leads of Fig. 5.4. In practice one works with a powerpack providing +250 volts and −250 volts with respect to earth. R_k is connected to −250 volts which enables one to receive a signal between grid and earth. This practical detail is omitted to show the circuits in their simplest form.

THE MAGNITUDE OF THE IMPROVEMENT

Naturally the push-pull stage cannot be expected to be completely symmetrical. It is therefore of interest to assess the output from variations in h.t. or filament voltage in comparison with the signal, with various reasonable assumptions about the performance of the stage.

(i) The stage is symmetrical, except for a difference in a.c. resistance

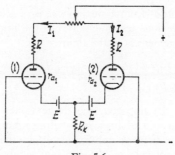

Fig. 5.6

of the two valves. The output from a variation in filament voltage is to be calculated.

From Fig. 5.6 we find

$$I_1 = [E-(I_1+I_2)R_k]\frac{\mu}{r_{a1}} + [E-(I_1+I_2)R_k-I_1R]\frac{1}{r_{a1}}$$

$$I_2 = [E-(I_1+I_2)R_k]\frac{\mu}{r_{a2}} + [E-(I_1+I_2)R_k-I_2R]\frac{1}{r_{a2}}$$

Therefore

$$I_1 = \frac{(\mu+1)E(r_{a2}+R)}{(r_{a1}+R)(r_{a2}+R)+(\mu+1)R_k(r_{a1}+r_{a2}+2R)}$$

$$I_2 = \frac{(\mu+1)E(r_{a1}+R)}{(r_{a1}+R)(r_{a2}+R)+(\mu+1)R_k(r_{a1}+r_{a2}+2R)}$$

Hence

$$\left|\frac{V_{a1}}{V_{a2}}\right| = \left|\frac{I_1}{I_2}\right| = \frac{r_{a2}+R}{r_{a1}+R}$$

The undesired output is

$$V_{a1}-V_{a2} = V_{a1}\left(1-\frac{r_{a1}+R}{r_{a2}+R}\right)$$

$$= \frac{(\mu+1)E \cdot R(r_{a2}-r_{a1})}{(r_{a1}+R)(r_{a2}+R)+(\mu+1)R_k(r_{a1}+r_{a2}+2R)}$$

This output may be compared with that from a single valve working without cathode feedback, bearing in mind that the gain for the desired signal is the same.

The undesired output from a single valve is $(\mu+1)E \cdot R/(r_a+R)$, as follows from the previous treatment. Hence the improvement due to the push-pull arrangement is in the ratio

$$\frac{(r_{a1}+R)(r_{a2}+R)+(\mu+1)R_k(r_{a1}+r_{a2}+2R)}{(r_a+R)(r_{a2}-r_{a1})} \sim \frac{r_a+R+2(\mu+1)R_k}{r_{a2}-r_{a1}}$$

This shows clearly the importance of large values of R and R_k. If $r_{a2} = 10$ kilohms, $r_{a1} = 9$ kilohms, $R = 0.1$ megohm, $R_k = 2$ kilohms, $\mu = 20$, the improvement is approximately in the ratio 200 to 1. A variation in filament voltage of 5 per cent, equivalent to $E = 0.05$ volt, would give an undesired output equal to that from a signal of $0.05/200$ volt or 0.25 mV.

If the output from variations of filament voltage were the only undesired one, it would be easy to avoid it by the use of a potentiometer in the anode circuit (Fig. 5.6). The effect of this would be to make the two anode load resistances different, say R_1 and R_2. In the above equations for I_1 and I_2 the anode load resistances appear in series with r_{a1} and r_{a2}. Hence we obtain directly

$$\frac{I_1}{I_2} = \frac{r_{a2}+R_2}{r_{a1}+R_1}; \quad \frac{V_{a1}}{V_{a2}} = \frac{(r_{a2}+R_2)R_1}{(r_{a1}+R_1)R_2}$$

The condition of equality of V_{a1} and V_{a2} is thus $R_1/R_2 = r_{a1}/r_{a2}$.

(ii) The conditions are assumed to be as in (i), but $r_{a1} = r_{a2} = r_a$, $\mu_1 \neq \mu_2$.

A calculation similar to that in (i) gives

$$I_1 = \frac{(\mu_1+1)E}{r_a+R+(\mu_1+\mu_2+2)R_k}; \quad I_2 = \frac{(\mu_2+1)E}{r_a+R+(\mu_1+\mu_2+2)R_k}$$

Hence the undesired output

$$V_{a1}-V_{a2} = \frac{(\mu_1-\mu_2)ER}{r_a+R+(\mu_1+\mu_2+2)R_k} \sim \frac{(\mu_1-\mu_2)ER}{r_a+R+2\mu R_k}$$

where μ is the average value for the two valves.

If $r_a = 10$ kilohms, $R = 0\cdot1$ megohm, $R_k = 2$ kilohms, $\mu_1 = 20$, $\mu_2 = 18$, $E = 0\cdot05$ volt, then the undesired output is 53 mV, equivalent to a signal of $2\cdot9$ mV. This shows that differences in μ are far more serious than those in r_a. A large value of R does not improve the conditions as was the case in (i), but a large R_k would be advantageous. However the use of a large R_k introduces new complications. For example, the voltage drop across R_k must be offset to prevent the valves from working practically at cut-off. This may be done by connecting the earth side of R_k to a potential negative with respect to earth. Then variations of the negative voltage supply become a new source of undesired output. The e.m.f. is then in the common cathode lead of the two valves, and hence the calculation is identical with that carried

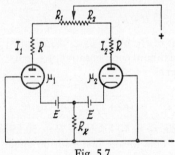

Fig. 5.7

out above for variations in filament voltage. An increase in R_k necessitates an increase of the negative supply voltage, and, since we may reckon with a certain fractional stability of this voltage, the magnitude of the undesired e.m.f. is likely to rise proportionally, with R_k. However the advantages of a large R_k are so pronounced that, as stated above, modern d.c. amplifiers employ powerpacks providing $+250$ volts and -250 volts with respect to earth.

Naturally it is possible to reduce the output from the negative supply voltage by the use of an anode potentiometer (Fig. 5.6), but it cannot be expected that the potentiometer will, at the same time, cancel the output from variations in filament voltage. A simple calculation will show the magnitude of the potentiometer required for zero output.

(iii) It is assumed that equal e.m.f.'s exist in both cathodes, owing to variations of either filament voltage or negative supply voltage (Fig. 5·7). The magnitude of the anode load resistances for zero output is to be found. The two relevant equations are

$$I_1 = [E - (I_1 + I_2)R_k] \frac{\mu_1 + 1}{r_a + R + R_1}$$

$$I_2 = [E - (I_1 + I_2)R_k] \frac{\mu_2 + 1}{r_a + R + R_2}$$

Solving these in the usual way gives

$$V_{a2} - V_{a1} = I_1(R + R_1) - I_2(R + R_2)$$

$$= E \cdot \frac{(\mu_1 + 1)(r_a + R + R_2)(R + R_1) - (\mu_2 + 1)(r_a + R + R_1)(R + R_2)}{D}$$

where D is the network determinant. The condition for zero output is

$$\frac{(\mu_1 + 1)(R + R_1)}{r_a + R + R_1} = \frac{(\mu_2 + 1)(R + R_2)}{r_a + R + R_2}$$

which is independent of R_k. When $\mu_1 > \mu_2$, R_2 must be larger than R_1. At the position of maximum compensation, $R_1 = 0$, when the condition of zero output becomes

$$R_2 = \frac{(r_a + R)(\mu_1 - \mu_2)R}{(\mu_2 + 1)r_a - (\mu_1 - \mu_2)R}$$

For $\mu_1 = 21$, $\mu_2 = 20$, $r_a = 10$ kilohms, $R = 50$ kilohms, we find that $R_2 = 18\cdot8$ kilohms. This means that with an anode potentiometer of $18\cdot8$ kilohms a difference of 5 per cent in μ could be compensated. When

$$\frac{\mu_1 + 1}{\mu_2 + 1} = \frac{r_a + R}{R}$$

$R_2 = \infty$, i.e. compensation is impossible.

This is understandable, because if $R \gg r_a$ the gain is hardly affected by changes in R, so that differences in μ cannot be compensated.

(iv) It is assumed that $r_{a1} \neq r_{a2}$, $\mu_1 \neq \mu_2$, $R+R_1 = R+R_2 = R$.

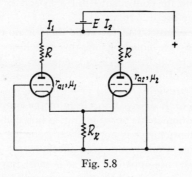

Fig. 5.8

The output due to variations in the h.t. supply is to be found. From Fig. 5.8 we obtain

$$I_1 = [E-(I_1+I_2)R_k-I_1R]\frac{1}{r_{a1}} - (I_1+I_2)R_k\frac{\mu_1}{r_{a1}}$$

$$I_2 = [E-(I_1+I_2)R_k-I_2R]\frac{1}{r_{a2}} - (I_1+I_2)R_k\frac{\mu_2}{r_{a2}}$$

The undesired output is

$$V_{a1}-V_{a2} = E-I_1R-(E-I_2R) = (I_2-I_1)R$$

$$= ER \cdot \frac{2R_k(\mu_1-\mu_2)+r_{a1}-r_{a2}}{(r_a+R)[r_a+R+2(\mu+1)R_k]}$$

r_a and μ being average values.

Two cases may be considered separately.

(a) $R_k = 2$ kilohms, $R = 0.1$ megohm, $r_{a1} = 10$ kilohms, $r_{a2} = 9$ kilohms, $\mu_1 = \mu_2 = 20$, $E = 1$ volt.

The undesired output is 4·6 mV corresponding to a signal input of 250 μV.

(b) As in (a), but $r_{a1} = r_{a2} = 10$ kilohms, $\mu_1 = 20$, $\mu_2 = 18$.

The undesired output is 38 mV, corresponding to a signal input of 2·1 mV.

Again, as previously, it is seen that differences in μ are more serious than those in r_a.

(v) The case of identical valves but different load resistances is of less interest and will not be discussed in detail. By using wire-wound resistances great accuracy in R, and at the same time absence of low-frequency noise, can be obtained.

(vi) The valve constants and the anode load resistances are the same for both valves, but the equivalent e.m.f.'s E_1 and E_2 due to variations in filament voltage are different.

Because of the symmetry of the stage there is no output if the two e.m.f.'s E_1 and E_2 are equal. From this it follows that the output is such as would result from an e.m.f. equal to E_1–E_2 being injected in the cathode lead of one of the valves. The output is the same as that from a signal of strength $(E_1 - E_2)$ $(1 + 1/\mu)$ (see p. 107), independent of the magnitude of R or R_k. Cancelling of the output with the help of the anode potentiometer is possible, but, as noted above, the required setting of the potentiometer is not likely to coincide with that needed for the cancellation of other undesired effects.

From this it becomes apparent that it is most important to choose a pair of valves as identical in behaviour as possible and use the anode potentiometer for minimizing the remaining undesired output. Double-triodes may be expected to be more suitable than individual triodes, because their two parts have been manufactured under the same conditions.

DESIGN OF THE D.C. AMPLIFIER

Numerical values of the various components and correct working conditions of the valves will be discussed with the help of Figs. 5.9 and 5.10. Only the first two stages are shown. We assume that the h.t.

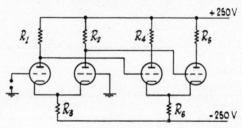

Fig. 5.9

supply is 250 volts. It is decided to run the valves with an anode current of 1 milliamp, a grid-cathode potential of -4 volts and an anode–cathode potential of approximately 100 volts. The following values follow automatically: $R_3 = 127$ kilohms, raising the cathode potential of the first stage to $+4$ volts; $R_1 = R_2 = 146$ kilohms, producing an anode potential of $+104$ volts.

To obtain, in the second stage, a grid bias of -4 volts, the cathode potential must be raised to $+108$ volts and hence the anode potential must be $+208$ volts. This gives the following values: $R_4 = R_5 = 42$ kilohms and $R_6 = 179$ kilohms. It is easy to see that, owing to the large cathode resistances, the valves adjust themselves automatically to a current of about 1 milliamp, and that tolerances in R_3 and R_6 are not serious. Let us assume that R_3 changes by 5 kilohms; this is equivalent to a voltage of 10 volts inserted in the cathode lead (p. 12). We can consider the two valves as being in parallel, acting as one valve of $\mu = 20$ and $r_a = 10$ kilohms (for $i_a = 1$ milliamp, $r_a = 20$ kilohms), with an anode load of 73 kilohms. Hence the change in anode current is $21 \times 10/(10+73+21 \times 127)10^3$ amps $= 0 \cdot 08$ milliamps. Clearly the same effect would be produced by a change of 10 volts at the anode of the first stage.

It is possible to increase the number of stages without having to increase the h.t., if the anodes are directly connected to the subsequent grids, but via potential dividers (Fig. 5.11). By proper choice of R_1

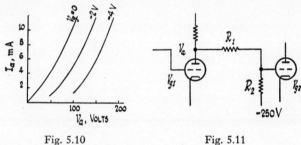

Fig. 5.10   Fig. 5.11

and R_2 the subsequent grid may be made to be at the same potential as that of the preceding stage. For example, let V_a be $+150$ volts, and $V_{g1} = 50$ volts. Now $V_{g2} = 150 - R_1 400/(R_1+R_2)$, hence the condition that $V_{g2} = +50$ gives $R_2 = 3R_1$. Values of $R_1 = 2$ megohms, $R_2 = 6$ megohms are likely to prove satisfactory, increasing the current in the anode load by about $0 \cdot 05$ milliamps. The grid leak resistance of the second valve is $1 \cdot 5$ megohms which is the parallel combination of R_1 and R_2. The maximum value of the grid leak permissible limits the size of R_1 and R_2. The stage gain is, in our example, reduced by 25 per cent.

To prevent a drop of gain at higher frequencies, owing to some stray capacitance C_2 across R_2, an additional capacitance C_1 must be connected across R_1. The stage gain is independent of frequency when $R_1 C_1 = R_2 C_2$.

Because of the large differences in the cathode potentials of the various stages it is not feasible to heat all the valves in parallel. The usual triode is designed for about 100 volts maximum potential difference cathode-heater, and therefore two, possibly three, different heater supplies must be provided. With a.c. heating this has the advantage that individual humdingers can be employed.

There are other versions of d.c. amplifiers in which the d.c. signal is changed into an a.c. signal by means of mechanical or electrical chopping. In these types the problem of slow drift is rendered harmless and, therefore, the smallest signal that can be received is considerably smaller in value than with the conventional amplifiers described in this chapter.

Chapter Six

POWER SUPPLIES

By S. W. Punnett

We have seen in chapters three and four, in a discussion of negative feedback and selective amplifiers, that variation in the gain m is undesirable. In fact in any electronic circuit which is used for quantitative measurements it is usually best to maintain m as constant as possible. Such constant gain, combined with the use of negative feedback, produces extremely stable circuits. Since m is dependent on the parameters μ, g_m and r_a of the valves, and since these are functions of the applied voltages, it is necessary to stabilize the latter. These voltages include the heater or filament voltage, for the operating temperature of the cathode has considerable influence on the valve parameters. Therefore the problem is the stabilization of all the supplies to the valves.

One solution is the use of trickle-charged accumulators for all supplies. This is cumbersome and needs continual attention. It is preferable, if possible, to design the equipment to operate from a.c. supplies, since these are most likely to be available. There are two lines of attack. The first is the stabilization of the a.c. supply. This stabilized supply is then used, after suitable transformation, to heat the valves and, after rectification and smoothing, to provide the h.t. voltages required. But this method is not the complete answer to all requirements for constant-voltage supplies. The rectifier units have appreciable internal impedance, and this results in a variation of the output voltage with variation of the current demand. Furthermore, this internal impedance gives rise to common impedance coupling between units attached to the same h.t. supply. It is thus necessary to stabilize the rectifier outputs against variations of load current, this is equivalent to a reduction of the internal impedance of the supply and thus also reduces the common impedance coupling. The second line of attack is to use an unstabilized source of alternating current to supply the rectifier units, whose outputs are fed into d.c. stabilizers. This provides satisfactory h.t. supplies for all the valves and sometimes that is sufficient without stabilization of the l.t. supply. If the l.t. voltages are important, the heaters of all the valves, including those in the stabilizers, can be connected in series and fed from a high-voltage stabilized supply of the same form as that supplying the high-tension voltage.

Suitable valves are obtainable which can be used in stabilizing circuits for output currents up to 300 mA; this current is sufficient for a large number of types of valve used in amplifiers or instruments.

This chapter is therefore divided into two sections. The shorter first section deals with the stabilization of a.c. supplies. The longer section is devoted to a consideration of stabilized d.c. supplies. It is not intended to treat a large number of methods nor to consider any particular circuit in great detail. A very extensive literature already exists covering this field, and the references cited in the footnotes should be consulted. Here a brief survey of the general field is given, and, in particular, the action underlying certain of the most used circuits is considered theoretically in detail.

STABILIZATION OF A.C. SUPPLIES

A number of low-power circuits have been described for stabilizing an a.c. supply.[1] Most of them produce a very distorted output waveform. Here only arrangements which will handle appreciable powers are considered, the largest versions of the apparatus being capable of outputs of the order of kilowatts. Those types of circuit which make use of magnetic saturation are dealt with first. These contain an element which saturates magnetically at relatively low applied voltages, and thus the output voltage does not vary linearly with the input voltage. Therefore if a transformer has a core which saturates readily, the output voltage varies with the current in the primary approximately as shown in Fig. 6.1. When such a transformer is connected in series with a normal transformer so that the output voltages of the two are in opposition, as shown in Fig. 6.2, then by the correct proportioning of the values

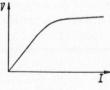

Fig. 6.1

The output-voltage and primary-current relationship for a transformer whose core saturates readily.

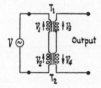

Fig. 6.2

Circuit arrangement for the stabilizer employing magnetic saturation.

an almost constant output voltage is obtainable. As the mains voltage rises, a point is reached where transformer T_1 saturates; its inductance therefore falls and further increase of voltage is almost wholly dropped across T_2; this is shown in Fig. 6.3 by the curves labelled V_1 and V_2. The resulting output voltages V_3 and V_4 are as shown; these voltages are in opposition.

If T_1 supplies the major portion of the output, then as this output is equal to (V_3-V_4), it can be very nearly constant. This type of circuit has three main disadvantages. Saturation of the core results in harmonics in the magnetizing current, and therefore the output is very distorted. The regulation is poor so that load variations cause changes in the output voltage. Finally, variations in the frequency of the supply voltage affect the output voltage. Slightly more complicated designs overcome these difficulties. One satisfactory arrangement is that employed in the 'stabilistor'[2] of which there are two designs. Fig. 6.4 gives the circuit

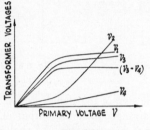

Fig. 6.3

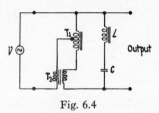

Fig. 6.4

The 'Stabilistor' circuit, which stabilizes the output voltage against input voltage and the load current charges.

arrangement of one of them which stabilizes against supply and load variations but not against the effects of frequency changes. The transformer T_1 of Fig. 6.2 is replaced by an auto-transformer, while the output is shunted by a circuit which is resonant at three times the supply frequency. Very little third-harmonic voltage, which is one of the main sources of distortion, can therefore appear in the output. Moreover, this series resonant circuit is capacitive at the fundamental frequency, and thus it draws a leading current which tends to offset the large magnetizing current in the transformer primaries. This tends to stabilize the output against load variations. This arrangement can be so constructed that input variations of 15 per cent are reduced to 2 per cent; when the current demand is altered from zero to full load current the output changes by approximately ± 2 per cent. A frequency variation of ± 1 per cent causes approximately $\pm 1 \cdot 5$ per cent variation in the output voltage. The second design is a modification of that given in Fig. 6.4; it is such that frequency variations produce no changes in output, but it must be used at full load. This is a distinct disadvantage when required as a general-purpose supply.

Next we consider the second class of stabilizer, which employs valves and can easily provide powers up to 2 kW. In fact the maximum power is limited only by the size of the power valves employed. A block diagram of the arrangement used is shown in Fig. 6.5. The output from the unit is connected across a bridge, one arm of which contains an element whose resistance varies with the power dissipated in it. Thus at one value of the output voltage V_0 the bridge is balanced: no voltage is applied to the voltage amplifier and hence there is no drive to the power amplifier. If the output V_0 changes, the bridge is no longer balanced and a voltage is applied to the amplifiers, the phase

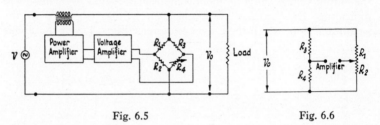

Fig. 6.5   Fig. 6.6

of the voltage being determined by the sign of the change in V_0. The connections to the amplifiers are so arranged that the output of the power amplifier tends to neutralize the change in V_0. We shall now consider certain aspects of the circuit in more detail, but for a full account reference should be made to the original paper. [3] The bridge may be arranged as shown in Fig. 6.6; with this arrangement the two arms R_1 and R_2 can easily be altered to provide a means of adjustment of the output voltage over a limited range. A thermistor [4] is probably the best element to use for the power-sensitive arm R_4, for the resistance of such an element changes a large amount with quite small powers dissipated in it. Patchett [3] shows that the output of the bridge contains an appreciable amount of third harmonic; this masks the desired fundamental-frequency output near balance and therefore should be removed by means of a suitable filter.

The voltage amplifier is normal, its gain being the factor controlling the stabilization obtained. The design of the power amplifier is not quite normal as may be seen by considering the manner in which it operates. Suppose a constant power is drawn from the stabilizer; then since the output voltage is also constant the current drawn from the unit must be constant. Therefore the secondary current of the transformer in the power amplifier stage must be constant as well, which implies that the alternating anode currents of the power amplifier valves are also constant. Therefore variations of the input voltage which are corrected by the stabilizer cause changes in the alternating anode voltages and not changes in the alternating anode currents. This is not true for an ordinary power amplifier working into a constant load, where both i_a and v_a vary throughout the cycle of the drive voltage. Thus the design of the power amplifier required for the stabilizer is unusual. The maximum anode currents of the valves and the output transformer ratio determine the maximum current which can be supplied. The range over which stabilization can be achieved is determined by the anode dissipation and transformer ratio used. It is to be noted that when the power amplifier is assisting the input voltage, because it is low, it is supplying power; then the anode dissipation is less than the static dissipation. This is the same as in normal use. If now the grid drive reverses because the input is too high, the anode voltage is in phase with the anode current and the valves are absorbing a.c. power so that the input voltage drops to V_0. Thus the anode dissipation increases above that for static conditions. This means that the valves must not be operated as in more normal use, for otherwise when bucking the input voltage the safe anode dissipation of the valves will be exceeded. Finally, various protective devices must be incorporated to prevent excessive anode dissipation and voltages in the event of changes in the input voltage greater than those for which the circuit is designed.

The third class of stabilizer to be mentioned is a servo-mechanism type. A block diagram of the arrangement is shown in Fig. 6.7. The

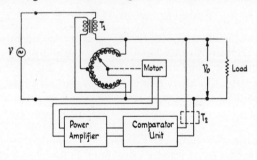

Fig. 6.7

output V_0 (the stabilized output) is applied to a comparator unit, which can be a bridge of exactly the same form as in the apparatus described in the previous section. Thus when the output is the correct value no voltage is applied to the amplifier and the motor remains stationary. If now V_0 changes, the bridge is no longer balanced and a signal is applied to the amplifier, whose output causes the motor to rotate. The direction of rotation is determined by the sign of the change V_0. The motor thus alters the tapping point on the variable transformer and a voltage is applied to the primary of transformer T_1. The secondary voltage of this transformer is such that it tends to cancel the change that has occurred in the output. Too great a degree of stabilization must not be attempted; it is liable to lead to hunting which is a form of self-oscillation of the system as a whole. A measure of control of the output voltage can be achieved by the insertion of a subsidiary transformer T_2 shown dotted in Fig. 6.7. If it is desired to have an output voltage of nV_0, the transformer T_2 must have a step-down ratio of $n:1$ so that a voltage V_0 is still applied to the comparator. This process cannot be carried too far. This is easily seen if a numerical example is considered. Suppose the unit is designed to give an output of 200 volts for an input which may vary between 180 and 220 volts. When the input is either of these limiting values the rotating arm is at one or other of its extreme positions, and is opposite the centre tap when the input is 220 volts. If an output of 220 volts is desired, a $22:20$ step-down transformer is required for T_2. Then when the input is 200 volts the rotating arm must be at its extreme position so that it gives the necessary output to boost the input to the required 220 volts. Thus the input may now vary only between approximately 200 and 240 volts. Furthermore the voltage ratings of the various transformers must be taken into consideration.

STABILIZATION OF D.C. SUPPLIES

It is not intended to deal with rectifier and normal smoothing circuits; these are extensively considered in many standard works. Here we consider only the stabilization of d.c. supplies after rectification and smoothing with LC filters. Almost all the various types of stabilizer employ gas-discharge tubes in some form and so these are discussed first.

Circuits with Gas-discharge Valves. The simplest type of circuit employs the cold gas-discharge valve. Such a valve consists of a cathode and anode structure in an envelope containing a suitable gas at low pressure. The current-voltage characteristic of these valves is sketched in Fig. 6.8. At voltages less than V_s, the striking potential, there is sensibly no current; once a discharge is started, the current rises rapidly and the voltage to maintain the discharge is considerably less than V_s. The voltage across the valve is now practically independent of the current flowing. It is found that the cathode is partially covered with a glow, the area covered being approximately proportional to the magnitude of the current. The region of almost constant valve voltage extends from the minimum current which will maintain a stable discharge up to the current at which the glow just covers the whole of the cathode area. If a greater current than this is passed through the valve, the voltage across the valve rises rapidly again, as shown in Fig. 6.8. The normal operating range extends from V_1 to V_2; a large number

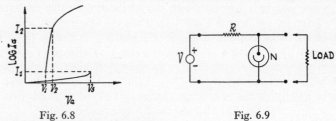

Fig. 6.8

The approximate relationship between the logarithm of the anode current and the anode voltage of a gas-discharge valve.

Fig. 6.9

of different types with various values of the current range (I_2-I_1) and the operating voltage V_1 are available.

The stabilization property of these valves depends on the above phenomenon and on the internal resistance of the supply. The latter may be artificially increased to secure desired operating characteristics. The circuit arrangement is as shown in Fig. 6.9; the resistance R

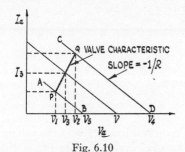

Fig. 6.10

A graphical method for the determination of the magnitude of the series resistance to be used in the circuit of Fig. 6.9.

includes the internal resistance of the supply. If only a reference potential is desired, the value of R to give maximum stabilization range against variations in the supply voltage V may be found by means of Fig. 6.10. A straight line is drawn from a point on the voltage axis equal to the supply voltage through the mid-point of the stabilizer characteristic

The reciprocal of the slope of this line is the required resistance R. The voltage across R is $(V - V_3)$, and this drives a current I_3 through R, where I_3 is the valve current due to the voltage V_3 across the discharge valve. If now V varies, the load line drawn moves parallel to itself, and the discharge valve characteristic is traversed from Q to P. The extreme positions beyond which the limits of the valve are exceeded are given by the lines AB and CD. Thus the extreme excursions of V from its mean position must be V_4 and V_5 A change $(V_4 - V_5)$ is reduced by the action of the neon valve to a change $(V_2 - V_1)$. We clearly see that the greater V is the greater R must be, and that the stabilization ratio defined as $(V_4 - V_5)/(V_2 - V_1)$ is also greater. It is to be noted that the percentage change in V is the same however large V is, provided that the characteristic is assumed linear.

If it is necessary to draw a current from V_0, i.e. if a load R_L is added, conditions are slightly altered. The relationship between current and voltage in the load is given by the line OR_L (Fig. 6.11). Thus the total

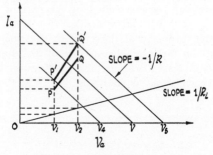

Fig. 6.11

A graphical method for the determination of the magnitude of the series resistor when a load R_L is connected to the stabilizer circuit.

current drawn by neon and load R_L over the voltage range V_1 to V_2 is given by P'Q', which is developed from PQ in Fig. 6.10, by adding the ordinates of the line OR_L. A line is now drawn joining the point representing the supply voltage V to the mid-point of PQ; the reciprocal of the slope of this line is the value of the required series resistance. As before, the maximum variation of V which can be stabilized is the range from V_4 to V_5. This is a smaller variation than is allowed in the no-load example first considered.

If the neon tube is to be used to stabilize against changes in load, a slightly different approach is necessary. Under no-load conditions, the neon tube is operated at or near Q as shown in Fig. 6.12, the maximum current permitted being drawn through the valve. This determines the value of R when V is given. When a load is applied, current flows through the load and the current through the neon tube decreases. Since the operating point must lie on VQC, the current in any given load is readily obtained. With the load R_L the difference between the ordinates of the VQC and the PQ curves must be the current in the load, and this must be driven through R_L by V_3. Thus V_3 is easily found; it is the voltage at which the current through R_L is equal to the difference of the two curves VRC and PQ. The limiting current is thus I_L, the largest difference between the ordinates of the two curves.

When both the input voltage and the current demand vary, the choice of series resistor is a matter of compromise. Obviously it is not possible to permit such great variations as when the quantities are varying alone.

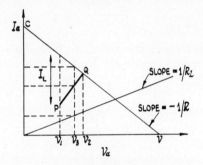

Fig. 6.12

A graphical method for the determination of the magnitude of the series resistor when the load is varying and the supply voltage V is constant.

Here, concern is directed chiefly to the case when the load current is nearly constant (or zero) and is small. The requirement is normally the provision of a constant reference potential in place of batteries, which are cumbersome and require replacement. All the various types of gas-discharge tubes may be used for this purpose; some are much better than others. For many tubes, the curve PQ is not smooth and contains abrupt changes; in others, the whole curve may be subject to sudden jumps. Further, the curve changes with age owing to alterations in gas pressure through clean up. Certain valves are produced which give exceptional stability against changes due to both age and conditions of operation.

Hard-valve Voltage Stabilizers. We turn now to the principles underlying the design of hard-valve voltage stabilizers. The basic circuit of one type is shown in Fig. 6.13. Essentially the load R_L is the cathode resistor of a cathode follower, the grid of this cathode follower being held at a fixed reference voltage V_R. A battery is shown as providing this reference voltage; a gas-discharge valve and a series resistor connected across the input supply can be used with a slightly inferior

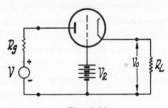

Fig. 6.13

performance. The action of the valve is such that the cathode potential must be approximately equal to that of the grid, and is thus very nearly constant. The actual values of the output voltage and of the internal impedance of the circuit are found below. In these calculations it is assumed that all valves have linear characteristics, and that the valve parameters are μ, g_m and r_a. The valve current I_a is given by

$$I_a = V_0/R_L$$

where V_0 is the output voltage. But the valve current is also given by

$$I_a = g_m V_g + V_a/r_a$$

where V_g and V_a are the grid and anode voltages respectively; these are given by

$$V_g = (V_R - V_0) \quad \text{and} \quad V_a = (V - V_0 - I_a R_g)$$

where V and R_g are respectively the voltage of the supply and its internal impedance.

These equations can be solved to give the value of the output voltage V_0 :

$$V_0 = (\mu V_R + V) \cdot \frac{R_L}{R_L(\mu+1) + r_a + R_g}$$

The current flowing through the load R_L is given by

$$I_a = \frac{\mu V_R + V}{R_L(\mu+1) + r_a + R_g} = \frac{[\mu/(u+1)]V_R + [1/(\mu+1)]V}{R_L + (r_a + R_g)/(\mu+1)}$$

Thus the action of the valve is to stimulate a generator of e.m.f. of approximately $\mu V_R/(\mu+1)$ with an internal resistance of $(r_a+R_g)/(\mu+1)$. Changes which occur in the supply voltage V are diminished by the factor $(\mu+1)$, and variations in the demand on the supply have a much smaller effect since the internal resistance is low, i.e. $(r_a+R_g)/(\mu+1)$. An expression for the improvement in the stability is found as follows. We differentiate the above equation for the output voltage with respect to V, which gives

$$\frac{dV_0}{dV} = \frac{1}{(\mu+1)+(r_a+R_g)/R_L}$$

The reciprocal of the quantity dV_0/dV might be termed the stabilization ratio, but it is not a really fair measure of the improvement. If the equation for dV_0/dV is rearranged, the following can be obtained:

$$\frac{dV_0}{V} = \frac{dV}{(\mu+1)+(r_a+R_g)/R_L} \cdot \frac{(\mu+1)+(r_a+R_g)/R_L}{\mu V_R+V}$$

$$= \frac{dV}{V} \cdot \frac{1}{1+\mu V_R/V}$$

Very approximately this may be written

$$\frac{dV_0}{V} = \frac{dV}{V} \cdot \frac{1}{1+\mu}$$

Thus the percentage variation of the output voltage is equal to that of the input voltage divided by the factor $(\mu+1)$. It is to be noted that V_R/V is involved and that this should not be too small; the input voltage should not be larger than necessary, but it must of course be sufficient to drive the required current through the regulator valve. These expressions show that a valve with a large value of μ should be used; special tetrode valves are available for this purpose which have large values of μ and g_m together with a large maximum current. The anode resistance r_a of the regulator valve appears in the expression for V_0 so that it should not be too large; a requirement met by having a large value of g_m as well as a large value of μ.

The factor which determines the output voltage variations due to changes in current demand is the internal impedance of the output circuit. Now the rate of change of output voltage V_0 with change of load resistance R_L is

$$\frac{dV_0}{dR_L} - \frac{\mu V_R + V}{(\mu + 1 + r_a/R_L + R_g/R_L)^2} \cdot \frac{r_a + R_g}{R^2_L}$$

and the rate of change of the output current with R_L is

$$\frac{dI_a}{dR_L} = -\frac{\mu V_R + V}{(R_L \mu + R_L + r_a + R_g)^2} \cdot (\mu + 1)$$

But the internal impedance of the output circuit is given by

$$Z = -\frac{dV_0}{dI_a}$$

The minus sign occurs since an increase in current causes a fall in the output voltage. If the expression for dV_0/dR_L is divided by that for dI_a/dR_L, the following expression is obtained for the internal impedance:

$$Z = \frac{r_a + R_g}{\mu + 1}$$

$$\sim \frac{1}{g_m} + \frac{R_g}{\mu}$$

Thus if in the valve employed $g_m = 10 mA/V$ and $\mu = 50$, and if the impedance of the voltage source V is 100 ohms

$$Z = 100 + 100/50 = 102 \text{ ohms}$$

In this example no improvement has been effected. It is seen that both g_m and μ should be large.

The next factor to be considered is the attainment of an output voltage which is approximately nV_R, where n is a positive number greater than unity. This is necessary since it is often impossible to employ

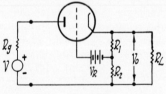

Fig. 6.14

a reference voltage as large as the desired output. The difficulty is overcome in the manner shown in Fig. 6.14. The voltage drop across the resistance R_1 is approximately equal to the reference voltage V_R.

Let R_2/R_1 equal $(n-1)$, and let us further assume that these two resistors are very much larger than R_L, so that the current flowing through them may be ignored in comparison with that through the load. Alternatively, they may be considered as part of the load so that R_L is modified slightly. This change in the circuit merely results in an alteration in V_g; it is the only change occurring in the equations which were set out for the first circuit. Here we have

$$V_g = V_R + V_0 \cdot \frac{R_2}{R_1 + R_2} - V_0$$

$$= V_R - \frac{V_0}{n}$$

$$V_a = V - V_0 - I_a R_g$$

$$I_a = g_m V_g + \frac{V_a}{r_a}$$

and

$$I_a = \frac{V_0}{R_L}$$

Solution of these equations yields

$$V_0 = \frac{\mu V_R + V}{(1 + \mu/n) + (r_a + R_g)/R_L}$$

Approximately the output voltage is $\mu V_R/(1+\mu/n)$. Therefore V_0 is very nearly nV_R provided that n is small compared with μ. If the exact expression for the output voltage V_0 is differentiated with respect to V to obtain the stability against changes in the generator voltage, the following expression results:

$$\frac{dV_0}{V_0} = \frac{dV}{V} \cdot \frac{1}{1 + \mu V_R/V}$$

This is exactly the same expression as for the simple circuit; it is to be remembered, however, that V_R is now a much smaller fraction of V. Thus if the approximate relationship for V_0 is made use of, the expression for dV_0/V_0 becomes

$$\frac{dV_0}{V_0} = \frac{dV}{V} \cdot \frac{1}{1 + \mu V_0/nV}$$

On the other hand, for the first circuit V_0 is nearly equal to V_R, and for this circuit it follows that

$$\frac{dV_0}{V_0} = \frac{dV}{V} \cdot \frac{1}{1+\mu V_0/V}$$

Therefore the stabilization ratio is degraded approximately n times. This must always be so when the reference voltage employed is only one-nth of the maximum value it may have, namely, when it is approximately equal to the desired output voltage.

The internal impedance of the output circuit may be determined in exactly the same manner as for the first circuit. Thus

$$Z = \frac{r_a + R_g}{1 + \mu/n}$$

If μ is considerably larger than n, this expression becomes very approximately

$$Z = \frac{n}{g_m} + \frac{nR_g}{\mu}$$

The internal impedance is thus increased about n times.

These effects are to be expected since the whole of any change occurring in the output is not applied between grid and cathode of the regulator valve; here only $1/n$th is so applied.

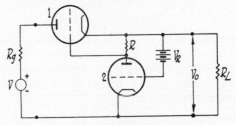

Fig. 6.15

A stabilizer circuit which employs an additional valve to amplify the variations in V before applying them to the control valve.

The next step is the inclusion of an amplifying stage so as to increase the controlling effect of small changes in the output voltage V_0. Thus the basic circuit of all electronic stabilizers of the type considered is that shown in Fig. 6.15. In this circuit the action is as follows. If for any reason the output voltage changes, the potential of the grid of the amplifying valve 2 undergoes the same change. Hence the anode voltage of this valve changes by an amount m times as great, where m is the amplification of this valve. The change at the anode is the opposite phase and this is applied to the grid of the regulator valve 1; it thus opposes the change at the cathode of 1, to which change it is due. Thus if the generator voltage V rises it tends to cause the grid of 2 to rise and its anode to fall. Therefore the grid of 1 becomes more negative with respect to its cathode, which results in a large voltage drop across valve 1, and this tends to limit the rise of the output V_0. Mathematically this is expressed by the following set of equations, in which the subscripts 1 and 2 refer to valves 1 and 2 respectively.

Valve 1

$$V_{g1} = -I_{a2}R$$

$$V_{a1} = V - V_0 - I_{a1}R_g$$

$$I_{a1} = g_{m1}V_{g1} + V_{a1}/r_{a1}$$

Valve 2

$$V_{g2} = V_0 - V_R$$

$$V_{a2} = V_0 - I_{a2}R$$

$$I_{a2} = g_{m2}V_{g2} + V_{a2}/r_{a2}$$

An exact solution of these equations can be made to obtain the value of V_0 which is equal to $R_L (I_{a1} - I_{a2})$; it is, however, a cumbersome expression which tends to mask the general characteristics. If it is assumed that I_{a2} is very small compared with I_{a1}, the approximation $V_0 = I_{a1}R_L$ yields on solving the equations

$$V_0 = \frac{m\mu_1 V_R + V}{1 + m\mu_1 + \mu_1 R/(R + r_{a2}) + (r_{a1} + R_g)/R_L}$$

where m is the amplification of valve 2 and is equal to $\mu_2 R/(r_{a2} + R)$. This expression for V_0 may be written approximately as follows:

$$V_0 \sim \frac{m\mu_1 V_R}{\mu_1(m+1)} \sim V_R$$

The stabilization ratio and the internal impedance of the output circuit are determined in the same manner as before; this results in the equations

$$\frac{dV_0}{V_0} = \frac{dV}{V} \cdot \frac{1}{1 + m\mu_1 V_R/V} \sim \frac{dV}{V} \cdot \frac{1}{1 + m\mu_1 V_0/V}$$

and
$$Z = \frac{r_{a1} + R_g}{1 + m\mu_1 + \mu_1 R/(r_{a2} + R)}$$

$$\sim \frac{1}{g_{m1}(m+1)} + \frac{R_g}{\mu_1(m+1)}$$

Thus if the mutual conductance of the valve 1 is 10 mA/V, the amplification factor is 50, R_g is 100 ohms as in the previous example, and m is equal to 29, then

$$Z = \frac{100}{30} + \frac{100}{1500} = 3 \cdot 4 \text{ ohms}$$

From these calculations we see that the amplifier valve effectively increases the amplification factor and the mutual conductance of the regulator valve by a factor m, where m is the amplification of this second valve. If a pentode is employed in place of a triode, a much higher value is obtainable for m with a resultant increase in stability. One important point arises with the use of a pentode; the screen must be supplied at its appropriate voltage. This screen supply must also be a low-impedance one, for otherwise the gain of the pentode is seriously reduced. Moreover since the d.c. impedance as well as the a.c. impedance is of interest here, the gain m must be maintained down to zero frequency. Thus decoupling by means of a capacitor is of no use by itself. The screen must be supplied by a battery, by a gas-discharge valve, or by a very low-resistance potentiometer connected across the mains supply.

In most cases the reference voltage is not of the magnitude desired for the output voltage; but V_0 can be made greater than in V_R in the same way as in the simple stabilizer. The arrangement is shown in Fig. 6.16. Again, if $R_1/R_2 = (n-1)$, similar calculations and approximations to those already used give

$$V_0 \sim nV_R$$

$$\frac{dV_0}{V_0} \sim \frac{dV}{V} \cdot \frac{1}{1 + m\mu_1 V_0/V} \sim \frac{dV}{V} \cdot \frac{1}{1 + m\mu_1 v/nV}$$

and

$$Z = \frac{1}{g_{m1}(m/n+1)} + \frac{R_g}{\mu_1(m/n+1)}$$

Since only $1/n$th of any change in the output voltage V_0 is applied to the grid of the amplifier valve, the valve gain is efficiently reduced by a factor n. This shows clearly that the reference voltage should be as large as possible. We can conveniently at this point consider the reference voltage more closely. With a valve amplifier present this voltage may be used to lower the d.c. level of the signal applied to the grid to a level below that of the cathode, as has been shown already. Alternatively, if the reference voltage supply is capable of passing a reasonable current, the cathode d.c. level may be raised above that of the grid. The latter alternative is not used with a battery owing to the current drain. A very convenient means lies in the use of a gas-discharge valve, as shown in Fig. 6.17. The series resistor may be connected

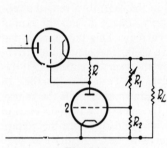

Fig. 6.16

The modification of the circuit of Fig. 6.15 to obtain an output voltage n times as large as the reference voltage V_R.

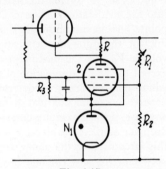

Fig. 6.17

A circuit which employs a gas-discharge valve to provide the reference voltage V_R. In addition it gives a reasonably stable supply for the screen grid.

to either the stabilized side of the supply or the unstabilized side as shown. Furthermore, this provides a reasonably low-impedance source for the screen voltage if R_3 is small (say 5000 ohms), and the current drain of the gas discharge valve is about 15 mA. It must also be noted that the stabilizer is only as good as the reference voltage. That this is so may be seen from a consideration of the formula for the output voltage V_0:

$$V_0 \sim \frac{\mu_1 m V_R}{1 + \mu_1(m/n + 1)}$$

Differentiation of this expression with respect to V_R yields

$$\frac{dV_0}{V_0} = \frac{dV_R}{V_R}$$

K

The percentage change in the output is equal to the percentage change in the reference voltage. Thus for extreme stability it is best to employ a battery despite the necessity of renewal at regular intervals. If a gas-discharge valve is used it appears better to connect its series resistor to the stabilized side of the circuit.

We shall next consider in rather more detail the action of the amplifier stage of the stabilizer circuit. It is obvious that m should be as large and as constant as possible. With the circuit arrangements sketched so far this is not easy to arrange. The grid base of the control valve, even with quite large valves, is not very great; therefore the voltage drop across the load resistor of the amplifier valve is limited to a small value. Some 20 or 30 volts is the maximum in most cases. A digression here into a consideration of the control-valve ratings tends to clarify this point. The maximum power dissipated in the control valve is the product of the difference between the supply voltage V and the output voltage V_0 and the maximum output current. This power must not exceed the anode dissipation of the valve used. The maximum current which may be drawn is determined by the cathode emission; if it is desired to exceed this two or more valves can be used in parallel. In any case, if the maximum current is to be drawn, this limits the voltage drop across the control valve owing to the anode dissipation. Thus in this circumstance the anode voltage is low, and therefore the voltage between grid and cathode must be small in order to drive a large current through the valve. This grid-cathode voltage is the drop across the anode load of the amplifier valve. Hence this valve is working with a very low anode current and, in consequence, a low value of mutual conductance. Therefore the gain m is not very large. A considerable improvement may be achieved by connecting the load resistor to the unstabilized side of the supply, as shown in Fig. 6.18. The voltage drop

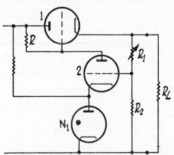

Fig. 6.18

A modification of the circuit of Fig. 6.17 in which valve 2 is operating under more satisfactory conditions.

across R is now large even when the grid-cathode voltage is small because the control valve is passing maximum current. The amplifier valve thus works with large values of anode current and mutual conductance. Furthermore there is not so great a change in its operating conditions, as the demand on the supply changes from no load to maximum load. In the first arrangement the amplifier valve is almost at cut-off when the maximum current is drawn from the supply, and the gain is very nearly zero. With the new arrangement the drop across the load resistance R must always exceed the drop across the control valve. The characteristics of this circuit are not quite the same as before, as may be seen from the following equations:

Valve 1

$$V_{g1} = V - I_{a2}R$$
$$V_{a1} = V - V_0$$
$$I_{a1} = g_{m1}V_{g1} + V_{a1}/r_{a1} \sim V_0/R_L$$

Valve 2

$$V_{g2} = V_0/n - V_R$$
$$V_{a2} = V - I_{a2}R$$
$$I_{a2} = g_{m2}V_{g2} + V_{a2}/r_{a2}$$

The expression for V_{a2} is the only term that is altered, the input voltage V appearing instead of the output voltage V_0. An approximate solution of these equations gives the following value of V_0:

$$V_0 \sim \frac{m\mu_1 V_R + V(\mu_1 + 1)}{1 + m\mu_1/n + r_a/R_L} \sim nV_R$$

One of the main approximations is that the drop in the generator impedance R_g caused by I_{a1} and I_{a2} has been ignored. The effect of this neglect is very small as can be seen from previous equations. The numerator of the expression for V_0 contains the term $(\mu_1 + 1)V$ instead of V as did the previous expression for the output voltage. Thus the control valve amplification factor has no effect on changes in the supply voltage. This can also be seen from the stabilization ratio dV_0/V_0, obtained by differentiation the expression for V_0 with respect to V. This gives

$$\frac{dV_0}{V_0} = dV \cdot \frac{\mu_1 + 1}{m\mu_1 V_R + V(\mu_1 + 1)} \sim \frac{dV}{V} \cdot \frac{1}{1 + mV_R/V}$$

$$\sim \frac{dV}{V} \cdot \frac{1}{1 + mV_0/nV}$$

The amplification factor μ_1 of the control valve is absent from this equation. The effectiveness of this circuit in respect of load variations is unaltered as can be shown by determining the internal impedance of the output circuit. This internal impedance z is found in the same manner as before by differentiating the output voltage and output current equations with respect to R_L, and then dividing the first result by the second. Thus

$$Z = -\frac{dV_0}{dI_{a1}} = \frac{r_{a1}}{1+m\mu_1/n} \sim \frac{1}{mg_{m1}/n}$$

If allowance is made for the missing term containing R_g, this is the same as before; thus the stabilizer is just as effective as far as load variations are concerned.

The circuit may be restored to its full sensitivity by the arrangement shown in Fig. 6.19. A gas-discharge valve and a series resistor are connected across the control valve, and the anode of the amplifier

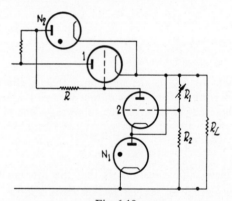

Fig. 6.19

A circuit arrangement providing an h.t. voltage
for the amplifier valve which is a constant amount
greater than the output voltage V_0.

is fed from the junction as shown. Variations in the input voltage V are no longer applied in full to the grid of the control valve, and thus the characteristics are restored to approximately the values obtained with the anode load connected to the stabilized supply. There is, of course, a small variation as V alters, but the anode voltage of the gas-discharge valve is very nearly a constant amount greater than the output voltage V_0. The connections shown are the most convenient when a variable supply voltage is required, as the output V_0 is varied the h.t. voltage applied to the amplifier valve follows V_0 almost exactly. Therefore the amplifier valve can be made to operate in its most sensitive condition whatever the output.

With a fixed output voltage the circuit arrangement of Fig. 6.20 is convenient. One or more gas-discharge valves are employed to secure

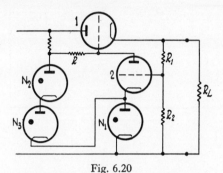

Fig. 6.20

A modification of the circuit of Fig. 6.9.

the requisite h.t. supply for the amplifier. In this circuit it is not necessary to make sure that the minimum current drawn from the supply is sufficient to keep the gas-discharge valve N_2 alight. Failure of this valve to strike in the circuit of Fig. 6.19 results in smaller stabilization against input voltage changes.

We turn now to two different modifications of the circuit of Fig. 6.17 which can result in almost perfect stabilization against both changes in the supply voltage V and in the load current. The first can be achieved by means of the circuit of Fig. 6.21. Variations in the supply voltage V now produce compensating variations at the grid of valve 2. Suppose V changes by ΔV, then the change at the grid of the amplifier valve is

$$\Delta V_{g2} = \Delta V \cdot \frac{R_1 R_2 / (R_1 + R_2)}{R_5 + R_1 R_2 / (R_1 + R_2)}$$

The load resistance R_L does not appear in this formula for the following reason. It is desired to make the output voltage independent of V, i.e. ΔV can generate no voltage across the output terminals. Thus, as far as ΔV is concerned, there is no impedance between these terminals, and so ΔV is driving current through R_5 and through R_1 and R_2 in parallel. If the gain of the amplifier is m, the voltage applied to the grid of the control valve as a result of this change ΔV is therefore

$$\Delta V_{g1} = -m \Delta V_{g2}$$

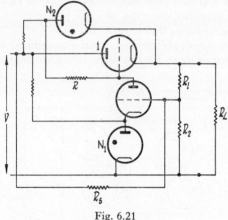

Fig. 6.21

The change in the anode voltage of valve 1 is

$$\Delta V_{a1} = \Delta V$$

But

$$I_{a1} = g_{m1}V_{g1} + V_{a1}/r_{a1}$$

and if the stabilization is perfect this current must not change; hence ΔV_{g1} must equal $-\Delta V_{a1}/\mu_1$. Therefore for perfect stabilization

$$\frac{\Delta V}{\mu_1} = m \cdot \Delta V \cdot \frac{1}{1 + [R_5(R_1+R_2)/R_1R_2]}$$

Rearrangement of this expression gives

$$R_5 = (m\mu_1 - 1) \cdot \frac{R_1R_2}{R_1+R_2}$$

If, for example, $\mu_1 = 20$, $m = 50$ and $R_1 = R_2 = 2 \times 10^4$ ohms, the value of R_5 required for perfect stabilization is 10 megohms.

The circuit arrangement for stabilization against variations of the current demand is shown in Fig. 6.22. The load current I_L flows through the resistor R_6, and thus a voltage proportional to it is applied to the grid of the amplifier valve. This voltage is of such a phase that it tends to compensate for the change in the output voltage due to variations in I_L. Thus, if I_L increases, the grid of the amplifier valve is made more negative with respect to the cathode, and the anode voltage rises. Therefore the grid of the control valve is less negative with respect to the cathode, and the control valve thus passes more

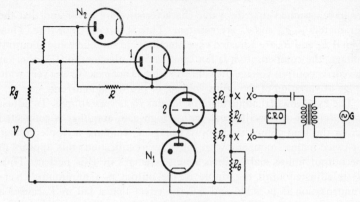

Fig. 6.22

A test circuit for adjusting R_6 is shown on the right of the main circuit.

current to compensate for the increase in I_L. The value of the resistor R_6 is found as follows. Let the load current change by an amount ΔI_L, so that the voltage applied to the grid of the amplifier is approximately

$$V_{g2} = -R_6 \Delta I_L \cdot \frac{R_1}{R_1 + R_2}$$

The voltage applied to the grid of the control valve is $-m$ times this quantity. The anode-cathode voltage of the control valve must not change if the stabilization is to be perfect, and so the change in anode current of this valve is

$$\Delta I_{a1} = g_{m1} m R_6 \Delta I_L \cdot \frac{R_1}{R_1 + R_2}$$

With perfect stabilization this extra valve current must equal ΔI_L, and thus

$$R_6 = \frac{1}{m g_{m1}} \cdot \frac{R_1 + R_2}{R_1}$$

It has been assumed that the input voltage does not change when the load current changes, which is equivalent to assuming that R_g is zero. As an example let $m = 50$, $g_{m1} = 10$ mA/V, and $R_1 = R_2 = 20$ kilohms; then the value of R_6 is 4 ohms.

The values obtained in the above calculations serve as guides only to those values which must be employed in an actual circuit. Apart from the fact that approximations are made in deriving the formulae, we have assumed that the valve characteristics are linear and that the parameters μ, g_m and r_a are constant. This is certainly not true. Thus even if R_5 and R_6 are adjusted experimentally to suit one value of output voltage, the compensation is not exact at any other output. Further, at the correct output voltage the compensation is not exact over a very wide range of variation of the input voltage, or of the load current.

The experimental adjustment of R_5 and R_6 is very simple. To adjust R_5 a cathode-ray oscilloscope with a high-gain amplifier is connected across the load. Since the supply voltage V contains a ripple voltage (at twice mains frequency with full-wave rectification) this appears in the output unless stabilization against changes in V is perfect. Thus R_5 is adjusted until the ripple in the output is a minimum. Over-compensation is possible and has the effect that a fall in V causes a rise in the output. This is undesirable and should be avoided. The

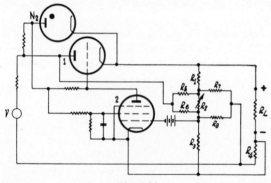

Fig. 6.23

The circuit diagram of a stabilized supply with variable output which incorporates the modifications of Figs. 6.21 and 6.22.

resistance R_6 is adjusted similarly. The arrangement of the apparatus is shown on the right of Fig. 6.22, terminals XX being connected to XX when an adjustment is being made. If the internal impedance of the stabilizer is zero the alternating current flowing into the supply from the generator G can set up no voltage across XX. R_6 is altered until no alternating voltage is observable between the output terminals.

At this point it is convenient to consider the reason for the use of a stabilized supply. If it is desired to have a supply which is stable enough to take advantage of the use of R_5 and R_6, a gas-discharge valve cannot be used for the reference voltage. It has been shown earlier in this chapter that $dV_0/V_0 = dV_R/V_R$, where V_R is the reference voltage. Hence a battery must be used as the source of the reference voltage;

for extreme stability a battery of standard cells may be used. If, on
the other hand, the object is to obtain a supply free from ripple and
with zero, or very low, internal impedance, the use of R_5 and R_6 is
justified even when a gas-discharge valve is used. The absolute value
of the output changes as V_R changes, but the internal impedance and
the ripple output are both low.

We now consider the use of the resistors R_5 and R_6 in circuits for
which it is desired to vary the output voltage V_0. The circuits sketched
in Figs. 6.21 and 6.22 cannot be used; variation of R_1 to change the
output voltage implies that R_5 and R_6 are of the correct values at one
value of R_1 only. This difficulty can be overcome by means of the circuit
arrangement[5] of Fig. 6.23. The various control resistors are arranged
to form a bridge circuit as shown in Fig. 6.24. Variation of R_2 produces

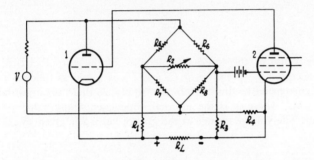

Fig. 6.24

The circuit of Fig. 6.23 redrawn to show that the variation of R_2
can have no effect on the correction voltages applied to valve 2.

changes in the output voltage. If the bridge formed by the resistors
R_5, R_6, R_7 and R_8 is balanced, variation of R_2 can have no effect on
the correction voltage fed through R_5 and R_6, or that fed through
R_7 and R_8. Reference should be made to the original paper for the
design formulae for the values of the various resistors used in the
circuit.

Up to this point the various stray capacitances in the circuits have
been ignored, but we shall now examine the effects of these. Three
important stray capacitances are shown in Fig. 6.25; for ease of calculation, only the simple circuit is considered and a number of approximations are made to obtain manageable results. The output voltage
is a d.c. one and its magnitude is not therefore affected by the capacitances. But, since the capacitances take a finite time to change their
potentials, there is a time delay in the compensation of any change in
the input voltage V, or in the load current. To keep this time delay

small the time-constants of the various circuits should be as small as possible. The other effect of the stray capacitances is that the output impedance is no longer purely resistive; this is considered below.

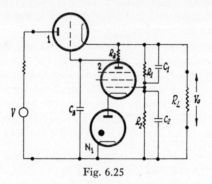

Fig. 6.25

The value of the internal impedance of the output circuit, with allowance for the presence of C_1 and C_2, is found as follows. Let an extra current ΔI be drawn from the supply, so that the output falls by $Z\Delta I$ volts, where Z is the internal impedance whose value we wish to find. The voltage change at the grid of valve 2 is given by

$$V_{g2} = -Z\Delta I \cdot \frac{\dfrac{R_2}{1+j\omega C_2 R_2}}{\dfrac{R_2}{1+j\omega C_2 R_2} + \dfrac{R_1}{1+j\omega C_1 R_1}}$$

$$= -\frac{Z\Delta I}{1 + \dfrac{R_1(1+j\alpha_2)}{R_2(1+j\alpha_1)}}$$

where $\alpha_1 = \omega C_1 R_1$ and $\alpha_2 = \omega C_2 R_2$.

The anode voltage of valve 2 changes by $-m$ times this grid voltage. Consequently the change in the anode current of valve 1 is

$$\Delta I_{a1} = \frac{g_{m1} m Z\Delta I}{1 + \dfrac{R_1(1+j\alpha_2)}{R_2(1+j\alpha_1)}} + \frac{Z\Delta I}{r_{a1}}$$

The change in the anode voltage of valve 1 due to the drop across R_g caused by ΔI is ignored. Now the current ΔI_{a1} must equal ΔI. Hence

$$1 = \frac{mZg_{m1}}{1+\dfrac{R_1(1+j\alpha_2)}{R_2(1+j\alpha_1)}} + \frac{Z}{r_{a1}}$$

The second term on the right-hand side of this equation is very small compared with the first, and thus

$$Z \sim \frac{1+\dfrac{R_1(1+j\alpha_2)}{R_2(1+j\alpha_1)}}{mg_{m1}}$$

$$= R_i + jX_i$$

where

$$X_i = \frac{R_1}{R_2} \cdot \frac{\alpha_2-\alpha_1}{1+\alpha_1{}^2} \cdot \frac{1}{mg_{m1}} \quad \text{and} \quad R_i = \frac{1+\dfrac{R_1}{R_2}\cdot\dfrac{1+\alpha_1\alpha_2}{1+\alpha_1{}^2}}{mg_{m1}}$$

Here interest is centred on the presence of a reactive term. This may be either positive or negative depending on the relative magnitudes of the time-constants C_1R_1 and C_2R_2. If C_2R_2 is greater than C_1R_1 the output impedance contains an inductive term.

As an example, let the various components have the following values: $R_1 = R_2 = 20$ kilohms; $C_1 = 10$ pF; and $C_2 = 100$ pF. Let the gain of the amplifier valve be 50, and the mutual conductance of the control valve be 10 mA. Then

$$X_i = \frac{\omega/(0{\cdot}5\times10^6)-\omega/(5\times10^6)}{1+[\omega/(5\times10^{-6})^2]} \times \frac{1}{50\times10^{-2}}$$

Up to frequencies of the order of 10^5 c/s this gives the approximate answer

$$X_i = \omega \times 3{\cdot}6 \times 10^{-6} \text{ ohms}$$

Thus the reactive component represents an inductance of $3{\cdot}6$ μH. This effect can be removed by making the two time-constants equal, and then the internal impedance is purely resistive.

The capacitance C_3 causes the gain of the amplifier to fall off as the frequency rises; approximately this gain is

$$G = g_{m2} \cdot \frac{R_3/j\omega C_3}{R_3 + 1/j\omega C_3} = \frac{m}{1+j\alpha_3}$$

where m is the low-frequency gain, being equal to $g_{m2}R_3$, and α_3 is $\omega C_3 R_3$.

Therefore the internal impedance of the supply is

$$Z = \frac{1 + \dfrac{R_1(1+j\alpha_2)}{R_2(1+j\alpha_1)}}{mg_{m1}} \cdot (1+j\alpha_3)$$

For simplicity let α_1 and α_2 be equal, and so

$$Z = \frac{(1+R_1/R_2)(1+j\alpha_3)}{mg_{m1}}$$

$$= R_i + jX_i$$

where

$$X_i = \frac{\alpha_3(1+R_1/R_2)}{mg_{m1}}$$

The reactive component is always inductive since α is a positive quantity.

As an example let the various quantities have the following values: $R_1 = R_2 = 20$ kilohms, $R_3 = 2 \times 10^5$ ohms, $C_1 = C_2$, $C_3 = 20$ pF, $g_{m1} = 10$mA/V, $m = 50$.

Then

$$X_i = \omega \times 16 \times 10^{-6} \text{ ohms}$$

Thus the reactive component represents an inductance of 16 μH.

As a result of these effects the impedance of the supply increases as the frequency rises. This may be important if large high-frequency currents are flowing in the h.t. line. These generate voltages across the inductance which may cause undesirable coupling between the various stages of the circuits attached to the supply. It is wise to connect a large capacitor of, say, 8 μF across the output terminals, for this ensures that the internal impedance of the supply is low at all frequencies. The addition of this capacitor also has one other useful effect. If the stabilizer circuit is redrawn as in Fig. 6.26, it is seen that it is a negative-feedback circuit. The output of the valve amplifier is applied to a cathode follower, and part of the output from this stage is applied as inverse feedback to the amplifier grid. For stability the loop phase must change by less than π until the frequency has risen to the point where the loop gain falls below unity.

In the circuit of Fig. 6.26 the capacitance C_1 is usually much smaller than C_2 and for the purposes of the argument set out below its presence is ignored. Therefore three phase-turning networks exist in this circuit owing to the presence of the stray capacitances C_2, C_3, and C_4. It is thus possible for self-oscillation to occur, as the phase may change by more than π before the loop gain falls to unity. [1] If a large capacitor is connected across the output the circuit contains two wide-band phase-turning networks and one narrow-band phase-turning network. There-

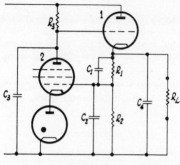

Fig. 6.26

fore large values of $m\beta$ may now be employed without the danger of self-oscillation. An alternative solution of this difficulty lies in increasing C_1 by the addition of an external capacitance so that the time-constant C_1R_1 is equal to the time-constant C_2R_2. Now only two phase shifts occur due to C_3 and C_4, so that the loop phase cannot change by more than π and self-oscillation is no longer possible.

Finally, we give attention to a number of points which affect the optimum performance of the stabilized supply. The most usual trouble encountered is that of an excessive amount of ripple on the output. This may be of two forms depending on its source. The ripple may be at mains frequency, or at twice mains frequency if full-wave rectification is used; it is also possible for the ripple to contain components of both frequencies. The likely sources of this output ripple are listed below.

1. *The Use of Alternating Current to Heat the Valves.* A careful selection of the valves employed together with the earthing of the centre-taps of the filament windings on the supply transformer should cure this source of trouble. With the control valve the maximum permitted d.c. potential between the heater and the cathode may prevent direct earthing of the centre-tap; here a large capacitor can be used. Where extreme stability and absence of ripple is required it is better to employ d.c. heating of the valves.

2. *Capacitive Pick-up on the Grid Leads.* There must be no capacitive pick-up on the grid leads of the amplifier or control valves. If a capacitance exists between these leads and any part of the circuit which is at a high a.c. potential,

the voltage produced at either grid causes a ripple output. The phase of this voltage is such that it cannot easily be cancelled by simple methods. Therefore these grid leads should be short and, if necessary shielded.

3. *Ripple on the Reference Voltage.* When a gas-discharge valve is used it is preferable to connect a 100 pF capacitor across the valve. The discharge is never quite steady, and is usually the source of high-frequency voltages which appear in the output unless suppressed.

4. *Ripple from the Supply Voltage.* The screen grid of the pentode amplifier valve must be free from ripple for otherwise the ripple output is much larger than the value expected from the design. The screen grid should be carefully decoupled or supplied by means of a gas-discharge valve.

With attention to these items it is not difficult to obtain an output with not more than a few millivolts total ripple.

References

1. MARTIN, D. J. R. 'A Low-Power Alternating Voltage Stabilizer'. *J. Sc. Instr.* (1951) **28**, p. 1, CHERRY, L. B. and WILD, R. F. 'Electronic Alternating-Current Power Regulators'. *Proc. I.R.E.* (1945), **33** p. 262.
2. WALKER, A. H. B. 'The Stabilistor'. *Wireless World* (1944) **50**, p. 339.
3. PATCHETT, G. N. 'Precision A.C. Voltage Stabilizers'. *Electronic Engineering.* (1950) **22**, pp. 371, 424, 470 and 499.
4. BECKER, J. A., GREEN, C. B. and PEARSON, G. L. 'Properties and Uses of Thermistors'. *B.S.T.J.* (1947) **26**, p. 170.
5. LINDENHOVIOUS and RIMA. 'A Stabilized Power Supply'. *Phil. Tech. Rev.* (1941), **6**, p. 54.

Chapter Seven

NOISE

By T. B. Tomlinson

The amplification of very small signal voltages calls for very-high-gain equipment, but there is a limit beyond which a further increase in amplification serves no useful purpose. This limit is reached when the total 'masking' or noise voltage produced by the amplifying circuits and valves, introduced into the circuit from the supplies and inherent in the signal source itself, is comparable in magnitude with the signal voltage. Thereafter one is more interested in the *signal/noise ratio* of the equipment than the gain of the amplifier as a measure of performance. Apart from 'man-made' noise disturbances of industrial origin introduced through the electric supply or by pick-up of electrostatic or magnetic fields (also noise due to poor contacts and microphonic sources, which may be eliminated by careful design), there are noise sources of a fundamental nature. It is with the latter that we are concerned in this chapter.

We shall make a general survey of the fundamental sources of noise one is likely to meet in practice, and illustrate by examples the manner in which the total noise to be expected in various kinds of apparatus and circuits may be calculated.

THERMAL-AGITATION NOISE

This type of noise is inherent in the circuit elements and may be best understood by reference to the process of electrical conduction in such elements. For this we must look into the atomic structure of conducting materials, and in particular investigate the potential field inside them. Fig. 7.1 shows the variation of this field within the lattice of a perfect crystal. We see that near the atomic nuclei (positive charge) the potential is low so that electrons in this neighbourhood have low energies—the so-called 'bound electrons'. Between two adjacent atomic centres the potential is high, i.e. electrons more distant from the nuclei have higher energies. Because of the large number of electrons involved, their energies have a distribution according to Fermi-Dirac statistics, so that even at a temperature of absolute zero there will be electrons present with high energy levels. Those electrons which are not bound close to atomic centres are free to roam within the lattice; in fact they are conduction electrons. These electrons form what is known as an *electron gas* and at room temperature they are in constant motion. This continuous random interchange of free electrons between atoms is known as *thermal agitation*. If now a p.d. is applied across the

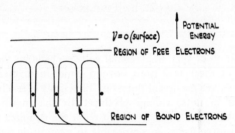

Fig. 7.1

Potential energy distribution within a metal.

ends of a conductor the conduction electrons acquire a drift velocity towards the positive end so that a conduction current flows. In the absence of such an external p.d., the statistical balance of electron motion is such that over a long period of time the average motion in any one direction is zero.

However, in either the presence or absence of such a p.d., there may be at any interval a preponderance of electron motion in a given direction, so that across the ends of the conductor there will appear a small fluctuation e.m.f. Such fluctuation e.m.f.'s will always be occurring and are due to the excess or deficit of electrons above or below the statistical average flowing between the ends of the conductor. A signal potential will cause an orderly movement of electron flow which is superimposed on the irregular fluctuation motion and so is only recognized provided the amplitude of the signal e.m.f. is sufficiently large compared with that of the thermal fluctuation, or noise, e.m.f. As the electron energy distribution is such that increasing temperature increases the number of electrons with higher energies, we see that the thermal fluctuations are temperature dependent, the noise increasing with temperature. This subject was investigated analytically by Nyquist, [1] applying the equipartition of energy principle to two similar resistances in thermodynamic equilibrium, and he deduced that

$$\bar{V}^2 = 4kT \int_{f_1}^{f_2} R\,df$$

where $\bar{V}$ = Root-mean-square fluctuation voltage, volts
  k = Boltzmann's constant, joules/°K
  R = Resistance, ohms
  T = Absolute temperature, °K
  f_1, f_2 = Limits of the frequency range involved, c/s

If R is independent of frequency in the range f_1–f_2, then

$$\bar{V^2} = 4kTR(f_2 - f_1) \tag{7.1}$$

Taking room temperature as 290° K, we have

$$\bar{V} \sim 1 \cdot 26 \times 10^{-10} (R \cdot \delta f)^{\frac{1}{2}} \tag{7.2}$$

where δf is the frequency interval. This formula holds regardless of the nature of the resistance. It has been investigated experimentally[2] and found to be correct in all respects.

As is to be expected, the mean-square noise voltage is independent of frequency since the fluctuations are completely random, i.e. it may contain slow or fast components so that there exists a continuous spectrum of uniform amplitude. Thus the mean square value of the thermal noise e.m.f. (as measured) is proportional to the frequency interval of the measurement, i.e. the bandwidth of the apparatus. This

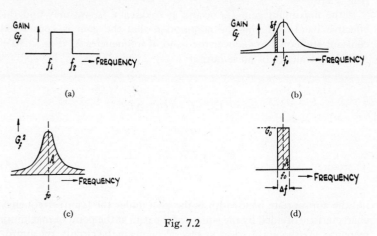

Fig. 7.2

means that in order to make calculations with the formula the overall frequency response characteristic of the apparatus concerned must be known. If the characteristic were uniform from frequency f_1 to frequency f_2, as depicted in Fig. 7.2(a), there would be no difficulty, the formula (7.1) being directly applicable. However, in most practical apparatus the response will be non-uniform, such as is depicted in

L

Fig. 7.2(b). In order to assess the total noise with such a response we must consider an elementary bandwidth δf centred on frequency f. The mean-square noise corresponding to this bandwidth will be

$$\bar{V}^2 = 4kRT.\delta f$$

At the output the mean-square noise voltage is

$$\bar{V}^2 = 4kRT\,\delta f.G_f{}^2$$

where G_f is the amplifier gain at frequency f. Combining the effects of all such elementary bandwidths gives an expression for the total mean-square noise:

$$\bar{V_t}^2 = 4kRT \int_0^\infty G_f{}^2.df \qquad (7.3)$$

$$= 4kRTA$$

where A is the area under the (gain)^2/frequency characteristic [Fig. 7.2(c)].

If the maximum gain G_0 occurs at frequency f_0, we may find the effective bandwidth, on the assumption that the gain is considered constant and equal to G_0 over the band of frequencies Δf [Fig. 7.2(d)].

For equivalence of noise output

$$\int_0^\infty G_f{}^2.df = G_0{}^2.\Delta f$$

Therefore

$$\Delta f = \frac{\int_0^\infty G_f{}^2.df}{G_0{}^2} = \frac{A}{G_0{}^2} \qquad (7.4)$$

i.e. the appropriate bandwidth is the area under the (gain)^2/frequency characteristic divided by the square of the gain at the point of maximum response. As the noise arises at several points in the circuit, the appropriate bandwidth for each noise source is the bandwidth from that point onwards. In multi-stage amplifiers the more important sources are those which occur in the early stages of amplification (see example 2, p. 168) so that the bandwidth for all these sources may be taken to be the overall bandwidth of the amplifier without introducing appreciable error.

Complex-Impedance Two-Terminal Network

If $R+jX$ is the total effective impedance measured between the two terminals of a complex network[3] such as the one in Fig. 7.3(a), then the mean-square fluctuation voltage $\bar{V}^2$ is given by

$$\bar{V}^2 = 4kRT\,\delta f$$

provided that all the impedances are linear and all at the same temperature T; thus the noise originates only in the resistive component

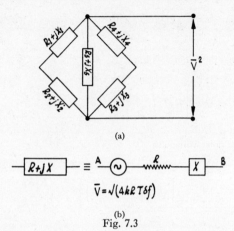

(a)

$$\bar{V} = \sqrt{(4kRT\delta f)}$$

(b)

Fig. 7.3

of the impedance. It follows that any impedance may be replaced by a hypothetical noise generator in series with a noise-free impedance as shown in Fig. 7.3(b).

Note that only the points A and B are available for external connection. When all the elements of a complex network are not at the same temperature we must replace each individual element by its equivalent circuit as above, using the value of T appropriate to that element. The total noise voltage may then be assessed in the normal manner.

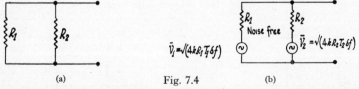

(a)   Fig. 7.4   (b)

Example 1. Consider two resistors R_1, R_2 at temperatures T_1, T_2 respectively connected in parallel as in Fig. 7.4(a). The equivalent circuit is given in Fig. 7.4(b). Using the superposition theorem, we may calculate the noise components due to $\bar{V}_1$ and $\bar{V}_2$ separately.

Noise voltage at output due to R_1 is

$$\bar{V}_1 \cdot \frac{R_2}{R_1+R_2}$$

i.e. $(4kR_1T_1\,\delta f)^{1/2} \cdot \dfrac{R_2}{R_1+R_2}$

Similarly, the noise voltage due to R_2 is

$$(4kR_2T_2\,\delta f)^{1/2} \cdot \frac{R_1}{R_1+R_2}$$

The total mean-square noise voltage is

$$\bar{V}_t^2 = 4k\,\delta f\left[R_1T_1\left(\frac{R_2}{R_1+R_2}\right)^2 + R_2T_2\left(\frac{R_1}{R_1+R_2}\right)^2\right]$$

Therefore r.m.s. noise voltage is

$$\bar{V}_t = \left[4k\,\delta f\left(\frac{T_1}{R_1}+\frac{T_2}{R_2}\right)\right]^{1/2} \cdot \frac{R_1R_2}{R_1+R_2}$$

Putting $T_1 = T_2 = T$ say, we have

$$\bar{V}_t^2 = 4kT\,\delta f\cdot\left(\frac{R_1R_2}{R_1+R_2}\right)$$

so that if R_1 and R_2 are at the same temperature we may consider them as a single resistance R equal to R_1 and R_2 in parallel.

Example 2. Calculate the approximate noise voltage across the terminals of the network of Fig. 7.5(a), if the whole network is uniformly at room temperature.

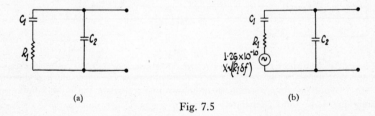

(a)   (b)

Fig. 7.5

First method

$$Z = \frac{\left(R_1 + \dfrac{1}{j\omega C_1}\right) \cdot \dfrac{1}{j\omega C_2}}{R_1 + \dfrac{1}{j\omega C_1} + \dfrac{1}{j\omega C_2}} = \frac{R_1 + \dfrac{1}{j\omega C_1}}{1 + \dfrac{C_2}{C_1} + j\omega C_2 R_1}$$

Therefore

$$Z = \frac{\left(R_1 + \dfrac{1}{j\omega C_1}\right)\left(1 + \dfrac{C_2}{C_1} - j\omega C_2 R_1\right)}{\left(1 + \dfrac{C_2}{C_1}\right)^2 + (\omega C_2 R_1)^2}$$

Now

$$R(Z) = \frac{R_1\left(1 + \dfrac{C_2}{C_1}\right) - \dfrac{C_2 R_1}{C_1}}{\left(1 + \dfrac{C_2}{C_1}\right)^2 + (\omega C_2 R_1)^2}$$

$$= \frac{R_1}{\left(1 + \dfrac{C_2}{C_1}\right)^2 + (\omega C_2 R_1)^2}$$

Therefore noise voltage

$$\sim 1 \cdot 26 \times 10^{-10} \left[\frac{R_1 \delta f}{\left(1 + \dfrac{C_2}{C_1}\right)^2 + (\omega C_2 R_1)^2} \right]^{1/2} \text{volt}$$

Second method

Replace R_1 by a noise generator and noise-free resistance as in Fig. 7.5(b). Then the noise voltage across the output terminals

$$= 1 \cdot 26 \times 10^{-10} (R_1 \delta f)^{1/2} \frac{\dfrac{1}{\omega C_2}}{\left[R_1{}^2 + \left(\dfrac{1}{\omega C_1} + \dfrac{1}{\omega C_2}\right)^2 \right]^{1/2}}$$

$$= 1 \cdot 26 \times 10^{-10} \left[\frac{R_1 \delta f}{(\omega C_2 R_1)^2 + \left(1 + \dfrac{C_2}{C_1}\right)^2} \right]^{1/2} \text{volt}$$

SHOT NOISE

The shot effect is observable as fluctuations in the current from an emissive surface which are a direct result of the corpuscular nature of electricity. The simplest example is that of a diode valve working under temperature-limited conditions. In these circumstances the anode voltage is sufficiently high to ensure that all the electrons emitted from the cathode will proceed to the anode, which thus collects all the available emission. The anode current cannot then be increased by an increase of anode voltage but only by an increase of cathode temperature, i.e. the filament voltage must be raised. This condition is illustrated by the flattening off of the I_a/V_a characteristic, as shown in Fig. 7.6.

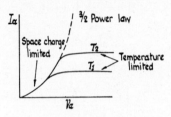

Fig. 7.6
Characteristic curves of a
high-vacuum diode.

In the temperature-limited condition the emission and consequent collection of an electron may be considered as an independent event. The number of such electrons passing to the anode at any instant will therefore be subject to fluctuations about a mean, and as is to be expected the subsequent fluctuations of current are dependent on the charge e of the individual electrons.

These variations about a mean current are governed purely by chance; in other words they are completely random, and as with thermal noise fluctuations the probabilities of rapid or slow fluctuations are equal. The frequency spectrum is therefore a uniform one up to frequencies where the transit time of an electron in passing from cathode to anode becomes an important factor and the noise components fall off in amplitude. Using purely statistical considerations, Schottky[4] derived the mean-square current fluctuation in a frequency interval δf for a temperature-limited diode passing a mean current I_a

$$\overline{i_a^2} = 2e\,I_a\,\delta f \tag{7.5}$$

where $e =$ the electronic charge $= 1 \cdot 59 \times 10^{-19}$ coulomb.

This formula is not of immediate use in general amplifier practice, because we use triode or pentode valves which are operated in the space-charge-limited region. If this were not so the anode current could not be varied by the grid and anode voltages and no amplification would be possible. In the space-charge-limited diode the mean anode current is only a fraction of the total mean emission current, the remainder of the emission returning to the cathode. The anode current can be increased by increasing the anode voltage, but not by increasing the filament voltage. The steady-state potential between anode and cathode has a potential minimum near the cathode. This is due to the presence of an electron cloud, the minimum occurring where the electron density is highest (see Fig. 7.7). Only those electrons with a component of the initial emission velocity normal to the

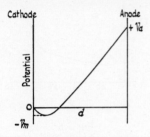

Fig. 7.7
Potential distribution in a
space-charge-limited diode.

anode that is greater than v, where $(1/2)mv^2 = V_m e$, will be able to proceed to the anode. The remainder are repelled by the retarding field due to the high electron density, and return to the cathode.

If a temporary spontaneous increase of emission occurs at some point, there is an increase in the magnitude of V_m at the potential barrier in this region due to the increased charge density in the electron cloud. Then certain electrons which have initial velocities such that they would previously have just managed to cross the potential barrier will now be prevented from doing so and consequently they return to the cathode instead of proceeding to the anode. Hence, for any spontaneous increase of emission there will be a compensating decrease of space current, and vice versa. We see then that the presence of space charge introduces a smoothing effect on the fluctuations and results in a reduced mean-square noise current.[5, 6, 7, 8] The Schottky formula must be modified to take this into consideration:

$$\bar{i_a}^2 = 2F^2 e\, I_a\, \delta f \tag{7.6}$$

where F^2 is known as the 'space-charge reduction factor'. It has a value which is always less than unity, but this is of course dependent on the working conditions of the valve.

A typical curve depicting the variation of F^2 with anode current is given in Fig. 7.8. The general shape of this curve is explained qualitatively when we consider the importance of the potential minimum in reducing shot noise fluctuations. At saturation current the minimum is non-existent and there is only the pure shot effect, for which $F^2 = 1$. As the anode current is reduced by reduction of the anode voltage, the potential minimum begins to appear, the compensation effect becomes

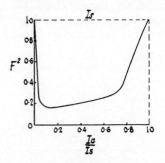

Fig. 7.8
Variation of F^2 with anode current.
I_s = saturation current.

operative and F^2 reduces to a value of about 0·2. When the current is further reduced by making the anode voltage negative with respect to cathode—the so-called retarding-field condition—the minimum is less prominent; it eventually disappears when the anode voltage is so negative that all electrons return to the cathode. This means that the value of F^2 rises again when the anode current becomes small and must finally reach the value unity when anode current ceases. For an oxide-coated-cathode valve working under normal conditions as an amplifier the value of F^2 is about 0·2.

      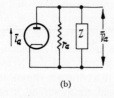

(a)   (b)
Fig. 7.9

A further effect of working under space-charge-limited conditions is the appearance in the circuit of the valve's anode characteristic resistance r_a, which now has a finite value. In the temperature-limited conditions, r_a is theoretically infinite and in practice very high. Then the shot-noise voltage across an impedance Z placed in the anode circuit will be simply $\overline{V_a} = \overline{i_a}|Z|$ [see Fig. 7.9(a)]. For space-charge conditions the equivalent circuit is as shown in Fig. 7.9(b), and the impedance Z and the a.c. resistance r_a must now be combined vectorially:

$$\overline{V}_a = \overline{i}_a \left| \frac{r_a \overline{Z}}{r_a + \overline{Z}} \right|$$

This is not generally important with pentodes, which have a high value of r_a so that $r_a \gg |Z|$, but it is important with triodes, where r_a may be of the same order as, or less than, $|Z|$.

It was at one time contended that the appearance of r_a in the noise formulae should introduce thermal noise inherent in r_a, since the Nyquist formula holds for any general form of resistance. But it is now agreed that the Schottky noise is the only kind to be considered, r_a therefore appears in the circuit as a noise-free resistance. That this doubt should have arisen is not surprising, since calculations involving the noise in a space-charge-limited diode had yielded the following result:

$$\overline{i_a^2} = 9\alpha k \, T_K \frac{I_a}{V_a} \delta f \tag{7.7}$$

where $\alpha = 2(1 - \pi/4) = 0\cdot429$
        $k =$ Boltzmann's constant and
        $T_K =$ cathode temperature

This is restricted to conditions where V_a is well below saturation value and well above the retarding field condition i.e. in the region of the flat part of the curve shown in Fig. 7.8. The full analysis yields:

$$\overline{i_a^2} = 0\cdot644 \, . \, 4kT_K g \, \delta f \tag{7.8}$$

The most interesting feature of this result is that the electronic charge e no longer appears in the formula but the cathode temperature does. Thus the formula has exactly similar form to the Nyquist formula for thermal noise, and indeed the two are identical if we ascribe to the cathode an equivalent temperature T_e where $T_e = 0\cdot644 \, T_K$. By comparing eqn. (7.7) with eqn. (7.6) we see that

$$F^2 = \frac{9\alpha k T_K}{2eV_a}$$

Thus $$F = 1\cdot39 \left(\frac{kT}{eV_a} \right)^{1/2} \tag{7.9}$$

This formula[7] has been tested experimentally and gives values of F that are generally higher than the calculated values. The discrepancy is thought to be due to elastic reflections of electrons from the anode, disturbing the field distribution and so causing additional fluctuations.

THE NEGATIVE-GRID TRIODE

We now proceed to examine the way this theory may be adapted to the more interesting problem of noise in amplifying valves, the most simple case being that of a triode operated with negative grid as the control electrode, the anode acting as electron collector. In such a valve, provided that it is operated in the temperature-limited range, the Schottky equation may be applied as for a diode since the equation refers fundamentally to the emission current. In the space-charge-limited range for a medium- or high-μ triode we may neglect the grid-anode region and apply the diode equation to the grid-cathode space, i.e. we may make an analysis in terms of the 'equivalent diode'. The equivalent anode voltage V_a' will be the effective potential in the grid plane, and g will then become g_m, the mutual conductance of the triode proper. The limitation to medium- and high-μ valves (say $\mu = 5$ or over) arises, since in a low-μ valve the potential variation could not be considered regular, especially near the grid wires. The electrons in the grid-anode space would also influence those in the grid-cathode space owing to the poor shielding effect of the grid. Then

$$V_a' = \sigma\left(V_g + \frac{V_a}{\mu}\right)$$

where σ is a valve parameter and usually has values between 0·5 and 1·0.

Thus $g_m = \sigma g$ and eqn. (7.8) becomes

$$\overline{i_a^2} = \frac{0·644}{\sigma}4kT_k g_m \,\delta f \qquad (7.10)$$

for a triode. Naturally this analysis is restricted to those frequencies for which transit times are negligible. For higher frequencies other fluctuation phenomena [6, 9, 10, 11, 12] become important, but their consideration is outside the scope of this chapter. Eqn. (7.10) has also been confirmed experimentally, the agreement being generally better than that for diodes, no doubt owing to the absence of elastic reflection effects.

SCREEN-GRID VALVES; PARTITION OR DISTRIBUTION NOISE

In the screen-grid valve electrons proceed from cathode to anode, passing through the screen-grid mesh *en route*. A fraction of these are collected by the screen grid, which is operated at a positive potential with respect to the cathode. It may then be expected that the noise in such valves (neglecting secondary-emission effects, which are generally avoided by using a pentode valve) will be higher since a new element of chance has been introduced. This is typified by the question whether an electron passing close to a screen-grid wire will be collected owing to the positive screen potential or will pass through the mesh and proceed to the anode. The division of current between anode and screen is not exactly constant but is subject to small fluctuations about a mean value, consequently the fluctuation in anode current is higher than the fluctuation in cathode current. Let us first assume that the cathode current exhibits no fluctuations and that the screen-grid wires are fine and widely spaced so that most of the emission current goes to the anode. Then the collection or non-collection of any electron by the screen grid may be regarded as an independent event determined purely by chance, and so the normal shot effect occurs. If I_s is the screen current, then

$$\overline{i_s^2} = 2e\,I_s\,\delta f$$

The fluctuations in I_a are equal and opposite, since the total current $I_a + I_s$ is constant. Then

$$\overline{i_a^2} = 2e\,I_s\,\delta f$$

If the cathode current fluctuations are taken into account, the total anode current fluctuations are given by

$$\overline{i_a^2} = 2e\frac{I_a}{I_a+I_s}(I_s+F^2 I_a)\delta f \tag{7.11}$$

Since the cathode current fluctuations are reduced to about 20 per cent by space charge ($F^2 = 0\cdot2$), it is obvious that the distribution fluctuations are the more important unless $I_s < 0\cdot2 I_a$, i.e. to keep the total noise current as low as possible the screen current must be kept to a minimum. For this reason 'optically aligned' grid valves have been used in specially developed 'low noise' pentodes.

Formula (7.11) for the total noise current in pentodes has also been obtained by D. O. North[13] using a different approach; this is based upon a loss of the space-charge compensation effect due to the division of current between the collecting electrodes. For instance, let a temporary excess of emission proceed mainly to the screen (or anode). This will result in a depression of the potential minimum, producing a compensation effect which reduces the fluctuations in the cathode current in the manner previously explained. However, the compensation is likely to be distributed over a considerable area so that the current decrease may be divided between screen and anode. Thus the screen (or anode) fluctuation is not fully compensated, and if the net cathode-current fluctuations are small the anode current fluctuations due to this cause are approximately equal to the screen current fluctuations. This theory is applied generally to a multi-collector valve and yields the result

$$\overline{i_q}^2 = F_q^2 . 2e\,I_q\,\delta f \tag{7.12}$$

where

$$F_q^2 = 1 - \frac{I_q}{I_t}(1 - F^2) \tag{7.13}$$

and I_q = space current to the qth electrode
I_t = total space current, i.e. the cathode current
F^2 = normal space-charge reduction factor for the total space current.

EQUIVALENT NOISE RESISTANCE

For convenience the total valve noise is expressed in terms of a resistance which if connected between grid and cathode would produce this noise output at room temperature according to the Nyquist formula for thermal noise. The noise performance of the valve is thereby summarized in terms of a resistance only,[14] the customary symbol being R_{eq}. For an r.m.s. noise current $\overline{i_a}$ the equivalent voltage at the grid is $\overline{i_a}/g_m$.

Then

$$\frac{\overline{i_a}}{g_m} = (4kTR_{eq}\delta f)^{1/2}$$

i.e.

$$\frac{F(2eI_a\,\delta f)^{\frac{1}{2}}}{g_m} = (4kTR_{eq}\,\delta f)^{1/2}$$

whence

$$R_{eq} = \frac{F^2\,e\,I_a}{2kT\,g_m^2} \tag{7.14}$$

By using the formula for F^2 as obtained from statistical considerations and substituting typical values for all parameters, several practical approximate formulae for R_{eq} have been obtained. Those for a triode and a pentode used as amplifier valves are listed below.

Triode amplifier

$$R_{eq} = \frac{2\cdot5}{g_m} \text{ ohms} \quad \text{(where } g_m \text{ is in amp/volt)} \tag{7.15}$$

Pentode amplifier

$$R_{eq} = \frac{I_a}{I_a+I_s}\left(\frac{2\cdot5}{g_m} + \frac{20I_s}{g_m^2}\right) \text{ (where } I_a \text{ and } I_s \text{ are in amp) (7.16)}$$

Numerical example

Triode: $\quad g_m = 3\text{mA/V} \qquad R_{eq} \sim 830 \text{ ohms}$

Pentode: $\quad g_m = 3\text{mA/V} \qquad I_a = 10\text{mA} \qquad I_s = 2\cdot5\text{mA}$

$$R_{eq} \sim 5110 \text{ ohms}$$

This illustrates the higher value of R_{eq} for a pentode of equal slope.

FLICKER NOISE IN VALVES

In 1925 J. B. Johnson[15] reported the discovery of a much increased valve noise at low frequencies. He suggested that this might be due to continual changes in the surface condition of the cathode caused by evaporation, diffusion, chemical action, etc., occurring at different rates and over areas of different size. The emission variations resulting from the slower surface changes and those connected with the larger areas would show an increased fluctuation effect as the frequency of the measuring equipment was made lower. His measurements indicated that the r.m.s. noise current I_a is proportional to $(\delta f)^{1/2}$ for this source of noise as for other noise sources, and that the noise amplitude depends on the magnitude and frequency of the steady current. In an analysis of Johnson's results, Schottky[16] derived

$$\overline{i_a}^2 \propto I_a^2$$

where I_a is the steady direct current and

$$\overline{i_a}^2 \propto \frac{\alpha}{\alpha^2+\omega^2}$$

where $1/\alpha$ is a time-constant, characteristic of the effect.

He considered that the fluctuations were due to the appearance of individual 'foreign' atoms on the emitter surface, each exerting a doublet effect and so increasing the emission. Moullin[17] has shown Johnson's results to be more nearly expressed by

$$\overline{i_a{}^2} \propto \frac{I_a{}^2}{\omega^{1.2}}$$

Experiments indicate a $1/f$ law for oxide-coated cathodes and a $1/f^2$ law for tungsten and thoriated-tungsten filaments. Theories on flicker effect have been put forward by Macfarlane[18] and Van der Ziel.[19] It appears that a $1/f$ law will be obtained provided that the distribution of the decay times of the active specks which appear on the cathode surface is a wide one. There is a possibility, however, that extra noise at low frequencies may be due to spontaneous fluctuations in the conductivity of the whole oxide coating since it has been shown[20] that the conductivity of the coating itself determines the emission current from an oxide-coated cathode.

Measurements of flicker noise have been made by Harris and others[21, 22, 23] and some typical figures for a particular valve are as follows:

Frequency	Bandwidth	Equivalent r.m.s. noise voltage at the grid	Corresponding value of R_{eq}
c/s	c/s	μV	kilohms
1000	1	0·005	1.5
100	1	0·0135	11
10	1	0·05	150

It appears that flicker noise may well be the main source of valve noise at low frequencies, and it is found that the order of the noise may vary widely between valve types and also between different valves of the same type. For all low-frequency work, then, the valves in a high-gain amplifier should be selected for low noise level; 'aged' valves have been found to have especially low values. More recent experimental work[24] indicates that the noise increases slowly with anode current, especially at a low-current level, but according to Brown[25] it is advantageous to use a valve in electrometer conditions, i.e. $I_a <$ about 100 μA, in the first stage of a high-gain amplifier for use at low frequencies. Under these conditions an effective equivalent resistance of the order of 50 kilohms may be obtained. For a given emission current it is doubtful if any advantage is to be gained by operating the valve with a reduced heater voltage.[26]

CONTACT AND BREAKDOWN NOISE

Another form of random noise which occurs in various network components is due to breakdown of insulation or change of conductivity over short paths. The most common example of this occurs in carbon resistors and is usually known as *current noise*. [23, 27, 28] The noise amplitude increases as the steady direct current through the resistor is increased and as the frequency is lowered, in a manner similar to that for flicker noise in valves. It is therefore wise to avoid the use of ordinary carbon resistors in a signal circuit where a steady direct current is involved, especially when the resistor has a high value such as with a grid leak. Wire-wound resistors are to be preferred, but these are not generally tested for noise performance and a small percentage of them are subject to insulation breakdown. The high-stability or cracked-carbon type of resistor may be used, but here again it will have a higher noise level if it has been subjected to ill treatment mechanically or electrically. If possible, all such components for use in the first stages of a sensitive amplifier should be tested before use, or specially selected specimens ordered from the manufacturer.

A few examples of the often unsuspected existence of this effect may be useful. For instance, current noise in a grid leak may arise through a leaky coupling condenser or through grid current in the valve. Incidently, grid current also has its associated shot noise; this produces an e.m.f. across the grid leak, which is then subject to amplification by the valve. Consequently grid current must be kept low either by choice of valve, by low screen dissipation or other means. Electrolytic capacitors have a reputation for contributing to the total noise; the manner in which this occurs is no doubt similar to that for noise in semiconductors. [19, 29, 30, 31] Their use should be avoided wherever possible. Dry batteries are often found to generate noise but this can be quite small for a battery which has always been operated at a current drain well below its maximum rating. For instance, a dry battery could be used as the h.t. supply for a pre-amplifier drawing only a few milliamperes or for grid-bias purposes.

NOISE IN PHOTOCELLS

In a vacuum photocell, where all the photoelectrons are collected by the anode, one would expect the noise to be the same as the shot noise for a temperature-limited diode drawing an equal current. This has been confirmed experimentally [32] for currents from $50\mu A$ to 1mA. It has also been shown that a space-charge reduction effect occurs under conditions of high illumination and low anode voltage. Values of F^2 down to 0·6 have been observed, with values approaching unity for both saturation and retarding-field conditions. [33] It is not yet certain whether flicker noise plays any part in photocell noise at low frequencies, although experimental results at audio frequencies have shown a noise voltage about 25 per cent greater than is given by the shot noise equation.[34]

SECONDARY-EMISSION NOISE[35, 36, 37, 38]

Let us first consider a single secondary-emitting surface and assume that for every primary electron striking the surface n secondaries are emitted. Then for a fluctuation δi of primary current there will be a resultant fluctuation $n\delta i$ of the secondary-emission current. The mean square fluctuation $\bar{i_a}^2$ will therefore be given by

$$\bar{i_a}^2 = \overline{I_{prim}^2} \cdot n^2$$

However, the value of n is not exactly constant since the number of secondaries freed by each primary electron is not an exact quantity but is itself subject to fluctuations about a mean value. In this case

$$\bar{i_a}^2 = \overline{I_{prim}^2} \cdot n^2 + \overline{I_{sec}^2} \qquad (7.17)$$

where n is now taken to be the average secondary emission ratio. To find a value for $\overline{I_{sec}^2}$ we must know more about the statistical distribution of the value of this ratio about its mean. If the primary current itself is subject to pure shot noise, i.e. no space-charge reduction factor is involved, we may write

$$\bar{i_a}^2 = 2eI_{prim} \cdot \overline{n^2} \cdot df = \overline{I_{prim}^2} \cdot \overline{n^2} \qquad (7.18)$$

where $\overline{n^2}$ is the mean square value of the secondary emission ratio. The final mean direct anode current will have a value nI_{prim} and so it would appear that a secondary-emission multiplier would introduce a higher noise level than that obtained by using a normal thermionic-valve amplifier having the same steady current and giving the same gain. This comparison cannot be made for a photo-electric multiplier, where the mean anode current is the 'dark' current of the multiplier and may be only a fraction of a microampere.

BARKHAUSEN EFFECT[39, 40, 41]

Changes in the magnetization of ferromagnetic materials do not proceed uniformly and continuously but in discrete steps as the domains readjust their orientation in the direction of the magnetizing field. Consequently the use of transformers in a signal circuit in the early stages of an amplifier may give rise to magnetic fluctuation noise. Normally the signal field involved is not sufficient to cause a noise effect comparable with thermal and valve noise, but more intense external fields may do so and they should be avoided. In any case magnetic shielding should be used to eliminate 50 c/s fields, thus giving protection against this source of noise also.

SPONTANEOUS FLUCTUATIONS OF TEMPERATURE AND RADIATION[42, 43, 44]

Sensitive elements subjected to radiation may introduce noise due to fluctuations inherent in the radiation intensity itself. This we may consider as a spontaneous fluctuation in the number of photons arriving at and leaving the element in unit time. Where such elements are used for radiation measurement purposes, there will be a limit to the sensitivity and accuracy of the measurement due to this cause. For instance, a bolometer for infra-red detection has a low thermal capacity and changes its electrical resistance in a manner dependent on the intensity of the incident radiation. A small steady current is passed through the element, usually in a bridge circuit, thus producing an e.m.f. which is a measure of the radiation intensity. This will also give rise to noise due to the fluctuations in the temperature of the element. If C is the heat capacity and $\overline{T^2}$ the mean square temperature fluctuation, then

$$\overline{T^2} = \frac{kT^2}{C} \tag{7.19}$$

There will also be thermal agitation noise in the resistance of the element, and if it consists of semiconducting material there will be excess noise at low frequencies. These two causes are the most important with present-day materials. In photo-electric cells no extra noise due to inherent fluctuations of the light intensity has been detected.

NOISE CALCULATIONS

To assess the total noise voltage in an amplifier, all individual noise sources must be referred to a common reference point and there added as *root mean squares*. This reference point is usually the grid of the first valve. It is to be remembered that the practical interest lies in the *signal/noise ratio* rather than in the total noise magnitude. This ratio is defined as

$$S/N = 20 \log_{10} \overline{V_s}/\overline{V_t} \text{ dB}$$

where $\overline{V_s}$ = r.m.s. signal voltage, and $\overline{V_t}$ = total r.m.s. noise voltage.

The manner of calculating the total noise is best explained by examples; the more difficult ones are chosen to be of particular interest to

M

the reader and it is hoped that the comments and deductions will be of practical use.

Example 1. *Grid circuit noise and valve noise.*

Let R_{eq} (Fig. 7.10) be the valve equivalent resistance and Z the total effective circuit impedance between grid and earth, where $Z = R + jX$.

Then

$$\bar{V} = (4kTR\,\delta f + 4kTR_{eq}\,\delta f)^{1/2}$$

$$= [4kTR\,\delta f(R + R_{eq})]^{1/2} \qquad (7.20)$$

i.e. the grid circuit resistance and the equivalent valve resistance *add directly* to give the total effective noise resistance. At low frequencies the true value of

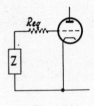

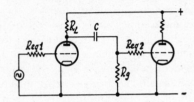

Fig. 7.10   Fig. 7.11

R_{eq} will be considerably higher than the specified value owing to flicker effect. An estimate must be made for a 'good' valve, e.g. $R_{eq} = 100$ kilohms at 5 c/s, say.

Example 2. *A simple resistance-coupled amplifier including thermal agitation noise in the anode circuit and valve noise in the first and second stages.*

It is assumed that C (Fig. 7.11) has no leakage and has negligible reactance at the frequency concerned. The effective anode load resistance R_1 is therefore the parallel combination of R_L and R_g

$$\text{i.e.} \quad R_1 = \frac{R_L R_g}{R_L + R_g}$$

(i) Thermal agitation noise $\overline{V_a}$ at anode is

$$\overline{V_a} = (4kT\,\delta f R_1)^{1/2} \times \frac{r_a}{R_1 + r_a}$$

owing to the potential divider effect of R_1 with r_a; r_a must be considered noise free, since valve noise is included in R_{eq}.

(ii) The total valve noise $\overline{V_t}$ in the anode circuit is therefore

$$\overline{V_t} = a\left[R_1\left(\frac{r_a}{R_1 + r_a}\right)^2 + R_{eq2}\right]^{1/2}$$

where

$$a = (4kT\delta f)^{1/2}$$

(iii) Referred back to the grid, $\overline{V_t}$ must be divided by the stage gain G, where

$$G = \frac{\mu R_1}{R_1 + r_a}$$

i.e.
$$\frac{\overline{V_t}}{G} = \frac{a\left[R_1\left(\dfrac{r_a}{R_1 + r_a}\right)^2 + R_{eq2}\right]^{1/2}}{\dfrac{\mu R_1}{R_1 + r_a}}$$

$$= a\left(\frac{R_1}{g_m^2 R_1^2} + \frac{R_{eq2}}{G^2}\right)^{1/2}$$

The total effective noise resistance is therefore

$$R_{eq}' = R_{eq1} + \frac{R_1}{g_m^2 R_1^2} + \frac{R_{eq2}}{G^2} \tag{7.21}$$

Note that for a pentode amplifier

$$G \sim g_m R_1$$

whence

$$R_{eq}' = R_{eq1} + \frac{R_1 + R_{eq2}}{G^2} \tag{7.22}$$

It follows that the procedure is simply to add all noise resistances in the anode circuit and divide by the square of the gain, and then add the total noise resistance in the grid circuit. In the triode as well as the pentode amplifier it is clear that the total noise is kept to a minimum by making G high. The total noise then approximates to the sum of the first grid-circuit and the first valve noise only.

Example 3. *Cathode follower, including the thermal noise generated in the cathode load and the shot noise of the following valve.*

Properties of the cathode follower (Fig. 7.12) are as follows

(i) Gain

$$G = \frac{\mu R_1}{r_a + (\mu + 1)R_1}$$

where

$$R_1 = R_L R_g / (R_L + R_g)$$

so that $G < 1$.

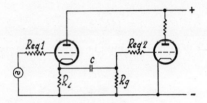

Fig. 7.12

(ii) Internal generator resistance $= r_a/\mu+1$.
The thermal noise $\overline{V_e}$ at cathode is

$$\overline{V_c} = \frac{a(R_1)^{1/2}}{\left(\dfrac{r_a}{\mu+1}+R_1\right)} \cdot \frac{r_a}{(\mu+1)} \quad \text{(where } a = (4kT\,\delta f)^{1/2})$$

$$= \frac{a(R_1)^{1/2} \cdot r_a}{r_a+(\mu+1)R_1}$$

Total noise $\overline{V_t}$ at cathode is

$$\overline{V_t} = a\left[\frac{R_1 r_a^2}{[r_a+(\mu+1)R_1]^2} + R_{eq2}\right]^{1/2}$$

The equivalent noise voltage at the grid

$$\frac{\overline{V_t}}{G} = a\left(\frac{R_1 r_a^2}{\mu^2 R_1^2} + \frac{R_{eq2}}{G^2}\right)^{1/2}$$

The total effective noise resistance R_{eq}' is

$$R_{eq}' = R_{eq1} + \frac{R_1}{g_m^2 R_1^2} + \frac{R_{eq2}}{G^2}$$

Note that this expression is the same as that for the valve amplifier in example 1, but here $G < 1$.

We may infer that the cathode-follower circuit will give a higher noise level if the valve noise of the second stage V_2 is important.

Using the result of example 1 to include the effect of the third stage, we have

$$R_{eq}'' = R_{eq1} + \frac{R_1}{g_{m1}^2 R_1^2} + \frac{R_{eq2} + \dfrac{R_2}{g_{m2}^2 R_2^2} + \dfrac{R_{eq3}}{G_2^2}}{G_1^2} \tag{7.23}$$

where R_2 is the effective anode load of the second stage.

If R_1 and R_{eq2} are of the same order,

$$R_{eq}' \sim R_{eq1} + \frac{R_{eq2}}{G^2} \text{ since } G \ll g_{m1}R_1$$

But $$R_{eq1} \sim R_{eq2} \text{ and } G \sim 1$$

Then $$R_{eq}' \sim 2R_{eq1}$$

This means that the valve noise is approximately doubled when the cathode-follower circuit is used.

In this example the gain for the cathode follower has been taken to be the same for valve noise as for the signal and other noise sources. This implies that negative current feedback due to a resistance in the cathode circuit is effective for shot noise and flicker noise. It has been stated that this type of negative feedback does not reduce flicker noise, and certain reported experimental results would appear to confirm this. On the contrary, the writer [45] has been able to show experimentally that the reduction of flicker noise in a triode due to negative current feedback is exactly equal to the reduction in gain from a signal point of view. The case of a screen-grid valve is complicated by the manner of connection of the screen by-pass condenser. In many practical valves the effect may be obscured by other noise sources due to imperfections of the valve, e.g. current noise in leakage paths, etc.; these latter become especially noticeable when the normal flicker effect is reduced to a low level by feedback, and their presence may have led to the view that this type of feedback is not effective for flicker noise itself.

It should be remembered that partition noise components do not appear in the cathode current, so that in a screen-grid valve an unby-passed cathode resistor will lead to a certain reduction of signal gain due to feedback, with no corresponding reduction of partition noise. This will result in a decrease in the signal/noise ratio, but at low frequencies the partition noise component will be smaller than the flicker noise component, and this decrease may be insignificant.

Example 4. Input circuit considerations

(i) Consider a signal source of internal resistance R_s connected directly in the grid circuit of a valve (Fig. 7.13).

Total noise voltage

$$= a(R_s + R_{eq}')^{1/2} \tag{7.24}$$

where R_{eq}' is taken to include noise in the anode circuit etc., as above. The ultimate minimum is achieved when $R_{eq}' \ll R_s$, so that the noise is nearly that due to the source only. But R_s may be $\ll R_{eq}'$ (for instance a thermocouple source, $R_s = 20$ ohms). In such cases it may be possible to achieve a higher signal noise ratio by connecting the source to the valve via a step-up transformer.

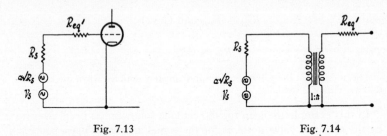

Fig. 7.13   Fig. 7.14

(ii) Connection via 'ideal' transformer (Fig. 7.14).
   Total noise voltage at grid

$$= a(n^2 R_s + R_{eq}')^{1/2}$$

Signal/noise ratio

$$= \frac{nV_s}{a(n^2 R_s + R_{eq}')^{1/2}}$$

$$= \frac{V_s}{a(R_s + R_{eq}'/n^2)^{1/2}} \qquad (7.25)$$

Obviously the effect of R_{eq}' is much reduced if we use $n > 1$. Practical considerations set a limit, since the reactance of the transformer primary must be greater than R_s at the frequency concerned. As the input impedance of the valve has been tacitly assumed to be infinite, the question of impedance matching

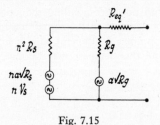

Fig. 7.15

does not arise. If now we take into account losses in the grid circuit, e.g. owing to the grid leak, if necessary, or simply the input leakage resistance of the valve due to grid current etc., the diagram of the circuit referred to the secondary of the transformer is as shown in Fig. 7.15.

The equivalent noise resistance

$$= R_{eq}' + \frac{R_g n^2 R_s}{R_g + n^2 R_s}$$

Then the signal voltage

$$= n V_s \cdot \frac{R_g}{R_g + n^2 R_s}$$

and the signal/noise ratio

$$= \frac{n V_s R_g}{R_g + n^2 R_s} \bigg/ a \left(R_{eq}' + \frac{R_g n^2 R_s}{R_g + n^2 R_s} \right)^{1/2}$$

$$= \frac{V_s}{a \left[R_s \left(1 + \frac{n^2 R_s}{R_g} \right) + \frac{R_{eq}'}{n^2} \left(1 + \frac{n^2 R_s}{R_g} \right)^2 \right]^{1/2}} \qquad (7.26)$$

This result shows that the value of R_g should be large, i.e. if possible omit the grid leak by direct coupling and use a valve specially selected for low grid current. There will be an optimum value of n which is obtained by maximizing the above expression. This gives:

$$n_{opt} = \left(\frac{R_g^2}{R_s^2} \cdot \frac{R_{eq}'}{R_g + R_{eq}'} \right)^{1/4} \qquad (7.27)$$

Inserting typical values, we have

$R_s = 30$ ohms, $R_g = 20$ megohms, $R_{eq}' = 150$ Kilohms (at 5c/s say)

Then

$$n = \left[\frac{(2 \times 10^7)^2}{30^2} \frac{150 \times 10^3}{2 \times 10^7 + 150 \times 10^3} \right]^{1/4}$$

$$\sim \left(\frac{2 \times 10^7 \; 5 \times 10^2}{3} \right)^{1/4} \sim 240$$

This figure is only an estimate, for R_g may vary over wide limits but it sets a target for design. Ratios of 300:1 at 5 c/s have been used in practice[46, 47] for a transformer connecting a thermocouple to a tuned amplifier.

Example 5. To calculate the noise in a galvanometer due to Brownian motion. [48, 49, 50]

This is a special case of thermal agitation, the fluctuations of the galvanometer coil about its mean position being due to both the random motion of electrons in the coil and to molecular bombardment of the assembly. The whole may be assumed to be in thermal equilibrium with its surroundings so that we may write

$$\tfrac{1}{2}c\overline{y^2} = \tfrac{1}{2}kT \tag{7.28}$$

where $\overline{y^2}$ = mean-square deflection, radians
c = restoring torque per unit angle of displacement
k = Boltzmann's constant
T = absolute temperature

Thus

$$\overline{y^2} = \frac{kT}{c}$$

What is the equivalent current fluctuation $\bar{i}$ in the coil? Now

$$y = \frac{nHA}{c}i$$

where n = number of turns on the coil
H = magnetic field strength
A = average area per turn

Therefore

$$\overline{i^2} = \frac{kT}{c} \cdot \frac{c^2}{(nHA)^2} = \frac{kTc}{(nHA)^2} \tag{7.29}$$

The undamped period τ of the movement is

$$\tau = 2\pi(I/c)^{1/2}$$

where I is the moment of inertia. When the damping is wholly electromagnetic the critical damping resistance R is given by

$$R = \frac{(nHA)^2}{2\sqrt{(Ic)}}$$

Hence

$$R\tau = \frac{\pi(nHA)^2}{c}$$

Eliminating c and nHA from eqn. (7.29), we have

$$\overline{i^2} = kT\frac{\pi}{R\tau}\text{e.m.u.} \tag{7.30}$$

But $k = 1 \cdot 38 \times 10^{-16}$ ergs and T may be taken to be 290°K at room temperature, and so, if i is measured in amperes and R in ohms,

$$\bar{i}^2 = \frac{1{\cdot}38 \times 10^{-16} \times 290\pi}{R \times 10^9 \times \tau} \times 10^2$$

whence

$$\bar{i} \sim \frac{1{\cdot}12 \times 10^{-4}}{\sqrt{(R\tau)}} \mu A (\text{r.m.s.}) \tag{7.31}$$

Note that this result is independent of the actual resistance of the coil or of the circuit in which it is connected. Inserting typical values for a short-period galvanometer, we find

$$R = 50 \text{ ohms}, \quad \tau = 0{\cdot}005 \text{ sec}$$

Then

$$\bar{i} = 2{\cdot}24 \times 10^{-4} \mu A$$

It is immediately obvious that if this galvanometer were connected to a signal source of a few microvolts then the signal/noise ratio would be greatly dependent on the internal resistance of the source. For instance, with a $1\mu V$ source of internal resistance 20 ohms (e.g. a thermocouple), and with a galvanometer resistance of 15 ohms, the signal current is $1/35 \ \mu A \sim 2{\cdot}86 \times 10^{-2} \ \mu A$, which is considerably above the noise level. On the other hand, if the resistance of the source is 1 megohm (e.g. a thermistor) the signal current is $10^{-6} \ \mu A$, which is well below the noise level. We conclude that a galvanometer amplifier will be of use only for very weak signals if the internal resistance of the source is low.

For a high-resistance source the signal must be fed directly into a thermionic amplifier. Sometimes a cathode-follower circuit is advocated, and the relative merits of the two methods are investigated in the following example:

Example 6. To investigate the relative noise performance of cathode-follower and normal-amplifier circuits as the first stage of a sensitive amplifier.

In order to make a true comparison we must assume that identical valves are used in each circuit. If a grid leak resistor is used it will be taken to have the same value in each case: if direct connection is possible then R_g in the diagram may be taken to be the input resistance of the valve due to leakage at the grid. Consider first the thermal noise in the grid circuit and valve noise in this first stage only.

A. CATHODE-FOLLOWER CIRCUIT

The effective input resistance between grid and cathode is $R_g(1+m)$ where $m = \mu R_L(r_a + R_L)$, assuming $R_g \gg R_L$.

A careful study of the circuit will show that, owing to the finite value of R_s, it is not a true cathode-follower circuit (Fig. 7.16) in that the feed back ratio is not unity but has a value $\beta = R_g/(R_L+R_s+R_g)$.

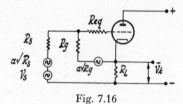

Fig. 7.16

It might well be described as an amplifier with the load circuit connected between cathode and earth. The gain from grid to cathode is

$$m' = \frac{m}{1+m\beta} = \frac{m}{1+m[R_g/(R_L+R_s+R_g)]}$$

Note that this depends on the magnitude of R_s, and that for a very high-resistance source the gain tends to the normal value, i.e. $m' \to m$ as $R_s \to \infty$, although the output voltage is always less than the input voltage and tends to zero as R_s is made larger. It will be an advantage to make the cathode our reference point.

(i) If i_s is the current in the grid circuit due to the signal voltage V_s then

$$i_s = \frac{V_s}{R_s+R_L+R_g(1+m)}$$

Therefore the signal voltage between grid and cathode

$$= R_g i_s = \frac{V_s R_g}{R_s+R_L+R_g(1+m)}$$

and the signal voltage at the cathode

$$= \frac{V_s R_g m}{R_s+R_L+R_g(1+m)}$$

$$= \frac{V_s m R_g/(R_s+R_L+R_g)}{1+m R_g/(R_s+R_L+R_g)}$$

$$= V_s \cdot \frac{m\beta}{1+m\beta}$$

(ii) Similarly, the noise voltage at the cathode due to R_s is

$$a(R_s)^{1/2} \cdot \frac{m\beta}{1+m\beta}$$

(iii) The noise voltage due to R_{eq} is

$$a(R_{eq})^{1/2} \cdot \frac{m}{1+m\beta}$$

(iv) The noise voltage due to R_g is calculated as follows:

The voltage between grid and cathode $\overline{V_{gc}} = aR_g^{1/2} - R_g\overline{i_g}$ where $\overline{i_g}$ is the current in the grid circuit due to this noise source.

Then

$$\overline{V_{gc}} = a(R_g)^{1/2} - R_g \cdot \frac{\overline{V_K} + a(R_g)^{1/2}}{R_s + R_L + R_g}$$

where $\overline{V_K}$ is the particular noise voltage at the cathode.

Now

$$\overline{V_K} = m\overline{V_{gc}} = m\left(a(R_g)^{1/2} - R_g \cdot \frac{\overline{V_K} + a(R_g)^{1/2}}{R_s + R_L + R_g} \right)$$

Therefore

$$\overline{V_K}\left(1 + \frac{mR_g}{R_s + R_L + R_g} \right) = a\,(R_g)^{1/2} \cdot m \cdot \left(1 - \frac{R_g}{R_s + R_L + R_g} \right)$$

i.e.

$$\overline{V_K} = a(R_g)^{1/2} \cdot \frac{m(1-\beta)}{1+m\beta}$$

As all four terms have a common factor $m/(1+m\beta)$, the signal/noise ratio is

$$\frac{V_s}{a\left[R_s + R_g\left(\frac{1-\beta}{\beta} \right)^2 + \frac{R_{eq}}{\beta^2} \right]^{1/2}} \qquad (7.32)$$

B. NORMAL AMPLIFIER CONNECTION

With the grid as reference point (Fig. 7.17), we have

The signal voltage

$$= V_s \cdot \frac{R_g}{R_s + R_g}$$

The total noise voltage

$$= a\left(\frac{R_s R_g}{R_s + R_g} + R_{eq} \right)^{1/2}$$

The signal/noise ratio

$$= \frac{V_s}{a\left[R_s + \frac{R_s{}^2}{R_g} + R_{eq}\left(1 + \frac{R_s}{R_g}\right)^2\right]^{1/2}} \tag{7.33}$$

Comparing eqns. (7.32) and (7.33), we conclude that the cathode-follower circuit will give an improved noise performance if

$$R_g\frac{(1-\beta)^2}{\beta^2} + \frac{R_{eq}}{\beta^2} < \frac{R_s{}^2}{R_g} + R_{eq}\left(1 + \frac{R_s}{R_g}\right)^2$$

i.e. if

$$\frac{(R_s+R_L)^2}{R_g} + R_{eq}\left(1 + \frac{R_s+R_L}{R_g}\right)^2 < \frac{R_s{}^2}{R_g} + R_{eq}\left(1 + \frac{R_s}{R_g}\right)^2$$

which is impossible, although the two expressions will be approximately equal if $R_L \ll R_s$.

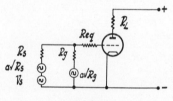

Fig. 7.17

The signal/noise ratio is improved in both instances by making R_g as high as possible, and as R_L will almost certainly be much less than R_g in practice, the difference between the two circuits will be only slight. The result indicates that the cathode-follower circuit is somewhat inferior to the normal amplifier circuit, except when the resistance of the source is considerably greater than the valve load resistance, and then the two circuits have approximately the same signal/noise ratio. If now we include the noise generated in the valve load resistance and the second valve, then, as we saw in example 3, the value of R_{eq} for the cathode-follower circuit will exceed that for the amplifier circuit (provided R_s is finite; the two are equal for infinite R_s).

We may therefore conclude that in all practical instances there is no case for the use of the cathode-follower circuit on the grounds of signal/noise ratio. The popular idea that an increase in signal/noise ratio is achieved through the cathode follower's high input resistance is a misconception. The reader should note that the cathode-follower circuit cannot have an increased input resistance if the grid leak resistor is returned to earth instead of to the cathode unless one considers that the inherent leakage path has a resistance lower than that of the grid leak resistor. But if this were so there would be no point in using a grid leak resistor.

Assuming that a.c. coupling and the consequent use of a grid resistor cannot be avoided, let us investigate the relative merits of the circuit connections of Fig. 7.16 and Fig. 7.18, where the grid leak is returned to earth or some suitable bias point. Here the input resistance

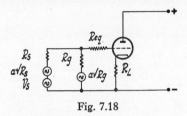

Fig. 7.18

is not increased by feedback but the circuit is a true cathode-follower circuit in that the feedback ratio is unity. The grid circuit of Fig. 7.18 is exactly similar to that for the valve as amplifier, and therefore for the grid-circuit and first valve noise only, we have

Signal/noise ratio

$$= \frac{V_s}{a[R_s(1+R_s/R_g)+R_{eq}(1+R_s/R_g)^2]^{1/2}} \tag{7.34}$$

Although there is no increase of input resistance in this instance, the signal/noise ratio is the same as that obtained for the amplifier circuit and is therefore superior to that for the circuit of Fig. 7.16. However, if the cathode circuit and second valve noise are included, this circuit will be somewhat inferior for a high-resistance source, since the signal voltage at the cathode is lower than in the other circuit. But both circuits are inferior to the normal amplifier connection, owing to the reduced effect of valve and anode circuit noise whatever the significance of R_g.

REFERENCES

1. NYQUIST, H. *Phys. Rev.* (1928) **32**, p. 110.
2. JOHNSON, J. B. *Phys. Rev.* (1928) **32**, 97.
3. WILLIAMS, F. C. *J.I.E.E.* (1937) **81**, p. 751.
4. SCHOTTKY, W. *Ann. Physik.* (1918) **57**, p. 541.
5. NORTH, D. O. *R.C.A. Review* (1940) **4**, p. 441, **5**, p. 106.
6. RACK, A. J. *Bell System Tech. Journ.* (1938) **17**, p. 592.
7. SCHOTTKY, W. and SPENKE, S. *Wiss. Veroff. Siemenswerken* (1937) **16**, p. 1.
8. WILLIAMS, F. C. *J.I.E.E.* (1941) **88**, Part III, p. 219.
9. MACDONALD, D. K. C. *Phil. Mag.* (1949) **40**, p. 561.
10. BAKKER, C. J. *Physica* (1941) **8**, p. 23.
11. VAN DER ZIEL, A. and VERSNEL, A. *Philips Research Reports* (1948) **3**, p. 13.

12. NORTH, D. O. and FERRIS, W. R. *Proc. I.R.E.* (1941) **29**, p. 49.
13. NORTH, D. O. *R.C.A. Review* (1940) **5**, p. 244.
14. HARRIS, W. A. *R.C.A. Review* (1941) **5**, p. 505.
15. JOHNSON, J. B. *Phys. Rev.* (1925) **26**, p. 71.
16. SCHOTTKY, W. *Phys. Rev.* (1926) **28**, p. 75.
17. MOULLIN, E. B. *Spontaneous Fluctuations of Voltage.* (Oxford: Clarendon Press (1938) Chapter 6, p. 165.
18. MACFARLANE, G. G. *Proc. Phys. Soc.* (1947) **59**, p. 366.
19. VAN DER ZIEL, A. *Physica* (1950) **16**, p. 359.
20. HANNAY, N. B., MACNAIR, D. and WHITE, A. H. *J. Appl. Phys.* (1949) **20**, p. 669.
21. HARRIS, E. J. and BISHOP, P. O. *Nature* (1948) **161**, p. 971.
22. HARRIS, E. J., ABSON, W. and ROBERTS, W. L. *T.R.E. Report* (1946) T.2051.
23. HARRIS, E. J. *Electronic Engineering* (1948) **20**, p. 145.
24. NICOLL, G. R. *T.R.E. Memo. No.* 147 (1949).
25. BROWN, D. A. H. *T.R.E. Memo. No.* 329 (1950).
26. TOMLINSON, T. B. *J. Appl. Phys.* (1953) **24**, p. 611.
27. CHRISTENSEN, C. J. and PEARSON, G. L. *Bell System Tech. J.* (1936) **15**, p. 197.
28. CAMPBELL, R. H. and CHIPMAN, R. A. *Proc. I.R.E.* (1949) **37**, p. 938.
29. MACFARLANE, G. G. *Proc. Phys. Soc.* (1950) **63**, p. 807.
30. DAVYDOV, B. I. and GUREVICH, B. *J. Phys. U.S.S.R.* (1943) **7**, p. 138.
31. TORREY, H. C. and WHITMER, C. A. *Crystal Rectifiers* (McGraw-Hill, 1948) Chapter 6.
32. MORRISON, R. F. *Electronics* (1948) **21**, p. 126.
33. FÜRTH, R. and MACDONALD, D. K. C. *Nature* (1947) **159**, p. 608.
34. KINGSBURY, B. A. *Phys. Rev.* (1931) **38**, p. 1458.
35. KURRELMEYER, B. and HAYNER, L. J. *Phys. Rev.* (1937) **52**, p. 952.
36. SHOCKLEY, W. and PIERCE, J. R. *Proc. I.R.E.* (1938) **26**, p. 321.
37. WOODWARD, P. M. *Proc. Camb. Phil. Soc.* (1948) **44**, p. 44.
38. RODDA, S. *J. Sci. Inst.* (1949) **26**, p. 65.
39. BARKHAUSEN, H. *Phys. Zeit.* (1919) **20**, p. 401.
40. KRUMHANSL, J. A. and BEYER, R. T. *J. App. Phys.* (1949) **21**, pp. 432 and 582.
41. NEWTON, R. R., AHEARN, A. J. and McKAY, K. G. *Phys. Rev.* (1949) **75**, p. 103.
42. LEWIS, W. B. *Proc. Phys. Soc.* (1947) **59**, p. 34.
43. MILATZ, J. M. W. and VEN DER VELDON, H. A. *Physica* (1943) **10**, p. 369.
44. FELLGETT, P. B. *J. Opt. Soc. Am.* (1949) **39**, p. 970.
45. TOMLINSON, T. B. *J. Brit. I.R.E.* (1954) **14**, p. 515.
46. ROESS, L. C. *Rev. Sci. Inst.* (1945) **16**, p. 172.
47. BROWN, D. A. H. *J. Sci. Inst.* (1949) **26**, p. 194.
48. ORNSTEIN, L. S. and MILATZ, J. M. W. *Physica* (1938) **5**, p. 971.
49. ASTBURY, N. F. *Proc. Phys. Soc.* (1948) **60**, p. 590.
50. HILL, A. V. *J. Sci. Inst.* (1948) **25**, p. 225.

BIBLIOGRAPHY (not referred to in text)

MACDONALD, D. K. C. 'Spontaneous Fluctuations', *Reports on Progress in Physics.* **12**, p. 56.
SCHREMP, E. J. 'Vacuum Tube Amplifiers'; (McGraw-Hill, 1948), Chapter 12.
GOLDMAN, S. 'Frequency Analysis, Modulation and Noise'; (McGraw-Hill, 1948) Chapters 6–9.
BAKKER, C. J. 'Fluctuations and Electron Inertia', *Physica* (1941) **8**, p. 23.
PIERCE, J. R. 'Noise in Resistances and Electron Streams', *Bell Syst. Tech. J.* (1948) **27**, p. 158.
BELL, D. A. 'Fluctuations of Electric Current', *J.I.E.E.* (1946) **93**, Part III, p. 37.
BAKKER, C. J. 'The Causes of Voltage and Current Fluctuations', *Phillips Tech. Rev.* (1941) **6**, p. 129.

Chapter Eight

AMPLIFIER DESIGN AND FAULT FINDING

By E. E. Zepler

The design of an amplifier depends to a large extent on the special requirements of its application, but in any design there are various fundamental principles which must be observed if the result is to be satisfactory. The subject is a vast one and an extensive treatment is beyond the scope of this chapter. The main points needing a careful consideration are input and output circuits, overall gain, distortion, signal/noise ratio and stability. They will be discussed in the order given.

THE INPUT CIRCUIT

The choice of input circuit depends on the nature of the signal and on the impedance of the generator. The object of the input circuit is to apply as large a signal as possible to the grid of the first valve without incurring distortion. We shall consider two typical cases of generator impedance.

(i) The signal is derived from a current generator, i.e. the generator impedance is so large that the current derived is practically independent of the load.

The condition is fulfilled in some types of photocell. In order to obtain a large signal it is desirable to connect in series with the photocell a very large resistance, with the p.d. across the resistance serving as the input signal. The size of the resistance is determined by the type of input valve. Because of the presence of positive ions or through electron emission from the grid, which is heated by the cathode, most valves pass a very small grid current under normal working conditions. Hence the size of the grid resistance must not be such that the grid current causes an appreciable p.d. between grid and cathode, and, because of variations in grid current, makes the valve behave erratically. The more powerful a valve, the larger is the power absorbed in the heater, and hence the smaller is the maximum grid resistance permissible. For average valves 10 megohms may be considered the upper limit. Valves made specially for the purpose may be used with a grid resistance many times larger.

A large grid resistance is useless if the frequencies to be amplified are so high that the input capacitance of the amplifier is the factor that determines the impedance. If, for instance, the input capacitance is 20 pF and the frequency 1000 c/s, the capacitive reactance is only 8 megohms and no benefit is derived from a 100-megohm grid resistance. At high frequencies it is essential to keep the input capacitance as low as possible, to avoid long leads and to use an input pentode rather than a triode. From Fig. 8.1 it can be seen that, with a stage

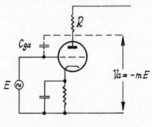

Fig. 8.1

gain m, the current through C_{ga} is $(E-V_a) j\omega C_{ga} = E(1+m)j\omega C_{ga}$. Hence, owing to the feedback through the grid-anode capacitance, E looks into a capacitance $C_{ga}(1+m)$ in parallel with the grid-cathode capacitance. In a pentode the effect is negligible because of the small value of C_{ga}. The sensitivity of the above input circuit may be seen from the following example.

Example. Owing to a chopped light beam, current pulses of 10^{-12} amp are obtained from a photocell; the duration of the pulses is $0\cdot02$ sec, and the repetition frequency is 25 c/s. A resistance of 10 megohms is connected in series with the photocell. The amplifier is tuned to 25 c/s. What is the input voltage?

Square pulses of 10 μV height are caused across the input. Only the amplitude of fundamental frequency is of interest, because the harmonics do not pass through the amplifier. From p. 17 it is seen that the r.m.s. signal is $20/\pi$ μV.

(ii) The generator impedance is a low resistance. In order to obtain a large signal across the grid-cathode of the first valve a transformer is inserted between the generator and the amplifier input. The step-up ratio of the transformer is determined by the generator resistance, by the capacitance across the secondary, by the highest frequency to be transferred and, possibly, by practical considerations such as the size of the transformer. If we assume unity a coupling factor, a secondary capacitance C, a primary inductance L and a step-up ratio n, the equivalent circuit seen from the generator is shown in Fig. 8.2 (compare p. 13). At the high frequency end $\omega L \gg R$, and therefore L may be neglected. Then the transfer ratio is independent of frequency as long as $1/\omega C n^2 \gg R$. For $1/\omega C n^2 = 3R$, the voltage across L is $-E\cdot j3/(1-j3)$; hence $|V| = |E|3/\sqrt{10} \sim 0\cdot95$ $|E|$; for many purposes this drop is not serious. For example, assuming $C = 100$ pF, $R = 5$

ohms, $f = 1000$ c/s, and allowing a drop of 5 per cent due to the secondary capacitance, we have $n = (30\pi 10^{-7})^{-1/2} = 300$.

The magnitude of L is given by the lowest frequency to be amplified, when ωL must be large compared with R. If, for instance, the lowest frequency is 20 c/s and if $\omega L = 3R$ is considered satisfactory, L is $15/2\pi \times 20 = 0.12$ henry. The secondary inductance would then be $0.12 \times 300^2 = 10,800$ henries. With a high-μ core such a transformer can be made without its being too bulky or expensive. In this example the voltage across L is practically equal to the generator e.m.f. for the frequency range 20-1000 c/s, and so the transfer ratio is 300.

If, in the above, the frequency band is only 19–21 c/s the design of the transformer is different. Because of the narrow bandwidth a tuned transformer can be used. We assume that 10,000 henries is the maximum secondary inductance practicable. We place a capacitance of 6000 pF across the secondary, tuning it to 20 c/s. The primary inductance

Fig. 8.2   Fig. 8.3

is chosen so that its reactance is about one-third of the generator resistance, i.e. $L = 5/(2\pi \times 20 \times 3) = 0.013$ henry. The equivalent circuit seen from the generator is as shown in Fig. 8.2. It may be assumed, as a reasonable approximation, that the Q-factor of the tuned transformer is 10, and therefore the transformer losses may be represented by a resistance $10\ \omega L_1 = 16.7$ ohms, in parallel with the primary (see p. 7). By Norton's theorem the circuit reduces to that of Fig. 8.3, R' being the parallel combination of the generator resistance of 5 ohms with a resistance of 16.7 ohms. The response of the circuit is naturally given by the Q-factor due to R', which is below 3. From this it is seen that the Q-factor of the transformer by itself is of secondary importance in the above problem. The response is easily wide enough for the frequency band 19–21 c/s. The transfer ratio is

$$\frac{R'}{R}n = \frac{R'}{R}\left(\frac{10,000}{0.013}\right)^{1/2} = 675$$

The Output Circuit

The maximum output power required determines the choice of the output valve and the h.t. supply. If the load into which the output valve works is a cathode-ray oscillograph without pre-amplifier, the

N

load impedance is a resistance of about 1 megohm in parallel with a capacitance of 20–30 pF. At audio frequencies this means a nearly infinite load impedance; the output power is negligible and the only consideration is the output voltage required. With the usual type of cathode-ray oscillograph this voltage is about 100 volts peak, and can easily be obtained from an output valve with a resistance in the anode lead. The correct anode resistance and distortion for a given anode voltage can be derived from the load line. If the oscillograph possesses a pre-amplifier, the maximum output voltage required is negligibly small and any type of amplifier valve will serve as output valve.

When considerations of output power enter, e.g. with a loudspeaker, it is usually necessary to employ an output transformer with a turns ratio such that the transferred load is the correct one for the particular valve. The direct voltage at the anode is very nearly equal to the h.t. voltage, because of the low d.c. resistance of the primary of the transformer. For the steepness of the load line, however, the determining factor is the transferred load. Hence the graph of Fig. 8.4, for an assumed a.c. load of 15 kilohms, should be easily understood. The ratio of second harmonic to fundamental is found from Fig. 8.4.

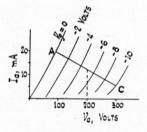

Fig. 8.4

The amplitudes of current and voltage of fundamental frequency are $(i_{max}-i_{min})/2$ and $(v_{max}-v_{min})/2$ respectively, thus the output of fundamental frequency is $(i_{max}-i_{min})(v_{max}-v_{min})/8$. For the load line AC in Fig. 8.4, the output is $0 \cdot 35$ watt.

OVERALL GAIN

The overall gain depends on the input available and on the required output. In the above example of square-wave current pulses of 10^{-12} amp it was stated that $20/\pi \,\mu V$ peak of fundamental frequency was produced at the input across a 10 megohm resistance. If the output is to be applied across the Y-plate of a cathode ray oscillograph, the amplifier gain from the first grid to the output anode must be of the order of 2×10^7.

If, on the other hand, an output power of, say, 4 watts is required, we have to find from the I_a/V_a graph of the output valve and from the appropriate load line the grid voltage required. For the normal type of output pentode this is about 10 volts peak; thus, in the above example the gain from the first grid to the grid of the output valve has to be about $1\cdot5 \times 10^6$. Such a large gain raises important problems which will be discussed later.

DISTORTION

If the waveshape of the output differs from that of the signal the amplifier is said to cause distortion. One distinguishes three types of distortion, frequency, phase, and harmonic. They will be discussed separately.

(A) *Frequency Distortion*

The effect is due to the amplifier gain being a function of frequency, and causes the amplitudes of the frequency spectrum to differ in their relative strength in input and output. The output is, however, proportional to the input, and hence no new frequencies are produced in the amplifier. The main causes of frequency distortion in the normal type of amplifier are the coupling capacitances, the stray capacitances and the transformers. In addition, the capacitances across the cathode resistors and the decoupling capacitances in the screen leads cause some frequent distortion, as has been shown in chapter two. Feedback through the grid-anode capacitance of a triode tends to aggravate the problem of stray capacitances.

In speech or music a certain amount of frequency distortion is permissible without serious effect. It results in what is usually called base or treble cut. In optical measurements, however, when an exact record of experimental results is essential, frequency distortion in the amplifier must be minimized as much as possible. If pulses of a small repetition frequency, such as 5 c/s, are to be faithfully reproduced, large coupling capacitances and transformers with large inductances

Fig. 8.5   Fig. 8.6

are required. The effect of too small a coupling capacitance on the shape of pulses may be seen from Figs. 8.5 and 8.6. (As will be shown later the distortion caused is due both to frequency and phase distortion.)

In Fig. 8.5 the switch is closed at $t = 0$; a simple calculation shows that the p.d. across R is given by $V = E \exp(-t/RC)$. Consequently the voltage at the following grid of an RC-coupled stage with a pulse applied at the previous grid is as shown in Fig. 8.6. The fractional drop in voltage over a cycle is $\Delta V/V = 1 - \exp(-T/RC)$, T being the duration of the pulse. If, for example, a drop of 2 per cent is considered permissible the relation is

$$1 - \exp(-T/RC) = 0.02$$

Therefore

$$RC = -\frac{T}{\log_e 0.98}$$

For square pulses of 5 c/s, $T = 0.1$ sec; hence $RC \sim 5$. A possible combination would be $R = 1$ megohm, $C = 5$ μF.

In a similar way the required magnitude of the primary inductance of the output transformer could be found. With the help of Thévenin's theorem the circuit of Fig. 8.7 simplifies to that of Fig. 8.8, where R'

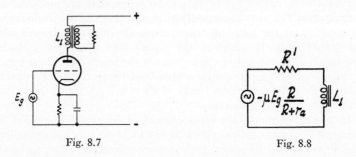

Fig. 8.7   Fig. 8.8

is the parallel combination of r_a and the transferred load resistance R. When a direct voltage E is applied in the circuit of Fig. 8.8, the p.d. across L_1 is $E \exp(-R'/L_1)t$, which is of the same form as that across R in Fig. 8.5. Allowing the same amount of distortion as that due to 1 megohm and 5 μF in Fig. 8.5 gives $L_1/R' = 5$. With an output pentode, the optimum anode load is about 6000 ohms, while r_a is approximately 50,000 ohms. Hence $R \sim 6000$ ohms, whilst the required magnitude of L_1 is 30,000 henries. Such a transformer is not easy to produce, in view of the problem of saturation by the anode current of the valve. The task would be considerably facilitated by using a push-pull output stage, when d.c. saturation would be avoided.

Insufficiently large decoupling capacitances affect the shape of pulses in a similar way as that shown above. The discussion on p. 29 may be studied for the purpose. If, in the circuit of Fig. 2.12, a direct voltage E is applied to the grid, the screen voltage becomes

$$V_s = -\mu_1 E \frac{R_1}{R_1+r_s} \left[1 - \exp\left(-\frac{t}{R'C_s} \right) \right]$$

and so

$$I_a = g_m E \left[1 - \frac{R_1}{R_1+r_s}(1-e^{-t/R'C_s}) \right] = g_m E \left(\frac{R_1}{R_1+r_s} e^{-t/R'C_s} + \frac{r_s}{R_1+r_s} \right)$$

From this it is seen that, when $r_s \ll R_1$, the time-constant $R'C_s$ is as important as that of C and R in Fig. 8.5. Because of the relatively small value of r_s (10–20 kilohms) the magnitude of C_s required would be prohibitive. Hence it is necessary to obtain the screen voltage by means of a low-resistance potential divider and leave out the decoupling capacitor altogether. For instance, if $r_s = 20$ kilohms and a potential divider of 10 kilohms is used with a centre tapping, the effective load in the screen is 2500 ohms and the varying screen voltage reduces the gain by only 12 per cent. Another possibility which would not sacrifice any gain would be the use of a neon lamp for producing a stabilized screen voltage.

The problem of frequency distortion exists whenever an input of an amplitude varying with time is applied to the amplifier. Let us assume that the absorption of light as a function of the light frequency is to be investigated. The light having passed the absorbing medium acts on a photocell, and thus the input to the amplifier will vary with time, according to the variations in light frequency. The more rapid the changes, the larger the audio-frequency band which the amplifier must pass. With a continuous light beam the response curve of the amplifier must start at zero frequency. If the light beam is chopped and the amplifier tuned to the chopping frequency, the frequency

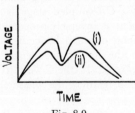

Fig. 8.9

band of the amplifier must be symmetrical with respect to the chopping frequency. Then the problem is the same as with broadcast reception, i.e. the amplifier must have a bandwidth sufficiently wide to pass all the relevant sidebands. The more rapid the changes in signal strength the larger must be the bandwidth of the amplifier. That means that the bandwidth is proportional to the speed with which records are to be taken. When the bandwidth is not sufficiently wide, a variation of input as shown by curve (i) in Fig. 8.9 might appear in the output as indicated by curve (ii).

(B) Phase Distortion

A variation of gain with frequency is always accompanied by a phase displacement of the various frequency components. In aural reception the phase conditions are of lesser importance, except in transient, because the ear does not react to changes in phase. This means that the wave form of the a.f. output need not be the same as that of the a.f. input, or, with a modulated wave, as that of the modulation envelope. In radar and television, however, phase relations are of first importance, because the waveform of the output determines the picture produced. An amplifier which is perfect from the point of view of phase distortion must fulfil one of the two following conditions:

(i) There is no phase displacement between input and output

(ii) The phase displacement between input and output is proportional to the frequency

Condition (i) cannot be fulfilled except in an ideal d.c. amplifier having no stray capacitances. Condition (ii) can be fulfilled with reasonable accuracy for frequencies up to several megacycles per second. If condition (ii) prevails, and if $E_1 \sin \omega_1 t$ and $E_2 \sin \omega_2 t$ are two input voltages, the corresponding output voltages are $E_1' \sin (\omega_1 t - \phi)$ and $E_2' \sin (\omega_2 t - \phi \omega_2/\omega_1)$ respectively. On rearranging the expressions, the output voltages become $E_1' \sin \omega_1(t - \phi/\omega_1)$ and $E_2' \sin \omega_2(t - \phi/\omega_1)$. This shows that the phase relation of the two signals in the output is the same as that in the input, both being delayed by the same time ϕ/ω_1. The tendency of a CR-coupled stage is to advance the phase by an angle whose tangent is inversely proportional to the frequency. This tendency is the wrong one and hence it is essential to choose the components so that at the lowest frequency concerned the phase shift is only a few degrees. If the lowest frequency concerned is 5 c/s, a value of $RC = 5$ restricts the phase shift to $0\cdot4°$.

(C) Harmonic Distortion

This type of distortion is due to the amplifier not acting as a linear network. It causes a change in the waveform of the signal as types (A) and (B) do, but in contrast to types (A) and (B) new frequencies are generated in the amplifier. For this reason there is a greater tendency for the output to sound objectionable than with frequency and phase distortion. There are three main causes of harmonic distortion:

(i)   Curvature of the valve characteristic
(ii) Grid current
(iii) The output transformer

(i) This point is discussed on p. 23. The load line gives information on the distortion incurred. As pointed out in chapter three, the distortion may be reduced by negative feedback in the ratio $(1-m\beta):1$.

(ii) If a valve is temporarily driven into grid current, it represents to the preceding valve a variable load, thus causing non-linear distortion of the signal. To prevent this effect it is essential to bias the valve so that the grid is always negative with respect to the cathode. This fact has been taken into consideration in discussing the load line of Fig. 8.4. If, for some reason, it is desired to drive a valve into grid current, distortion can be minimized by using a generator of very low internal impedance. If, for instance, the variable load resistance is always large compared with the generator resistance, the p.d. across the load is nearly equal to the e.m.f. and the distortion is small. For this reason the valve acting as a generator should either use a step-down transformer or it should be a cathode follower. Using a push-pull stage has the advantage of removing the even harmonics and thus reducing distortion considerably.

(iii) An output transformer may be the cause of harmonic distortion for two reasons: (*a*) indirectly by its effect on the load line, aggravating the influence of the non-linear valve characteristic; and (*b*) directly, because of hysteresis.

(*a*) If the reactance of the primary is not large compared with the transferred load, the anode load is a parallel combination of resistance and inductance. The anode voltage and the anode current are not in

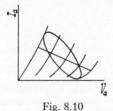

Fig. 8.10

phase and the load line becomes an ellipse. Because of the reduced anode load the slope of the ellipse is greater than that of the load line. As is seen from Fig. 8.10, the valve is driven into lower anode current, and hence the distortion due to the curvature of the valve characteristic is increased. The lower the frequency the more marked will be the effect. The magnitude of the primary inductance is thus determined by the anode load and by the lowest frequency to be amplified. Good modern output transformers designed for aural reception have a primary inductance of not less than 100 henrys. Such transformers, if used with an output pentode and an anode load of, say, 6 kilohms, limit the phase displacement between anode current and anode voltage to about 10°. Therefore they cannot be expected to be satisfactory when slow changes are to be recorded, involving frequencies of a few cycles per second.

(*b*) Because of the hysteresis of the iron core the transformer is a non-linear impedance and is thus the cause of harmonic distortion. In order to minimize the effect it is important to keep the flux density B well below saturation. The p.d. across the primary is given by $N_1 A dB/dt$, where N_1 is the number of turns in the primary and A is the area of cross-section of the iron core. The larger N_1 and A, the smaller the flux density for a given p.d. Since the inductance is proportional to $N_1^2 A$ it is clear that a large primary inductance results in a small flux density and hence keeps distortion down. As with (*a*) the effect is largest at the low frequencies, because $dB/dt = \omega B$, so that for a given voltage, B is inversely proportional to the frequency. A primary inductance of 100 henries is adequate for good aural reception.

SIGNAL/NOISE RATIO

The smallest signal that can be detected depends on the noise in the amplifier. If the signal is strong, the noise may be unimportant, but usually it is essential to reduce the noise to the lowest possible value. The main sources of noise are shot noise, thermal-agitation noise, mains hum and microphonic noise. Here only the two latter will be discussed, the other two being dealt with in chapter seven.

Mains Hum

Hum may enter the amplifier in various ways: (i) through the h.t. leads, (ii) through the filament leads, (iii) through electrostatic pick-up, and (iv) through magnetic pick-up.

(i) With a full-wave rectifier the ripple frequency is twice that of the a.c. mains. When a power pack with capacitance input is employed (Fig. 8.11) the r.m.s. voltage at the fundamental ripple frequency is approximately $V = 150\ I/2fC_1$, where I is the steady current in milliamp, f is the mains frequency and C_1 is in μF. Assuming $I = 60$mA, $f = 50$ c/s and $C_1 = 10\ \mu$F, we find that the r.m.s. ripple voltage across C_1 is 9 volts at 100 c/s. The inductance-capacitance filter LC_2 reduces the ripple voltage to

$$V\frac{1/j\omega C_2}{j\omega L + 1/j\omega C_2} = \frac{V}{1-\omega^2 LC_2}$$

Since $\omega L \gg 1/\omega C_2$, the reduction factor is approximately $\omega^2 LC_2$.

Average values are $L = 20$ henries, $C_2 = 10\,\mu\text{F}$; for a mains frequency of 50 c/s, the reduction factor is $(200\,\pi)^2 \times 20 \times 10^{-5} = 80$, leaving a ripple voltage of $0\cdot1$ volt in the h.t. supply to the amplifier. The point most sensitive to h.t. ripple is the anode (or possibly the screen grid)

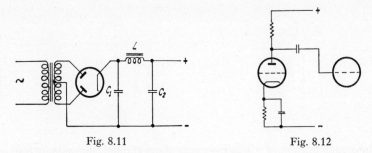

Fig. 8.11   Fig. 8.12

of the first valve. If the first valve is a triode of $r_a = 10$ kilohms and $\mu = 20$ and has an anode load resistance R of 50 kilohms (Fig. 8.12), the ripple voltage at the anode would be $0\cdot1 r_a/(r_a+R)$ volts $= 17$ mV. The stage gain being $16\cdot7$, the ripple output is equal to that from an input of approximately 1 mV across the grid of the first valve. This is at least 100 times the ripple permissible in a sensitive amplifier, and so means of further reducing the ripple must be provided.

Another LC-section in the general h.t. leads would fulfil the purpose. A cheaper way would be to insert an RC-section into the h.t. leads of the first and second valves only. Frequently, for the sake of constancy of gain, it will be found desirable to employ a stabilized h.t. supply as described in chapter six. Then the ripple voltage is automatically reduced to a very low value. Another possibility is the use of push-pull stages throughout the amplifier, which greatly reduces the ripple output.

(ii) Hum from the filament leads is mainly due to capacitance between the grid and filament leads inside the valve. The effect can be much reduced by a *humdinger*, i.e. a potential divider across the filament (Fig. 8.13). By connecting the sliding point to earth, it is possible to cancel the two voltages induced at the grid. There is no hum pick-up when the grid is at a.c. earth potential, and so the condition for mutual cancellation is $R_1/R_2 = C_1/C_2$. It cannot be expected that the correct position of the potential divider is the same for all valves. In addition, there are always other sources of hum, so that the best position of the humdinger gives a minimum, rather than a zero, of hum output. The frequency of the hum picked up from the filament leads is that of the mains and its harmonics.

Another way in which hum can be introduced from the filament leads is through leakage resistance, often caused by filament emission, between the filament and cathode. As can be seen from Fig. 8.14, an

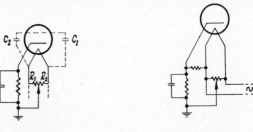

Fig. 8.13   Fig. 8.14

alternating current of mains frequency flows through the cathode lead and causes a p.d. between cathode and grid. A large capacitance, bypassing the cathode resistor minimizes the effect, but frequently it is necessary to change the valve.

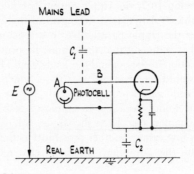

Fig. 8.15

(iii) Electrostatic pick-up may take place from the mains outside the amplifier or from leads inside. The effect is in principle the same as that described in connection with Fig. 8.13, the main difference being that the coupling capacitance is outside the valve. It is thus possible to provide a cure by correct electrostatic screening. The method may be understood from Fig. 8.15. Between the mains lead shown and true earth there exists an alternating potential E at mains frequency. C_1 is the capacitance between the mains lead and the grid input lead of the amplifier, C_2 is that between the amplifier chassis and true earth and Z is the input impedance of the amplifier. C_2 is likely to be large compared with C_1, and is infinite when the receiver chassis is earthed. The voltage applied across the input is approximately $E . Z/(Z+1/j\omega C_1)$, from which it is seen that the effect is the more serious the larger Z is. The pick-up disappears when, in the circuit of Fig. 8.15, the photocell and the connecting lead AB are surrounded with a metal screen which is connected to the chassis of the amplifier. The same method applies if pick-up is due to leads inside the amplifier. It is advisable to keep leads carrying large alternating voltages, such as the mains leads, the leads connected to the h.t. rectifier, etc., as far away as possible from the input valve of the amplifier.

If capacitance C_1 exists, not between the mains lead and point B, but between the mains lead and chassis, a p.d. $EC_1/(C_1+C_2)$ is produced between the chassis and earth. Therefore capacitance between the earth and point B will cause electrostatic pick-up. Hence the chassis should be earthed as a matter of routine.

(iv) Magnetic pick-up of hum need be taken into account only when the amplifier works with an input transformer. The most important source of hum is the mains transformer, and so it is essential to keep the two transformers as far apart as possible. It often helps to place the two transformers at right angles in a position of symmetry, so that the mutual inductance is a minimum. However, with amplifiers of large gain it is necessary to surround the input transformer with a box of high-permeability material. The amplifier chassis and box should not be iron, since this tends to increase the coupling between the two transformers.

Microphonic Noise

Mechanical vibrations cause movements of the electrodes of a valve; those of the grid are the most serious. The movements produce variations in anode current and therefore an undesired output component. Rubber mountings of the first and second valves and careful selection of these valves are essential in working with amplifiers of large gain. In exacting conditions it is useful to suspend the amplifier as a whole by means of springs.

STABILITY

Constancy of Gain

In many amplifiers it is important that the gain does not vary over an appreciable period, for otherwise measurements taken would not be reliable. Therefore, the design has to be such that (i) the supply voltages vary as little as possible and (ii) the gain is hardly affected by such variations. Stabilization of the filament voltage is always laborious, unless accumulators are used, and hence the design emphasis should be on (ii). The means of achieving this is the application of ample negative feedback. For large feedback, the stability of gain is primarily determined by the feedback ratio β and any further improvement can be achieved only by increasing the stability of the components in the feedback path. Temperature stability is the major factor to be considered. For further details the reader is referred to chapter three.

Instability of the Amplifier

One of the most important aspects of the design of an amplifier is the avoidance of undesired feedback over several stages. With amplifiers having a gain of, say, 10^5 the possibility of instability caused by undesired feedback is appreciable. (An amplifier, when oscillating, maintains its driving voltage due to the existing feedback. This is fulfilled when $m\beta = 1$, the phase angle of $m\beta$ being zero.) In the following a list of the most common sources of undesired feedback in a.f. amplifiers is given, together with means of combating them.

(i) *Feedback through the Common h.t. Supply.* The problem will be understood from Fig. 8.16. The capacitance C_3 is common to the anode circuits of the three valves. Because of the gain involved only the coupling between the first and third anode circuits need be considered. The

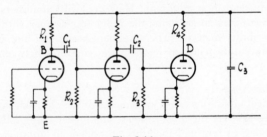

Fig. 8.16

p.d. across C_3 caused by the anode current of the third valve is fed back via R_1 to the grid of the second valve. The first valve only acts as a resistance r_a between B and E and thus reduces the feedback factor approximately in the ratio $(R_1+r_a):r_a$. We may, therefore, treat the circuit as an amplifier with the input terminals B and E and the output terminals D and E (Fig. 8.17). At higher frequencies, when the coupling capacitances C_1 and C_2 may be considered short-circuits, the output voltage at D is in phase with that at B. Therefore the voltage fed back, owing to the very low reactance of C_2, lags by 90° behind the input voltage. At lower frequencies C_1 and C_2 cause a phase advancement, and there will be one particular frequency at which the voltage fed back is in phase with the input voltage. If at this frequency the feedback factor $m\beta$ is larger than unity, oscillation will take place. It may be

Fig. 8.17

assumed that in the circuit of Fig. 8.16, $C_1 = C_2$, $R_2 = R_3$ and $R_2 \gg R_1$. Then $m\beta$ is a real positive number when $1/\omega C_1 R_2 = 1/\omega C_2 R_3 = 1$, the phase shift being 45° in each stage and the total gain being half that at higher frequencies.

Assuming identical valves and anode loads, we have as the amplitude condition for oscillation

$$m\beta = \frac{1}{2}\left(\mu\frac{R_1}{r_a+R_1}\right)^2 \cdot \frac{1}{\omega C_3 R_4} \cdot \frac{r_a}{R_1+r_a} = 1$$

The frequency at which the phase is right for oscillation is given by the relation $1/\omega C_1 = R_2$, and thus the amplitude condition for oscillation becomes

$$\frac{1}{2}\left(\mu\frac{R_1}{r_a+R_1}\right)^2 \cdot \frac{C_1 R_2}{C_3 R_4} \cdot \frac{r_a}{r_a+R_1} = 1$$

whence

$$C_3 = \frac{1}{2}\left(\mu\frac{R_1}{r_a+R_1}\right)^2 \cdot \frac{R_2}{r_a+R_1} \cdot \frac{r_a}{R_4} C_1$$

Example. $r_a = 10$ kilohms, $R_1 = R_4 = 50$ kilohms, $R_2 = 0.5$ megohm, $C_1 = 0.01\ \mu F$, $\mu = 24$.

The value of C_3 for which oscillation would just start is

$$C_3 = 200\frac{0.5\times 10^6}{0.6\times 10^5}\frac{1}{5}0.01\ \mu F = 3.3\ \mu F$$

The frequency of oscillation is

$$\frac{1}{2\pi 10^{-8}\times 0.5\times 10^6}c/s = 100/\pi\ c/s$$

Feedback through the common h.t. supply is not always easy to cure. In the simple circuit of Fig. 8.16 there are essentially three ways of doing so:

(*a*) C_3 is increased so that feedback is negligible. Increasing it to only 6–7 μF might be considered. This would have the advantage of leaving enough positive feedback at $100/\pi$ c/s so that the gain would be the same as at higher frequencies.

(*b*) C_1 and C_2 are reduced to half their values. The disadvantage of this is that the response curve of the amplifier falls off at about 60 c/s; furthermore, because of the small value of C_3 the hum is likely to be troublesome.

(*c*) An RC-filter is inserted in series with R_1; for the above circuit a resistor of 10 kilohms and a capacitor of 4 μF would be adequate.

Addition of a further stage in the circuit of Fig. 8.16 would not aggravate conditions, in spite of the increased gain, because the phase in the overall feedback is not correct for oscillation. The addition of a fifth valve, however, would raise a serious problem. With a gain of 100,000 between the second grid and the last anode, and with the phase correct for oscillation, it is clear that even a very low impedance in the common h.t. supply is likely to cause trouble. For this reason it is advisable not to use more than four stages altogether, unless this is essential. By the use of pentodes one can easily achieve, with four stages, a gain of 10^6 or more, even allowing for a good deal of negative feedback to provide stabilization.

If, on the other hand, one is forced by circumstances to use more than four stages one should employ either a stabilized h.t. supply or have a separate h.t. supply for the last few valves. The use of push-pull stages is another possible solution.

(ii) *Feedback due to Electrostatic Coupling.* Any stray capacitance between input and output provides a source of feedback that may cause instability. Oscillation is likely to take place at the high-frequency end of the amplifier, since the feedback factor β increases with increasing frequency. Phase conditions may be discussed with the help of Fig. 8.16. It is assumed that a small capacitance, of the order of 0·1 pF, exists between the first grid and the last anode, and, for the sake of simplicity, that the first valve is a pentode. Then the input impedance of the first valve is determined by the grid leak resistance and by the capacitance between grid and earth; with a triode the effect of feedback through the grid-anode capacitance would have to be taken into account. It is easy to see that the voltage fed back leads the voltage at the last anode by an angle ϕ, which at low frequencies tends towards 90° and at high frequencies towards zero. Hence, for oscillation to take place, the voltage at the last anode must lag by the same angle ϕ behind the voltage at the first grid. At intermediate frequencies, when the coupling capacitances act as short-circuits and when the stray anode-earth or grid-earth capacitance may as yet be disregarded, the output voltage is in antiphase with the input voltage. Hence for the output voltage to be lagging behind the input voltage by an angle ϕ, a phase retardation of $180°+\phi$, or a phase advance of $180°-\phi$, must be produced by the capacitances in the amplifier. The coupling capacitances advance the phase while the stray capacitances retard it. Hence there will be two frequencies at which the phase is right for oscillation; one will be at the low-frequency end of the amplifier, the other at the high-frequency end. However, at low frequencies β is extremely small, and when $m\beta$ becomes real its absolute magnitude is usually well below unity. For instance, with the values assumed above, the phase would be right at a frequency of $100/\pi$ c/s. At this frequency the input impedance is resistive, so that the voltage fed back leads the output voltage by $90°$. The reactance of the $0 \cdot 1$ pF feedback capacitor is $0 \cdot 5 \times 10^5$ megohms; allowing for an input resistance of 1 megohm, a gain of $0 \cdot 5 \times 10^5$ would be needed to cause oscillations.

At the high-frequency end of the amplifier the input impedance is determined by the grid/earth capacitance of the first valve and its grid lead. If we assess this at 20 pF, a gain of 200 will be sufficient for oscillation. The phase shift required in the amplifier would be $180°$, which is possible with three stages.

Capacitive feedback as described above can be avoided by correct design. Points of the amplifier between which there is a large gain should be as far apart as possible. If this proves insufficient, metal partitions connected to the chassis may be placed at appropriate points. The use of screened leads at the first grid and the last anode should prove equally helpful. By choosing the right type of screened lead (50–60 pF/m) the added stray capacitance is negligibly small.

(iii) *Magnetic Feedback.* Magnetic feedback is likely to cause trouble only when there is an input and an output transformer and a large gain between them. Phase conditions need not be discussed; from the above it will have become clear that with several stages there is always a frequency at which the phase is correct for oscillation. The methods of prevention are the same as those given for magnetic pick-up of hum, namely:

(*a*) Placing the transformers as far apart as possible
(*b*) Setting the transformers at right angles in a position of symmetry

(c) Surrounding one or both transformers with boxes of high-permeability material

It may be mentioned that at low frequencies partitions of copper or aluminium have practically no effect on magnetic fields.

(iv) *Parasitic Oscillations.* By a *parasitic oscillation* is usually understood instability of the amplifier at a frequency quite outside the range for which it is designed. The type of parasitic oscillation that frequently occurs in a.f. amplifiers may be understood from Fig. 8.18. Between the grid and cathode of the last valve there is a loop *abcd*, consisting of

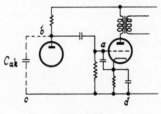

Fig. 8.18

the inductances of the leads marked in full and the stray capacitance C_{ak}. At very high frequencies, such as 60 Mc/s, the loop forms a tuned circuit with the grid-cathode capacitance of the valve. In the anode circuit there is a similar loop, from the anode through the capacitance of the primary of the transformer and the capacitance across the h.t. supply. Hence there are tuned circuits at the anode and the grid, coupled through the grid-anode capacitance of the valve. If the two circuits happen to have resonant frequencies fairly close to each other and if the valve is powerful, with a mutual conductance of 5–10 mA/V, oscillation takes place. Oscillation of this kind is not always easily noticeable. The frequency is quite outside the audible range, and even a cathode-ray oscillograph often fails to indicate it, because either the frequency is too high for the oscillograph to respond or the oscillation stops as soon as the oscillograph is connected.

The symptoms by which a parasitic oscillation may be recognized are distortion of the wanted signal, erratic changes in the behaviour of the valve, sensitivity to the hand being brought near, etc. It is usually the output valve which is prone to parasitic oscillation, because of its high mutual conductance. It is fairly easy to stop parasitic oscillations by inserting a grid stopper (a resistance of about 1,000 ohms) in the grid lead as close as practicable to the grid terminal of the valve. Such a resistance damps the r.f. resonance circuit, without harming the a.f. performance. By keeping the leads involved as short as possible the tendency to parasitic oscillations is greatly reduced, but insertion of a grid stopper as a matter of routine can be recommended in any case.

Fault Finding

Skill in finding faults in a circuit is a very important and time-saving feature, which, however, cannot be acquired without a good deal of experience. While it is impossible to convey experience through a book, it is possible to teach the right outlook in these matters and to enable the reader to acquire experience more quickly than he otherwise would. It is not intended to go through a whole list of faults that might occur, but simply to show, with the help of a few examples, the correct procedure in tracing the causes of trouble. The circuit of Fig. 8.16 is used for the following discussion.

Example 1.

An amplifier is found to oscillate at an audible frequency. The following tests should quickly reveal the source of feedback.

Short-circuit the grid of the first valve to earth.

If oscillation stops it must be capacitive feedback to the grid of the first valve, probably from the output leads going to the cathode-ray oscillograph.

If oscillation does not stop, short-circuit the grid of the second valve to earth.

Let us assume that oscillation stops. There are two possible causes:

(*a*) Capacitive feedback to the grid of the second valve, or to the anode of the first valve. This is not at all probable because the grid of the second valve is connected to earth through the comparatively low a.c. resistance of the first valve, the coupling capacitor being considered as a short-circuit.

(*b*) Feedback through the common h.t. supply. Interrupt the connection between h.t. lead and the anode load of the first valve. This removes feedback through the h.t. supply but increases capacitive feedback to the grid of the second valve, because of the increased impedance between grid and earth. If oscillation stops it is clearly h.t. feedback. There is a very slight chance that oscillation will persist, although the original cause was feedback through the h.t. supply, oscillation being maintained by the now increased capacitive feedback. If, therefore, the test is not conclusive a *CR*-filter might be inserted in the first valve instead of interrupting its h.t. supply. This should, without doubt, clarify the situation.

Example 2.

The source of a large hum is to be traced. The following test will quickly reveal the source.

Short-circuit the grid of the first valve to earth. It is assumed that the hum persists.

Short-circuit the grid of the second valve to earth. The hum disappears. There are three different possibilities:

(a) Capacitive coupling from an unknown source to the grid of the second valve.

(b) An insufficiently smoothed h.t. supply.

(c) Leakage between heater and cathode of the first valve.

o

Short-circuit the cathode resistor of the first valve. The hum will disappear if the cause is leakage between heater and cathode. The short-circuit should be applied for a very short time only, because of the possibility of excessive anode current.

If the hum persists, tests similar to those in the previous example will easily trace the source of the trouble.

Example 3.

The response of an amplifier shows a sharp peak at high frequencies which is not to be expected from the design. The response is obtained when a crystal microphone is connected across the input, the microphone being subjected to sound waves of varying frequency.

For clarification a signal generator is connected between the earth side of the microphone and earth. The response of the amplifier to signals from the signal generator is found to be the same as that to signals from the microphone. This shows that the cause is in the amplifier, and not in the microphone.

Next the signal generator is connected across input grid and earth, thus by-passing the microphone. The response is found to be normal. That demonstrates that the effect is due to capacitive feedback to the grid of the first valve, which practically disappears when the grid is short-circuited to earth by the low impedance of the signal generator.

Chapter Nine

THE APPLICATION OF SEMICONDUCTORS
TO THE DETECTION OF RADIATION

By E. Schwarz

The detection of radiation by means of semiconductors started with the discovery of the light sensitivity of selenium by Smith[1] in 1873. Since then, many other substances have been found which are, in certain circumstances sensitive to electromagnetic and corpuscular radiation; all these substances belong to the class of solids classified as semiconductors. In order to explain why these solids are particularly useful as radiation detectors, an elementary account of the properties of semiconductors is given first. It is especially concerned with those properties which up to now have led to the development of radiation detectors of practical importance, and only brief reference is made to experimental results that are of interest to the theory of semiconductors.

General Properties of Semiconductors

The term 'semiconductor' denotes a solid which shows electronic conductivity that increases with increasing temperature. Contrary to the behaviour of metals, the conductivity of these solids is usually small in the pure state, and increases with the presence of impurities. The actual value of the conductivity is very sensitive to the kind and amount of impurities. Furthermore, the conductivity of most semiconductors depends on the mechanical treatment they have received and on the vapour pressure of the gases of their constituent atoms in the surrounding atmosphere.

Some elementary substances which are semiconductors are selenium, tellurium, germanium, silicon and tin in the grey modification; but these substances very likely owe their semiconducting properties to the presence of minute amounts of impurities. A great number of oxides, sulphides, selenides and tellurides, and some nitrides, halides and carbides belong to the semiconducting group of solids. Recently it has been found that certain inter-metallic compounds, e.g. $CdSb$, $InSb$, Mg_3Sb_2, $AlAs$, may exhibit semiconducting properties. [2] It should be emphasized that as a consequence of the very strong dependence of conductivity on the nature and amount of impurities the same substance may behave as an insulator, a semiconductor, or a metal.

A short description will be given of those properties which are important to the practical application of semiconductors as radiation detectors and more details will be included for the special semiconductors under discussion. Since most of these substances crystallize in the ionic type of structure, semiconductors are usually hard and brittle, which, as will be seen later, is a great difficulty for many applications. The thermal conductivity of semiconductors is usually several orders lower than that of metals, and the melting point varies within very wide limits. Similarly the optical properties show great variations, some semiconductors being colourless, brightly coloured or black, with high or low reflectivity.

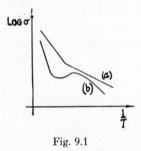

Fig. 9.1

For most semiconductors the temperature dependence of electrical conductivity can be expressed by the sum of two terms

$$\sigma = A_1\, e^{-E_1/kT} + A_2\, e^{-E_2/kT} \qquad (9.1)$$

where T is the absolute temperature, k is a constant, and A_1, A_2, E_1, E_2 are nearly constant for a given specimen. The coefficient A_1, is about 1–10 (ohm-cm)$^{-1}$ for many semiconductors, whereas the *activation energies* E_1 and E_2 vary considerably for different substances and for different specimens of the same substance.[3] The first term in eqn. (9.1), due to the conductivity of the pure substance (or *intrinsic semiconductor*), has a large activation energy E_1 and a large coefficient A_1 while the second term, due to impurities, has much smaller values of E and A. The graph of log σ plotted against $1/T$ has a kink at the junction of two straight lines [Fig. 9.1(a)]. Other possibilities occur where the curve representing the low-temperature conductivity is not a straight line and has a temperature range with the metallic direction of slope [Fig. 9.1(b)].

It follows from eqn. (9.1) that the temperature coefficient of resistance β of a semiconductor is negative

$$\beta = \frac{d(\sigma^{-1})}{dT} = -\sigma\frac{E}{k}\cdot\frac{1}{T^2} \tag{9.2}$$

and it is usually much greater than for a metal.

Much work has been done on the effect of vapour pressure upon the conductivity, starting with the classical work of Baedeker[4] on cuprous iodide, in which it was found that the conductivity of this substance increases with increasing iodine vapour pressure. Similar work has been done, investigating the effect of oxygen pressure with oxides and sulphur pressure with sulphide semiconductors. Figs 9.2 and 9.3

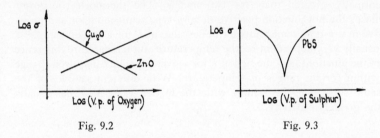

Fig. 9.2   Fig. 9.3

show the dependence of conductivity upon vapour pressure for cuprous oxide, zinc oxide and lead sulphide. As a result of work done with a great number of semiconductors it is possible to distinguish four groups of semiconductors.

(i) Substances in which the conductivity increases with increasing vapour pressure of the electronegative atom (e.g. CuI, Cu_2O, Cu_2S, NiO).

(ii) Substances in which the conductivity decreases with increasing vapour pressure of the electronegative atom (e.g. Ag_2S, ZnO, CdO).

(iii) Substances in which the conductivity is practically not affected by the vapour pressure of the electronegative atom (e.g. CuO, Fe_2O_3, Fe_3O_4).

(iv) Substances in which the conductivity increases with increasing vapour pressure of the electronegative atom and also with excess of the electropositive atom (e.g. PbS, SnS).

Substances of the first group are called *defect* or *p-type* semiconductors, and those of the second group are known as *excess* or *n-type* semiconductors. It should however, be mentioned that all investigations do not agree upon the values of conductivity for a certain substance at a given temperature and vapour pressure, and even upon the nature of conductivity in certain cases.

The Thermoelectric Effect in Semiconductors

A current flows in a closed circuit consisting of two different conductors if the two junctions are kept at different temperatures. The thermoelectric coefficient $P = dE/dT$, which is the e.m.f. developed for one degree difference in the temperature of the junctions, is additive. It is, therefore, possible to find the value of P for any pair of conductors if the value of each relative to a standard is known. The thermoelectric effect is observed in semiconductors but not in ionic conductors, and is normally greater than for two metals. The thermoelectric power makes the hot junction positive in an n-type semiconductor and negative in a p-type semiconductor. The value of P for a certain sample is usually very dependent on the temperature and temperature difference of the junctions, and the sign of P for a given substance may even change within certain ranges of temperature. With different samples of the same substance, the sample with the higher value of P has usually the greater resistivity.

The Contact between a Metal and Semiconductor

The contact between some metals and semiconductors has a resistance which varies considerably with the direction of the current. The first observation of unipolar conductivity was made by Munck in 1835, and Braun[5] in 1874 observed rectification with copper sulphide and so discovered the crystal detector. Since then an enormous amount of work on rectification has been done, and many more substances investigated. The best known example of non-linear conductivity occurs in the cuprous-oxide rectifier.[6] This consists of a copper plate on which a layer of cuprous oxide has been formed by heating and on whose surface another metal plate is pressed. This rectifier and the selenium rectifier have been the only ones of practical importance up to now with a large area of contact between the semiconductor and metal. There are many semiconductors where rectification takes place only when the contact area is very small, the best-known ones being germanium and silicon. The type of resistance-voltage curves obtained with these rectifiers is shown in Fig. 9.4, but it must be emphasized that the shape of the curve and even the direction of rectification depend on the special sample and on the nature of the contact. For n-type semiconductors the direction of easy flow of electrons is from the semi-conductor to the metal, for p-type semiconductors from the metal to semiconductor. Schottky, Störmer and Waibel[7] postulate a layer of

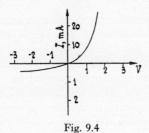

Fig. 9.4

high resistance between the semiconductor and the metal contact where the rectification occurs. This layer of high resistance is called the block-ing layer and it gives to the rectifier a considerable capacitance in an alternating field.

PHOTOELECTRIC EMISSION

External Photo-effect

The classical experiments of Hertz[8] and Hallwachs[9] showed that a metal irradiated with light of suitable wavelength emits electrons into the surrounding space. The fundamental theory of this external photo-effect was given by Einstein[10], who postulated that the energy V of electrons after leaving the surface is

$$V = \frac{h\nu}{e} - \phi = \frac{hc}{e\lambda} - \phi = \frac{12000}{\lambda} - \phi \qquad (9.3)$$

where e is the electronic charge, c the velocity of light, ν the frequency, and where the electron energy and the *work function* ϕ are expressed in volts and the wavelength λ in angstroms. It follows from eqn. (9.3) that only light with wavelength $\lambda < \lambda_0$ will release electrons, where

$$\lambda_0 = \frac{12000}{\phi} \qquad (9.4)$$

λ_0 is called the *threshold wavelength* see also chapter eleven, p. 245.

In order to achieve a high efficiency of photoelectric emission some essential conditions must be fulfilled.

(i) The absorption of light must be high, and therefore highly reflecting metals and transparent insulators are excluded.

(ii) The work function should be low.

(iii) The electrical conductivity should have an intermediate value.

The great electrical conductivity of metals is closely connected with their high reflectivity and therefore unfavourable according to (i). On the other hand the very high specific resistance of insulators avoids the replacement of electrons released by light. The group of solids which best fulfil the above conditions are semiconductors and in practice the most sensitive photocathodes consist of special semiconductors, as will be discussed later.

Internal Photo-effect

Since the discovery of the resistance change of selenium under illumination, many more substances have been found with a similar behaviour. They include some natural minerals like Bi_2S_3, MoS_2, Ag_3SbS_3, PbS,[11] and many artificially produced semiconductors can under certain circumstances be made photoconductive, e.g. Te_2S, Cu_2O, PbTe, CdS, CdSe, GeSi. The conditions under which these substances become photoconductors are not yet fully understood, but the presence of oxygen in one form or another seems to be essential (although this has been questioned by some authorities). As will be described in detail later, the quantum yield of most photoconductors is greater than unity and can in certain circumstances be very high indeed.

Photovoltaic Effect

The term *photovoltaic effect* is used to include phenomena associated with the production of an electromotive force in a system consisting of two electrodes, separated by a semiconductor or an electrolyte, when the electrodes are asymmetrically illuminated. The photovoltaic effect was first observed by Becquerel[12] with metal electrodes immersed in dilute acid; later electrodes consisting of oxides, sulphides or halides of certain metals in different electrolytes were investigated. The only important systems from a practical point of view are those using a semiconductor between metal electrodes. Schottky[13] has shown that the photovoltaic effect in the semiconductor cuprous oxide is closely connected with the presence of a barrier layer of high resistance and with the rectifying properties of the illuminated contact. This is also true for selenium as a semiconductor, which shows the close connection between the photovoltaic effect and rectification of p-type semiconductors.

Outline of the Theory of Semiconductors

Within the limits of this book only a short account of the theory of the properties of semiconductors can be given. A comprehensive treatment will be found in the many books on the subject.[14]

The quantum theory of the atom has shown that the electrons associated with the nucleus can exist only in a limited number of energy states or levels. In an ordered assembly of atoms like a crystal, however, these discrete energy levels are spread out into energy bands of permitted energy states, separated by bands in which the electrons cannot remain in equilibrium—the forbidden bands. When an external electric field is applied to a solid, containing free electrons, the only electrons which can be accelerated are those able to move to a higher energy level; as the Pauli exclusion principle prevents more than two electrons from occupying the same energy level, this movement is restricted to electrons in an energy band which is not already completely occupied. On this basis it is possible to understand the vast difference in electrical conductivity of solids of different types. A metal has its uppermost band only partly filled (Fig. 9.5). An applied electric field therefore easily raises the electrons from the highest occupied levels

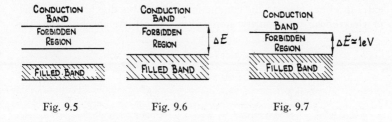

Fig. 9.5   Fig. 9.6   Fig. 9.7

into the adjacent empty levels, and conduction results. On the other hand, an insulator with a band structure consisting of a number of filled bands and the higher permitted band completely empty and separated by a wide forbidden region (Fig. 9.6) could become a conductor only if the electrons were forced into the empty band by the applied field. Such a process is, however, very improbable, for the width of the forbidden region is of the order of several electron-volts.

According to Wilson[15] intrinsic semiconductors have a band structure similar to that of insulators, but the width of the forbidden region is relatively small, of the order of 1 eV (Fig. 9.7). The probability of an electron being raised to the conduction band from the filled band is then appreciable. The electron leaves behind in the full levels a locality in which an electron is missing and which therefore has a positive charge with respect to its surroundings. Such a locality is called a *positive hole*. An electron from a neighbouring ion can fall into the positive hole and neutralize it, leaving behind another hole, so that in effect the original hole can be considered to have moved. It can be shown that such a positive hole behaves very similarly to a normal electron, the only essential difference being the positive charge. Thus electron and positive hole contribute to the conduction of an intrinsic semiconductor. However, it is doubtful whether examples of intrinsic semiconduction exist at normal temperatures.

As already mentioned, most semiconductors owe their conductivity at the ordinary temperatures to the presence of impurities. The concentration of impurities may vary within a range of 10^{15}–10^{19} centres of impurity per cubic centimetre. The distribution may be uniform throughout the volume of the semiconductor, or impurities can be concentrated on the external and internal surfaces of it. Wilson's theory assumes that the energy required to bring an electron from an impurity centre into the conduction band is considerably less than that required to bring it from the full band of the pure substance into the conduction band. Most properties of semiconductors can be accounted for if it is assumed that these new levels—the impurity levels—lie within the forbidden band of the crystal. In one case of practical importance the extra level lies close to the conduction band and is due to the presence of electropositive impurity atoms [Fig. 9.8(a)]. At absolute zero the

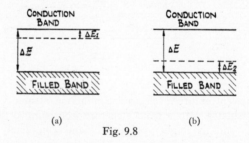

(a)   (b)

Fig. 9.8

level is filled, but at finite temperatures electrons from this level can easily be raised into the conduction band. This level is therefore called a *donator* level and the semiconductor is called an excess, normal or n-type semiconductor, since the current is carried by electrons. In the second important case an extra level lies just above the full band of the crystal, is normally empty at absolute zero temperature and is due to the presence of electronegative atoms [Fig. 9.8(b)]. At finite temperatures this level may accept electrons from the full band, thus giving rise to the formation of positive holes which take part in the conduction. The extra level is called an *acceptor* level and the semi-conductor is a definite or *p*-type semiconductor, since the current is carried by positive holes. Excess and deficit centres can be present simultaneously and the character of the semiconductor is then deter-mined by the predominating type. The type of conduction may be distinguished by the sign of the Hall effect, and, as already mentioned, by that of the thermoelectric power. In some substances complications[16] arise, however, and the interpretation of these measurements is then ambiguous.

With the donation as in Fig. 9.8(a) a calculation[15] of the number *n* of ionized impurity centres in equilibrium gives, for weak ionization,

$$n = \sqrt{(N\nu)}\epsilon - (\Delta E/2kT) \tag{9.5}$$

In this equation ϵ is the logarithmic constant and N is the number of impurity centres per cubic centimetre and

$$\nu = 2\left(\frac{2\pi mkT}{h^2}\right)^{3/2} \tag{9.6}$$

where $h =$ Planck's constant, $m =$ free electron mass and $T =$ absolute temperature.

As the conductivity $\sigma = ebn$, where e is the electronic charge and b is the mobility of the carrier, the conductivity–temperature relation is given by an equation of the form (9.1).

Within the last few years it has been realized that the surface of a semiconductor may play an important role in the conduction process. As the normal periodicity of the crystal at the surface is destroyed, new permitted energy levels may appear within the forbidden band of the crystals. Levels of this type are called *surface states* or *Tamm levels*.[17] They are important for rectification,[18] and may be essential for the photoconductivity of semiconducting layers. It has been suggested[19] that in photoconductors the surface states are closely connected with the activity of a dispersed system of semiconductor particles, which gives rise to the adsorption of oxygen on internal and external surfaces of the particles. These adsorbed layers provide boundary potential hills between the *n*-type particles of the semiconductor, and may be the seat of *p*-type conductivity along the surface of the particles.

The thermoelectric coefficient P is related to the Peltier coefficient π by the equation

$$P = \frac{\pi}{T} \tag{9.7}$$

where T is the absolute temperature and in n-type semiconductors, with small ionization of the impurity centres of concentration N, we have

$$\pi = \frac{E}{2\epsilon} - \frac{kT}{\epsilon} \log \frac{h^{3/2}N^{1/2}}{(2\pi mkT)^{3/4}} \tag{9.8}$$

where ϵ is the logarithmic constant.

The value of P should therefore be given by

$$P = \frac{E}{2\epsilon T} - \frac{k}{\epsilon} \log \frac{h^{3/2}N^{1/2}}{(2\pi mkT)^{3/4}} \tag{9.9}$$

which is approximately $E/2\epsilon T$ and therefore of the order of several hundreds of microvolts per degree.

In practice it has been found that the thermoelectric behaviour of many semiconductors is much more complicated and does not obey the $1/T$ law. According to Moench[20] the measured value of P for Cu_2O is the sum of a volume and a surface effect, and the contribution of the two parts to the total e.m.f. may vary from sample to sample. It is important to note that the addition of a small amount of certain impurities to semiconductors with high values of P may greatly increase the electrical conductivity, while the thermoelectric power and the heat conductivity are altered only slightly.

RADIATION DETECTORS USING SEMICONDUCTORS

The general conditions which a radiation detector must fulfil to be of practical value will now be given. From the previous remarks in this chapter, the reader will appreciate that semiconductors are most suitable for these devices. It should become clear why only relatively few out of the great number of known semiconductors have up to now found practical application.

The most important properties required from a radiation detector are:

(a) High sensitivity, i.e. the minimum energy detectable over the background noise should be as small as possible.

(b) High speed, i.e. the time between application of the signal and reaching of the new equilibrium should be shorter than the time lag of the indicating instrument.

(c) Convenience of use. No special apparatus and only few accessories should be needed. A self-generating device is the simplest possible.

(d) Linearity of response, for otherwise special calibration will be required.

(e) It should cover a very wide range of wavelengths, and the response should be independent of wavelength.

(f) It should be stable under the conditions of use, i.e. after a possible preliminary ageing, the properties should be constant.

The requirements mentioned above are very often mutually exclusive, so that in practice the kind of detector must be chosen which fulfils best the problem in hand, at the sacrifice of certain valuable properties.

It is possible to divide existing radiation detectors into three groups:

A. Thermal or non-selective detectors
B. Electronic or selective detectors
C. A combination of A and B

The working principle of detectors of group A consists in the transformation of the radiant energy into heat and retransformation of the heat into electrical energy. Consequently these receivers are non-selective and linear, but relatively slow and of medium sensitivity. Detectors of group B depend for their response on the energy increase and liberation of electrons by the absorbed radiation. The sensitivity of these receivers is usually high but varies enormously with the wavelength, and there may be deviations from linearity. A very high speed is possible, but the stability may be limited.

Group C at present consists of one type of detector, which combines certain properties of group A and B. Receivers of group A are represented by the bolometer and the thermopile, and existing devices of this kind using semiconductors will be described.

NON-SELECTIVE DETECTORS

Bolometer

The high negative temperature coefficient of resistance of a semiconductor, as expressed by eqn. (9.2), has found practical applications in radiation measuring devices. These are frequently referred to as *thermistors* and consist of small beads of a semiconducting material with small heat capacity. For usefulness the following conditions must be fulfilled:

(i) Pure electronic conductivity at the temperature of use.

(ii) The value of β should be high, giving high sensitivity.

(iii) They should be rugged even when in the form of a thin flake, and as previously mentioned this may constitute a great difficulty.

(iv) The contact must be reliable, avoiding barrier layers.

(v) They should be reproducible, a great difficulty which has been overcome by using a semiconductor that is not highly sensitive to impurities.

Originally UO_2[21] was used but later it has been found that more stable and reproducible materials could be achieved by mixing two or more different oxides,[22] e.g. $MnO+NiO$, $MgO+TiO_2$, or $TiO_2+Cr_2O_3$.

The oxide powders are mixed, and, with a suitable binder, ground to a creamy consistency. After forming and drying, the flakes are heated in a reducing atmosphere until the correct resistance is obtained. The values of β and R are strongly temperature-dependent, as can be seen from Table 9.1, which applies to a sample of $MnO+NiO$.

TABLE 9.1

T	R	β
°C	ohms	
0	145000	−5·2
25	46000	−4·4
50	16400	−3·8
100	3200	−3·0
200	305	−2·0

To reduce the noise, one must look carefully at the raw material, the grain size, the degree of sintering and reduction, and the contacts with the metal electrodes. The minimum detectable power, limited by semiconductor noise, is about 10^{-9} watt.

Thermopile

The oldest non-selective method of measuring radiation is based on the thermoelectric effect, and as the thermopile is a self-generating device it is also the most convenient method. The first method of construction used thin wires or strips of metal.[23] Advances were made by the use of bismuth, antimony and certain alloys of these elements,[24] and the theory has been developed by several workers.[25] To design a thermopile giving optimum response in the shortest possible time, several conditions must be fulfilled. The current I generated by a vacuum thermopile in a circuit consisting of the thermopile with resistance R_T and galvanometer of resistance R_G is given by

$$I = \frac{P}{R_G+R_T} \cdot \frac{\epsilon F}{L(F)+L(W)} \qquad (9.10)$$

where P is the thermoelectric coefficient, ϵ the radiation absorbed in unit time by the receiver in watts/cm^2, F the area of the receiver, $L(F)$ the losses due to re-radiation from the receiver and $L(W)$ the conduction losses through the wires in unit time. It follows from eqn. (9.10) that I will be large if the radiation is concentrated onto a small receiver, if R_T and the losses $L(W)$ and $L(F)$ are as small as possible and if P is as large as possible. The resistance R_T is proportional to $(1/\sigma).(l/q)$ and $L(W)$ is proportional to $\kappa(q/l)$, where l is the length and q the cross-section of the wires, and σ and κ are electrical and heat conductivities respectively. In order to minimize R_T and $L(W)$ simultaneously, a compromise must be made over the wire dimensions, and the ratio of κ/σ should be small, i.e. the Wiedemann-Franz coefficient

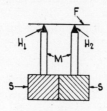

Fig. 9.9

$Z = \kappa/\sigma T$ should be small. The value of Z for metals is about 2·5 $\times 10^{-8}$ watt-ohm/(deg. C)^2, but unfortunately there are unfavourable deviations from this value for most metals and semiconductors with high thermoelectric power. The use of semiconductors for the combination of thermopiles is suggested by the high value of P, as already mentioned, but in order to construct an efficient device of high voltage sensitivity, high speed and rigidity, the conditions discussed above must be fulfilled simultaneously and the mechanical properties must be satisfactory. After an extensive search, the writer has found substances [26] which have led to a new construction of radiation thermopiles; these are called *pin-type thermopiles* or *Schwarz-Hilger Thermopiles*. Fig. 9.9 shows the principle of the construction. The metal rods M are fixed in a support S by resilient pressure, and fused to the top of the rods are the semiconducting substances H_1 and H_2. The blackened foil F is spot-welded to the two semiconductors constituting the receiver. H_1 is an excess semiconductor, consisting essentially of a mixture of silver sulphide and silver selenide with some minor impurities and H_2 is a defect semiconductor, consisting of a mixture of silver, copper, tellurium and selenium, with a small addition of suitable impurities. The value of P for H_1 can be varied between 120 and 1000 μV/(deg. C) and for H_2 between 100 and 480 μV/(deg. C) at will, giving a total thermoelectric power between 220 and 1480 μV/(deg. C.). This possible variation of P is essential, if the optimum conditions for different types are to be achieved. The reproducibility is very good, as can be judged from the fact that a compensation within ± 0.5 per cent can be achieved. In order to minimize the heat conduction losses $L(W)$ through the substances, the semiconductors H_1 and H_2 are ground in the form of cones with sharp points for a vacuum type and to sharp wedges for an air type. As the Wiedemann-Franz coefficient is relatively low $[\sim 10^{-7} \text{ watt-ohm}/(\text{deg. C})^2]$, a sufficient length for H_1 and H_2 is only 0.2–0.5 mm, which thus reduces R_T. Owing to the possible variation in the composition of the semiconducting materials, the resistance per junction can be varied between very wide limits, say from 1 ohm to 10,000 ohms. This permits a convenient adaptation to the measuring circuit.

Some characteristic data of performance for different types and sizes are given in Table 9.2.

TABLE 9.2

Type	Area mm	Resistance ohms	Sensitivity $\mu V/\mu W$	Response time sec
Air	2×0.2 10×1	35 150	4 2.4	0.005 0.03
Vacuum	2×0.2 4×0.2 9×0.5	200 35 100	90 30 28	0.01 0.01 0.3

The minimum detectable power is fixed by the Johnson noise, and for a vacuum type with small-area receiver it is of the order of 10^{-10}–3×10^{-11} watt for a bandwidth of 1 c/s and a chopping frequency of 13 c/s.

The construction of a semiconductor thermopile based on the same principle was announced independently and later [27] without details of the kinds of semiconductor used.

SELECTIVE DETECTORS

Photo-emissive Cells

According to the Einstein relation (9.3), for each absorbed quantum greater than $h\nu_0$ one electron should be liberated from the surface of the cathode. If P_R is the incident light power and V is the electron energy in volts, the quantum efficiency $\eta = VI/P_R$ should therefore be unity. The theoretical value for the photocurrent I produced by radiation with wavelength $\lambda < \lambda_0$ and a power P_R would therefore be

$$I = \frac{P_R \lambda}{12000}$$

and a plot of I/P_R against λ gives a straight line [Fig. 9.10, curve (a)]. The values of I/P_R observed in practice are much smaller and do not

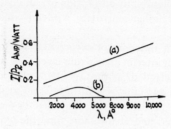

Fig. 9.10

vary linearly with λ [Fig. 9.10, curve (b)]. This represents a small value for η, and is a consequence of the relative opacity of the cathode and of the very small penetration of the electrons. Deviations from the linearity and the presence of a peak in the sensitivity curve are referred to as the *selective photo-effect*, which will be discussed later.

The first photocathodes, consisting of thin films of alkali metals adsorbed on a metal case such as platinum,[28] had an efficiency η of only 0·001–0·01 per cent for visible light, owing to the high reflectivity of the metal. Thin films of alkali metals on tungsten surfaces have later been studied extensively by several workers.[29] They have found that λ_0 reaches a maximum when the coverage is nearly complete, and begins to decrease again when more than a monatomic layer of the alkali metal is formed, approaching eventually the value for the alkali metal in bulk. Further experiments with films of different thickness[30] have led to the conclusions that the normal photo-effect arises from the excitation of the electrons of the metal base, whose escape may be facilitated by the adsorbed film; and that the selective photo-effect, excited by light polarized parallel to the plane of incidence, results from photo-excitation of the adsorbed atoms.

Elster and Geitel[31] replaced the highly-reflecting alkali-metal cathodes by cathodes of alkali halides of lower reflectivity, and this has led to higher quantum yields and to higher values of λ_0. Later researches established that with such photocathodes an adsorbed layer of alkali-metal atoms on the surface of the halide is responsible for the higher sensitivity and for a pronounced selective photo-effect.

P

The adsorption of electronegative atoms, such as oxygen, on the surface of metal electrodes generally gives rise to the formation of a double layer whose polarity is such as to impede electron emission and to increase the work function. In certain circumstances the adsorbed oxygen may however lead to higher sensitivity and to an increase in λ_0. Thus Pohl and Pringsheim[32] found that the introduction of dry oxygen into an evacuated potassium phototube caused the formation of a layer of potassium oxide coloured by adsorption of colloidal potassium metal. This cathode showed higher sensitivity, a selective maximum at 4050 Å and an increase in λ_0.

Observations on the influence of oxygen have led to the development of photocathodes with intermediate oxide layers, e.g. the silver-oxygen-caesium cathode, referred to as the Ag–O–Cs photocathode. In order to reach high sensitivity in the near infra-red and visible regions, many highly active places in the oxide layer must be created which will adsorb caesium atoms; and at the same time the oxide layer must be sufficiently conductive to allow the replacement of the liberated electrons from the silver base. Both conditions have been fulfilled by the technique introduced by Koller.[33] The silver layer is first oxidized by an electric discharge in oxygen; caesium is then admitted and the tube baked at 150–250°C. According to the reaction $2Cs+Ag_2O = 2Ag+Cs_2O$, the layer of caesium oxide will contain silver impurities, which make it an excess semiconductor with caesium atoms adsorbed on active spots of the surface; this reduces the work function. A further increase of sensitivity has been attained by evaporating metal atoms, in particular silver and gold, on the prepared cathode and by subjecting the cathode to a second thermal treatment.[34] The increase in emission is accompanied by a shift of λ_0 into the visible spectrum and by reduced photo-electric fatigue.

The optical and electrical conditions for high sensitivity of a cathode are still better fulfilled by a new photosensitive surface consisting of an inter-metallic compound of an alkali metal with bismuth, antimony and arsenic.[35] In the making of an antimony-caesium cathode, an antimony layer is prepared first by evaporation. The tube is then raised to a temperature of 150°C, and the caesium admitted gradually until the photosensitivity reaches a maximum. Subsequent baking in oxygen at low pressure may increase the sensitivity and produce a shift of the maximum towards the red. The inter-metallic compound caesium antimonide, formed during the preparation, may react with oxygen as follows:

$$4SbCs_3+3O_2 = 6Cs_2O+4Sb$$

This reaction forms free antimony, thus increasing the conductivity of the semiconducting base. Furthermore, the polarization of caesium atoms adsorbed on the caesium oxide will be stronger than when adsorbed on the antimony as is so before oxidation, and therefore a larger threshold wavelength is to be expected.

The characteristics of vacuum phototubes with the best known cathodes are summarized in Table 9.3 and in Fig. 9.11. The spectral response of the Ag–O–Cs cell is shown in Fig. 9.11(a), and that of

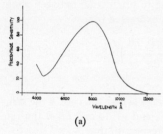

(a)

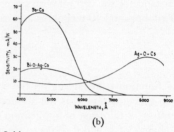

(b)

Fig. 9.11

the Sb–Cs and the Bi–O–Ag–Cs cells in Fig. 9.11(b). The Ag–O–Cs response is also included in Fig. 9.11(b). Common to all types is a very fast response of a fraction of a microsecond and, with proper geometrical design of the tube, the linear relation between photocurrent and light intensity. Thick-layer phototubes may exhibit certain fatigue effects, which depend on the wavelength of the illumination and on the light intensity.

TABLE 9.3

Cathode	Sensitivity
	μA/Lumen
Ag–O–CS	20
Ag–O–Rb	6·5
Sb–Cs	50
Bi–Cs	30

Photoconductive Cells

The high quantum yield of photoconductive cells is one of the properties which offer a great advantage over photo-emissive cells. Furthermore, the range of sensitivity for some kinds extends well into the infra-red and ultra-violet regions, respectively. The size of sensitive area can be varied and reduced to a fraction of a square millimetre in order to measure the intensity of spectral lines. Some cells are stable in air, eliminating the light absorption in the window material, and the operation of the cell is extremely simple. Against these advantages must be set the lower speed compared with the phototube, certain very marked slow effects, some instability and deviations from a linear relation between photocurrent and light intensity.

The first photoconductive cell, made of selenium, showed the unfavourable effects to a great extent. Although it is obsolete now, its properties will be described to indicate the difficulties.[36] The dark resistance of the cell may vary according to production between about 50 kilohms and 10 megohms and can be expressed by

$$R_D = f\left(V, \theta, t, \frac{\partial V}{\partial t}, \frac{\partial \theta}{\partial t}\right) \tag{9.11}$$

the function f depending on the sample.

In this equation V is the applied voltage across the cell; θ the temperature, t the time of application of V; and $\partial V/\partial t$ and $\partial \theta/\partial t$ the rate of change of V and θ respectively with respect to time.

For most selenium cells, R_D decreases with increasing V, an effect which is not caused by heating of the layer and shows marked hysteresis. Sometimes a range of voltages exists within which R_D increases with increasing V, and this voltage effect, moreover, is dependent on the temperature. For a constant applied voltage the value of R_D usually decreases with time. The temperature coefficient β of the usual variety of metallic selenium has a large negative value, causing a decrease of

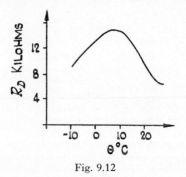

Fig. 9.12

cell resistance with rising temperature, but, with some cells a positive value of β within certain temperature ranges has been observed, giving rise to a curve as illustrated in Fig. (9.12).[37] The influence of the rate of change of temperature and applied voltage is rather complicated and being of less practical importance will not be discussed here.

The behaviour of the selenium cell is still more complicated when the cell is exposed to radiation and may be expressed by

$$R = F(E, \lambda, t, \theta, V, h) \qquad (9.12)$$

the function F again depending on the sample.

The resistance R under illumination is thus determined not only by the illumination E and wavelength λ of the light to be measured, but also by the time t of exposure, the temperature θ, the applied voltage V and the past history of the cell, i.e. whether kept in the dark or exposed to radiation previous to the radiation to be measured, which is expressed by the variable h.

The sensitivity is defined as

$$S = \frac{R_D - R}{R} = \frac{I - I_D}{I_D}$$

It is usually higher for cells with higher dark resistance R_D. As expected, the relation between the photocurrent I and illumination E is non-linear, as shown in Fig. 9.13 for white light; being dependent on the previous illumination it shows hysteresis effects.

The selenium cell exhibits very pronounced time-delay effects, greatly dependent on the processing techniques and cell construction. Fig. 9.14 shows the time-lag for two different types of cells. The recovery of the dark resistance after exposure to illumination is usually the more protracted and may be of the order of minutes or even hours. Furthermore, these slow effects are much more pronounced for weak light than

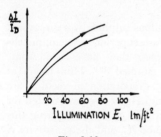

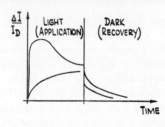

Fig. 9.13   Fig. 9.14

for strong light and may also depend on the previous dark period, the voltage V, the temperature θ and the colour of the light. The inertia effects and the sensitivity of the cell for weak light are decreased after previous exposure to strong light,[38] and are also dependent on the applied voltage.

The spectral sensitivity of the selenium cell was first measured by Pfund, [39] who found a very decided maximum at 7000 Å for light rays of equal energy (Fig. 9.15). The optical absorption curve for a selenium layer is also plotted in Fig. 9.15, and it offers no explanation for the photo-electrical maximum. Later investigations [40] have shown that the

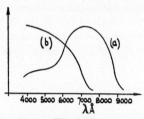

Fig. 9.15

Properties of a selenium photoconductive cell.
(a) Spectral sensitvity.
(b) Optical absorption.
Ordinate, relative spectral sensitivity or optical absorption

character of the spectro-photoelectrical sensitivity curve may change very much indeed, depending on the process of manufacture, the illumination, the previous illumination, the exposure time, the applied voltage and the temperature, i.e. on the conditions of the experiment.

The same general phenomena as for the selenium cell have been observed in many other photoconductive substances, but fortunately some semiconductors and methods of preparing photoconducting layers of them have been discovered in which the unfavourable properties are much less pronounced or even completely absent.

(a) The Thallous-Sulphide Cell.

The photoconductivity of oxidized thallous sulphide was discovered by Case, [41] and as cells made from it are superior to selenium cells both in sensitivity and dynamic response they have found some applications and have been carefully studied. [42] Thin layers of thallous sulphide deposited on glass by evaporation in vacuum are exposed to oxygen at a pressure of 1 mm Hg or less, and heated for several minutes to temperatures between 250° to 350°C. During this treatment an increase in the dark resistance R_D and the sensitivity S takes place, and the semiconductor changes from n-type to p-type, as indicated by a change in the sign of the thermoelectric coefficient P (Fig. 9.16). [42] As with the selenium cell, the variation of photocurrent with light intensity is non-linear and there are wide and uncontrollable variations in the response characteristics. With increasing temperature the photo-response decreases and the relative dynamic response increases, owing to the decreasing time-constant (Fig. 9.17).

The sensitivity extends into the near infra-red region to a wavelength of approximately 1·4 μ, and the maximum value is for a wavelength close to 9000 Å (Fig. 9.18). Early thallous sulphide cells showed a marked voltage effect and deterioration after illumination with strong light, but these properties have now been much improved.

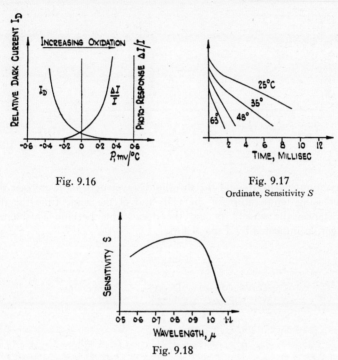

Fig. 9.16

Fig. 9.17
Ordinate, Sensitivity S

Fig. 9.18

(b) Infra-red-Sensitive Cells

The light sensitivity of natural crystals of galena was observed by Bose [43] as early as 1901, but systematic investigations started only during the Second World War; these were made in Germany by Gudden and his school. [44] A layer of sensitive lead sulphide may be obtained either by a chemical reaction between lead acetate, thiourea and sodium hydroxide in dilute solution, or by evaporation of purified lead sulphide in an atmosphere of oxygen or air at a pressure of about 0·2 mm Hg. The layer is then baked at about 400°C for about 10 minutes, and, after cooling down, the cell is evacuated and sealed off. Cells prepared by the wet process are usually stable in air, but the evaporated layers deteriorate quickly after exposure to the atmosphere. The spectral sensitivity curve varies according to the method of preparation (Fig. 9.19). At room temperature the sensitivity usually has a maximum value near a wavelength of 2·5 μ, with another maximum at a wavelength of 1·2–1·5 μ, and the threshold wavelength near 3·0 μ but there are great variations according to the method of preparation. The wavelength for

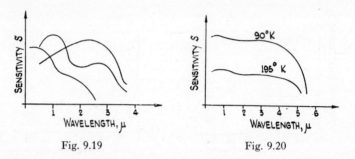

Fig. 9.19   Fig. 9.20

maximum sensitivity and the threshold wavelength both increase with decreasing temperature of the cell, and at the same time the dark resistance, the sensitivity and the decay time become considerably larger, as indicated by Table 9.4.

TABLE 9.4

Threshold wavelength λ_0	Decay time	Temperature
μ	μ sec	°C
2·92	14	20
3·33	210	−80
3·84	490	−180

The dark resistance at room temperature is of the order of 0·1–10 megohms, and the response may be linear over a great range of illumination. Very slow effects have been observed after exposure of the cell to visible and ultra-violet light.[45] There are great variations of the frequency response to interrupted light, depending on the sample, the illumination and the wavelength. The minimum detectable energy is of the order of 10^{-8} to 10^{-10} watt, and the quantum yield about 10.

(c) The Lead-Selenide and the Lead-Telluride Cells

Photosensitivity extends even further into the infra-red region for photoconducting cells prepared from lead selenide and lead telluride by methods similar to that described for lead sulphide. The spectral sensitivity of the lead-selenide cell for different temperatures is illustrated in Fig. 9.20, but there are also wide variations of the spectral response according to the preparation of the cell and the method of measurement. The minimum detectable energy is of the order of 10^{-8} to 10^{-9} watt and the quantum yield about 10. The optical and photoelectric properties have been investigated by various workers[46] and contrary to expectation the sensitivity of the lead selenide cell seems to extend even further into the infra-red region than that of the lead telluride cell.

(d) The Silicon Cell

In the course of research on crystal rectifiers interesting photoeffects have been observed in both silicon and germanium.[47] Photoconductivity has also been observed in high-purity silicon, when deposited on a ceramic or quartz surface as a hard smooth film through reduction of silicon tetrachloride by hydrogen at a temperature of 1100°C or higher.[48] The spectral response has a maximum near 9000 Å, and the cut-off wavelength is near 1·5 μ (Fig. 9.21). The sensitivity is

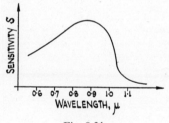

Fig. 9.21

intermediate between those of the thallous-sulphide and the selenium cell, but its speed of response is faster than that of either. The relation between photocurrent and illumination is nearly linear for low intensities, and a great advantage is the remarkable stability of the cell in air even when heated to high temperatures.

(e) The Germanium Cell

Photo-effects in germanium rectifiers have been observed by American investigators.[49] They occur most frequently in the boundary region separating p-type and n-type germanium and are associated with two special types of current/voltage characteristics. The first type (Fig. 9.22), which has been called a *photodiode*, shows a saturation effect in the forward direction, and the effect of white light on this characteristic is illustrated in Fig. 9.23.

The photocurrent is nearly proportional to the illumination over a wide range, and the spectral distribution shows a maximum at a wavelength of about $1 \cdot 3$–$1 \cdot 6 \, \mu$, with a threshold wavelength of about $1 \cdot 9 \, \mu$.

The second type (Fig. 9.24), which has been called *photopeak*, exhibits a voltage peak followed by a negative-resistance region;

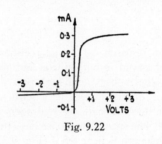

Fig. 9.22

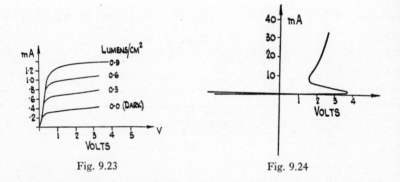

Fig. 9.23   Fig. 9.24

the resistance becomes positive again for higher currents. The peak voltage decreases with decreasing illumination, and for low values of illumination the peak voltage is proportional to the illumination. This type has a possible application as a triggering device, for under illumination the current jumps to a value limited by the spreading and circuit resistances and may be large enough to actuate a relay.

For both types a photo-response for light flashes as short as 10 microsec may be obtained.

To the knowledge of the writer no photoconductive cells consisting of thin layers of germanium have yet been produced.

(f) *Photoconductivity of Cadmium Sulphide*

Ribbon-shaped single crystals of cadmium sulphide have been prepared[50] by heating cadmium metal, placed in a quartz tube in a stream of hydrogen, which brings the metal into contact with a stream of hydrogen sulphide. Small crystals of cadmium sulphide are thus formed

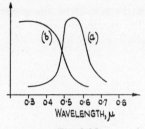

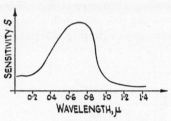

Fig. 9.25

Fig. 9.26

Properties of Cadium Sulphide.
(a) Spectral sensitivity.
(b) Optical absorption.
Ordinate, sensitivity *S*.

and deposited on the walls of the reaction tube. The optical absorption and spectral sensitivity of these crystals are shown in Fig. 9.25, indicating that the peak of response occurs where the absorption falls off rapidly. These crystals are also sensitive to ultra-violet rays, X-rays, α- and β-rays, but they may be very slow in response,[51] especially for weak light, and they exhibit strong fatigue for radiation in certain wavelength-regions. The measured photocurrents are of the same order as for thallous sulphide cells, but the dark resistance is very much higher, being about 10^8–10^{10} ohms. They have been the subject of many investigations[52] with the aim of clarifying the fundamental mechanism. The photoconductance and luminescence associated with it are usually explained by a model based on the band structure of semiconductors, as previously discussed, with the addition of some extra energy levels, called *trapping levels*, in order to explain the slow processes observed.[53]

(g) *Photoconductive Cells of Cadmium Selenide*

Polycrystalline layers of cadmium selenide have been prepared by new methods based on the assumption that adsorption of oxygen during the evaporation of a semiconductor is one essential condition for photoconductivity.[54] They are extremely sensitive to visible light, with a maximum at about 7000 Å and a long wavelength threshold of about $1 \cdot 4$ μ (Fig. 9.26). These cells are also sensitive to ultra-violet rays and X-rays, with high quantum yields. The sensitivity to visible radiation is about 10–50 amp/lumen, and the minimum detectable energy at 7000 Å about 10^{-12} watt, for a chopping frequency of 800 c/s and a bandwidth of 1 c/s. Currents of the order of 30 mA can be passed through the cell under strong illumination without undue fatigue. The dark resistance for a small-area cell may be as high as 10^{11} ohms, and the quantum yield for visible light of the order of 10^4–10^5.[55] The relation between photocurrent and illumination can be altered by the manufacturing process, which allows cells with the maximum sensitivity for either weak light [Fig. 9.27(a)] or strong light [Fig. 9.27(b)].

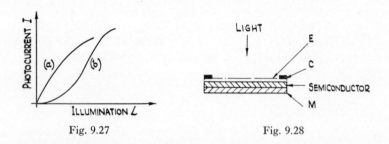

Fig. 9.27   Fig. 9.28

Photovoltaic Cells

The development of a spontaneous e.m.f. in an asymmetrically illuminated system consisting of a semiconductor and metal electrodes was first observed by Adams and Day in 1887; and the first photovoltaic cell, incorporating nearly all the features of the modern cell, was constructed by Fritt in 1884.[56] This cell was then forgotten for many years, and the first modern photovoltaic cell, rediscovered in connection with the rectifying properties of cuprous oxide, was due to Grondahl.[6] In 1930, Lange[57] constructed selenium photo-elements similar to the Fritt cell with the additional improvement of sputtering a semi-transparent front electrode on to the selenium. Fig. 9.28 shows the construction. The semiconductor is supported by a metal base M, the transparent top electrode E applied by sputtering or evaporation and a metal contact ring C sprayed on. With cuprous oxide cells the *barrier layer*[13, 16] may be located between the mother copper and the oxide (*back-wall cells*), or between the oxide and the front electrode (*front-wall cells*), but all selenium barrier-layer cells are invariably front-wall cells. Since the selenium cells are more sensitive and more stable than cuprous oxide ones, practically all photo-elements on the market at the present time are selenium cells. Electrically a barrier-layer cell can be represented (Fig. 9.29) as a current generator *E*, shunted by a capacitance C—due to the barrier layer—and the resistance R_i depending on the illumination and the load resistance R. In series with E is the small external resistance R_{sl} due to the translucent front electrode, and the semiconductor resistance. In accordance with the equivalent circuit, the open-circuit variation of p.d. with illumination is highly non-linear (Fig. 9.30). The short-circuit current is a

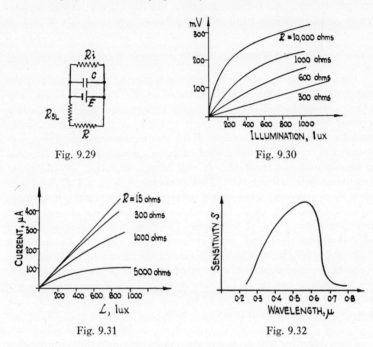

Fig. 9.29   Fig. 9.30

Fig. 9.31   Fig. 9.32

practically linear function of the illumination but for finite values of R the variation of current becomes increasingly non-linear as the internal resistance R_i decreases through stronger illumination (Fig. 9.31). Selenium photocells have a very small temperature coefficient of photocurrent for low external resistances, and the independence of the spectral sensitivity and the temperature is very favourable.

The spectral sensitivity of selenium photo-elements referred to a constant-energy spectrum is illustrated in Fig. 9.32. There are slight variations for different cells, but the maximum lies at a wavelength somewhere between $0.5\,\mu$ and $0.6\,\mu$, and with the addition of suitable filters most cells match the response of the average human eye very well.

Although the response of barrier-layer cells is practically instantaneous, the current decreases rapidly for interrupted light signals, owing to the high capacitance C of the barrier layer. Furthermore, barrier-layer cells exhibit temporary fatigue on exposure to light, which increases fairly rapidly with the illumination. The amount and speed of this effect vary greatly from cell to cell and no explanation has been forthcoming up to the present. As the photovoltaic cell is a self-generating device of great long-time reliability it is well suited for use in light meters, and for the operation of relays. Short-circuit sensitivities range from about 150 to 500 μA/lumen.

COMBINATIONS OF THERMAL AND ELECTRONIC RADIATION DETECTORS

The only existing radiation detector belonging to this group is the superconducting bolometer. It is based on the fact that certain substances when cooled through a small temperature interval around a critical low temperature lose their normal resistance characteristics and the resistance drops to zero. If the temperature of a suitable superconducting material is maintained at a point within the range of normal resistance and zero resistance, it will have a high rate of change of resistance with temperature. This property of high dR/dT has been used[58] to construct a bolometer of very high sensitivity; it employs columbium nitride, which has a transition temperature around 15° K, near the triple point of hydrogen. The bolometer consists of a strip of columbium nitride of small area, say 5mm$\times$0·5mm, fastened to a base of copper, from which it is electrically insulated by lacquer but in good thermal contact. Lead wires are soldered on to the copper-plated ends of the strip. The time-constants for different bolometers of this type range from 0·7 to 17 millisec and figures of merit[59] have been calculated ranging from 14·0 to 1·3.

These bolometers used as radiation detectors fulfil the requirements stated above fairly well, with the exception of (c) (p. 210) for rather complicated apparatus and accessories are needed to keep the temperature low and constant.

REFERENCES

1. SMITH, W. *J. Soc. Tel. Eng.* (1873) **2**, p. 31.
2. WELKER, H. *Z. Naturforsch* (1952) **7a**, p. 744.
3. MEYER, W. *Z. Phys.* (1933) **85**, p. 278.
4. BAEDEKER, H. *Ann. Phys.* (1909) **29**, p. 566.
5. BRAUN, H. *Ann. Phys. Pogg.* (1874) **153**, p. 556.
6. GRONDAHL. *Phys. Rev.* (1926) **27**, p. 813.
7. SCHOTTKY, STÖRMER, WAIBEL, *Hochfrequ* (1931) **37**, p. 162.
8. HERTZ, W. *Ann. Phys.* (1887) **31**, p. 983.
9. HALLWACHS, W. *Ann. Phys.* (1888) **33**, p. 301.
10. EINSTEIN, A. *Ann. Phys.* (1905) **17**, p. 132.

11. CASE, T. W. *Phys. Rev.* (1917) **9**, p. 305.
12. BECQUEREL, *Comptes Rend* (1839) **9**, 144, 561.
13. SCHOTTKY, W. *Z. Phys.* (1930) **31**, p. 913.
14. MOTT, N. F. and GURNEY, R. W. *Electronic Processes in Ionic Crystals*, 1940; SEITZ, F. *The Modern Theory of Solids* (1940); SHOCKLEY, W. *Electrons and Holes in Semiconductors* (Van Nostrand, 1950); WRIGHT, D. A. *Semi-Conductors* (Methuen, 1950).
15. WILSON, A. H. *Proc. Roy. Soc., A.* (1931) **133**, p. 458. *Semiconductors and Metals* (Cambridge, 1939).
16. SCHOTTKY, W. and WAIBEL, F. *Phys. Zs.* (1934) **34**, p. 858. DAUBER, F.I.A.T. Report 706, 1946.
17. TAMM, I. *Z. Phys.* (1932) **76**, p. 849.
18. BARDEEN, J. *Phys. Rev.*, (1947) **71**, p. 717; BRATTAIN, W. H. *Phys. Rev.* (1947), **72**, p. 345.
19. SCHWARZ, E. *Proc. Phys. Soc., A.* (1949) **62**, p. 530.
20. MOENCH, G. *Ann. Phys.* (1936) **26**, p. 481, *Ann. Phys.* (1939) **34**, p. 265.
21. MEYER, W. *Z. techn. Phys.* (1933) **14**, p. 126.
22. BECKER, GREEN and PARSONS; *Bell Syst. Techn. J.* (1947) **26**, p. 171; PRINGENT, J. *J. de Phys. et Rad.* (1949) **16**, p. 58.
23. RUBENS, H. *Z. f. Instrumentenk* (1898) **18**, p. 65; PASCHEN, F. *Ann. Phys.* (1910) **33**, p. 330; MOLL, W. *Inaug. Dissertation Utrecht* (1907).
24. CARTWRIGHT, C. H. *Z. Phys.* (1934) **92**, p. 153.
25. JOHANSEN, E. S. *Ann. Phys.* (1910) **33**, 517; FIRESTONE, F. *Rev. Sci. Instr.* (1930) **1**, p. 630; MOLL, W. and BURGER, H. C. *Z. Phys.* (1925) **32**, p. 575; FELLGETT, P. W. *Proc. Phys. Soc.* (1949) **62**, p. 35; GEILING, L. *Z. f. angew. Phys.* (1951) **3**, p. 467.
26. SCHWARZ, E. U.K. Patent Nos: 578,187 (1941) 578,188 (1941); U.S. Patent Nos: 2,397,756; 2, 398,196 (1946); Dutch Patent Nos: 65.724 65.725 (1950); *Research* (1952) **5**, p. 407.
27. LISTON, M. *J. Opt. Soc. Amer.* (1947) **37**, p. 515.
28. GEITEL, H. *Ann. Phys.* (1922) **67**, p. 420.
29. TAYLOR, J. B. and LANGMUIR, J. *Phys. Rev.* (1933) **44**, p. 423; BECKER, J. A. *Phys. Rev.* (1926) **28**, p. 341.
30. BRADY, J. J. *Phys. Rev.* (1932) **41**, p. 613; FLEISCHMANN, R. *Naturwiss.* (1931) **19**, p. 826; IVES, H. E. and BRIGGS, H. B. *J. Opt. Soc. Amer.* (1938) **28**, p. 330.
31. ELSTER, J. and GEITEL, H. *Phys. Z.* (1910) **11**, p. 257.
32. POHL, R. W. and PRINGSHEIM, P. *Verh. d. phys. Ges.* (1913) **15**, p. 625.
33. KOLLER, L. R. *Phys. Rev.* (1930) **36**, p. 1640.
34. ASAO, S. and SUZUKI, M. *Proc. Phys. Math. Soc. Japan* (1930) **12**, p. 247.
35. GOERLICH, P. *Z. Phys.* (1936) **101**, p. 335.
36. BARNARD, G. P. 'The Selenium Cell and its Applications' (1930).
37. MARC, R. *Z. Anorg. Chemie* (1903) **37**, p. 459.
38. RIES, C. 'Das Selen' (1918).
39. PFUND, A. H. *Phil. Mag.* (1904) 6, 7, p. 27.
40. DIETERICH, E. O. *Phys. Rev.* (1914) 2, **4**, p. 467; BROWN, F. C. and SIEG, L. P. (1915) 2, **5**, p. 236.
41. CASE, T. W. *Phys. Rev.* (1920) **15**, p. 289.
42. HIPPEL VON, A. *et. al. J. Chem. Phys.* (1946) **14**, p. 355.
43. BOSE, J. U.S. Patent 755840 (1901).
44. GUDDEN, B. 'Infrarote Strahlungsempfänger' (OKH/WaF, 1944).
45. GENZEL and MÜSER. *Z. Phys.* (1950) **127**, p. 194.
46. GIBSON, A. F. *Proc. Phys. Soc., B.* (1950) **63**, p. 756; *Proc. Phys. Soc., B.* (1952) **65**, p. 196; SOSNOWSKI, A. *et. al. Nature* (1947) **159**, p. 818; STARKIEWICZ. *J. Opt. Soc. Amer.* (1948) **38**, p. 481; MOSS, T. S. *Proc. Phys. Soc. B.* (1949) **62**, p. 741; CHASMAR, R. P. and MOSS, T. S. *Nature* (1948) **161**, p. 244; KRENZIEN, O. *Z. Phys.* (1949) **126**, p. 666.
47. MILLER, P. H. and GREENBLATT, M. H. N.D.R.C. 14–412, *University of Penn.* (1945).

48. TEAL, G. K., FISHER, J. R. and TRAPTOW, A. W. *J. Appl. Phys.* (1946) **17** p. 879.
49. BENZER, S. N.D.R.C. 14–342 *Purdue University*, 1944.
50. FRERICHS, R. *Naturwiss.* (1946) **33**, p. 281. *Phys. Rev.* (1949) **76**, p. 1869.
51. BROSER, J. and WARMINSKY, R. *Ann. Phys.* (1950) **6**, p. 289.
52. KALLMANN, H. and WARMINSKY, R. *Ann. Phys.* (1948) **4**, p. 69; FASS-BENDER, J. *Ann. Phys.* (1949) **3**, 33; SCHOEN, M. *Ann. Phys.* (1948) **3**, p. 333.
53. RIEHL, N. and SCHOEN, M. *Z. Phys.* (1939) **114**, p. 682; GARLICK, C. F. 'Luminescent Materials' (Oxford, 1949).
54. SCHWARZ, E. *Nature* (1948) **162**, p. 614. *Proc. Phys. Soc., A.* (1949) **62**, p. 530.
55. SCHWARZ, E. *Proc. Phys. Soc. B* (1951) **64**, p. 821.
56. FRITTS, E. *Elect. Rev.* (1885) p. 208.
57. LANGE, B. *Z. Phys.* (1930) **31**, p. 139. 'Photo-elements' (Reinhold, New York), 1938.
58. ANDREWS, D. H., MILTON, R. T. and DE SORBO, W. *J. Opt. Soc. Amer.* (1946) **36**, p. 518; MILTON, R. M. *Chem. Rev.* (1946) **39**, p. 419; FUSON, N. *J. Opt. Soc. Amer.* (1948) **38**, p. 845.
59. CLARK JONES, R. *J. Opt. Soc. Amer.* (1947) **37**, p. 888.

Chapter Ten

DETECTOR AND AMPLIFIER SYSTEMS IN INFRA–RED SPECTROMETRY

By J. C. O. Rochester*

THE INFRA-RED SPECTROMETER

In recent years the infra-red spectrometer has become increasingly important in chemical research and industry, for several reasons. [1]

Organic chemistry has developed so quickly that the need has arisen for more rapid and accurate methods of analysis, particularly where chemical methods are difficult or impossible. This need may often be met by the use of analytical methods based on the measurement of infra-red absorption spectra.

Modern infra-red spectrometers are reliable instruments capable of recording the infra-red absorption spectrum of a sample with speed and accuracy. The improvements in these instruments have been brought about largely through improvements in infra-red detectors and amplification systems.

Much research has been done on the development of infra-red analytical techniques, the accumulation of spectra of known compounds, and the correlation of infra-red absorption frequencies with molecular structure.

In a typical infra-red spectrometer (Fig. 10. 1), the radiation from a Nernst filament or globar source S is focused onto the entrance slit F of a monochromator by a system of front aluminized spherical mirrors A and D, after passing through a cell containing the sample E. The radiation passing through the entrance slit of the monochromator is collimated by an off-axis paraboloidal mirror J to give a parallel beam through a prism of rock salt K.

Behind the prism, a plane mirror L, which can be rotated to alter the wavelength setting, reflects the beam back through the prism a second time to the collimator mirror, which now focuses the spectrum on to the exit slit G. Radiation of the required wavelength passes through the exit slit and is focused by means of an elliptical mirror N onto the thermal detector O.

---

* The author wishes to thank Sir Howard Grubb, Parsons and Co. for permission to publish this chapter, and Dr A. E. Martin for his guidance and encouragement.

The output from the detector is amplified and used to operate an indicating instrument or a pen recorder. In operation the wavelength control is driven slowly by a motor so that the recorder plots a curve of energy against wavelength. The absorption bands of the sample will be superimposed on the background energy curve which would be obtained with no sample in position.

D.C. DETECTOR SYSTEMS

(a) The early work in infra-red spectroscopy was carried out using very sensitive galvanometers to measure the output from thermopiles and metal strip bolometers. To obtain the required sensitivity these galvanometers had to be of very long period and were inherently very sensitive to vibration. Point-by-point readings needed to be taken, and the time required to obtain a spectrum was considerable. As these detector systems were very sensitive to temperature drifts, as well as to vibration, elaborate experimental techniques were required to obtain reliable results. [2]

(b) In an attempt to overcome the difficulties involved in using the most sensitive galvanometers, photoelectric amplifiers were introduced. [3, 4] In this system a less sensitive primary galvanometer is used to throw a spot of light onto the cathodes of two photoelectric cells connected in opposition, in such a way that a very small deflection of the primary galvanometer produces a much larger deflection in a secondary galvanometer connected to the output of the photoelectric cells.

The performance of this type of amplifier may be greatly improved by the application of negative feedback. To do this the secondary galvanometer current is passed through a small resistance inserted in series between the thermopile and the primary galvanometer coil, in such a direction that the p.d. across the resistance opposes the thermopile. As in other types of amplifier, negative feedback increases the stability and the linearity and reduces the response time.

(c) The best true electronic d.c. amplifiers that have been made up to now are still subject to drifts which are large compared with the required signal from a thermopile or bolometer detector. A method of circumventing troubles due to these amplifier drifts is provided in the contact-modulated d.c. amplifier. [5] Two contact-breakers are driven mechanically in synchronism; one switches the thermopile output to the primary winding of a step-up input transformer, successively in alternate directions, to produce an increased alternating voltage in the secondary winding. A three-stage resistance-capacitance-coupled amplifier is connected to the input transformer, and the amplifier in turn feeds an output transformer. The output from the secondary of the transformer is reconverted to direct current by means of the second breaker, and provides enough current to drive a pen recorder.

This type of amplifier has been made to measure potentials of 0·01 μV–300 μV from a 5–20-ohm source, with a noise level of less than 1·5 $\times 10^{-3}$ μV and a drift of less than 5×10^{-3} μV over a period of 8 hours under laboratory conditions. Very thorough magnetic screening of the input circuit is necessary to avoid pick-up troubles. It is also necessary to take great care in the design of the input breakers to avoid stray thermo-electric effects.

A number of different circuit arrangements may be used in conjunction with the contact-modulated amplifier, by applying negative feedback from the output or from the slide wire of a self-balancing potentiometer recorder.[6] This type of amplifier can also be used with a modulated light system to overcome the effects of thermal drifts, if the chopping frequency is not greater than about 15 c/s.

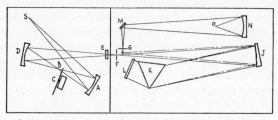

FIG. 10.1

OPTICAL LAYOUT OF AN INFRA-RED SPECTROMETER

S	Source	G	Exit slit
A	Spherical mirror	J	Collimator mirror
B	Primary focus	K	Rock-salt prism
C	Chopper disk	L	Littrow mirror
D	Spherical mirror	M	Plane mirror
E	Sample cell	N	Ellipsoidal mirror
F	Entrance slit	O	Thermal detector

A.C. DETECTOR SYSTEMS

In a.c. detector systems, the radiant energy is interrupted at a suitable frequency (generally between 5 and 30 c/s) by a chopper disk, before falling on the detector.[7, 8, 9] The output from the detector then consists of an alternating voltage, the amplitude of which is proportional only to the intensity of the radiation and is free from any drifts due to temperature changes. The detector output may be stepped up by a transformer with a low-resistance detector, and amplified by means of a high-gain a.c. coupled amplifier. This is much easier to design than a d.c. amplifier, and can be made to give very stable amplification. The a.c. amplifier can easily give an output of the order of 100 volts, which is enough to obtain sensibly linear rectification with diode rectifiers; alternatively, rectification may be obtained by means of mechanically driven switches running in synchronism with the chopper disk.

Most modern infra-red spectrometers use some form of chopped-beam a.c.detector system. Another advantage of this system is that the output responds only to energy incident on the detector which has been chopped at the correct frequency; so it is not necessary to provide elaborate heat-insulating screens to protect the detector from the effects of stray radiation from surrounding objects, as in d.c. systems, in which any temperature change at the detector is registered.

Requirements of Spectrometer Amplifier and Detector System

(a) High Resolution

For a given design of spectrometer, the highest resolution is obtained by using the narrowest slit possible, until the diffraction limit set by the prism size is reached. Other conditions being the same, this means that the energy available at the detector will usually be very small, so that it is necessary to use a detector which is very sensitive and which has a very low noise level. The minimum detectable energy is fixed by the noise level and sensitivity of the detector—assuming that the noise introduced by the amplification system used can be made less than that of the detector. The limit of resolution is usually set by the minimum detectable energy.

(b) Speed of Recording

In d.c. systems the detector must respond uniformly up to the highest speeds at which the energy changes when scanning the spectrum. In the contact-modulated amplifier d.c. system the modulating frequency must be high compared with the highest frequency at which the energy changes.

With a.c. systems, the chopping frequency must be high compared with the frequency of energy variations produced by scanning the spectrum. It follows from this that, for fast recording, the time-constant of the detector should be short, so that the sensitivity may not be reduced too much when the chopping frequency is reasonably high.

Noise

Whatever form of detector is used, if the gain of the amplifier is sufficiently high a limit is reached when the noise from the detector becomes comparable to the wanted signal.

For information about noise and its effects see chapter seven.

SPEED OF RESPONSE

In this section, expressions will be developed to show the relations between bandwidth, speed of recording and resolution.[10]

If the energy passing through the spectrometer is assumed to be varying sinusoidally at a frequency f_1, the instantaneous amplitude of the energy may be represented by $(a+b \sin 2\pi f_1 t)$. When this is chopped sinusoidally at a frequency f, the resultant energy at the detector is

$$(a+b \sin 2\pi f_1 t) \sin 2\pi f t$$
$$= a \sin 2\pi f . t + \tfrac{1}{2} b \cos 2\pi t (f-f_1) - \tfrac{1}{2} b \cos 2\pi t (f+f_1)$$

This represents three sinusoidal signals at frequencies f, $(f+f_1)$ and $(f-f_1)$, the two latter being known as side-band frequencies. For the amplifier to transmit the whole signal without distortion the pass-band must include these side-band frequencies $(f+f_1)$ and $(f-f_1)$. The minimum permissible bandwidth of the amplifier is thus $(f+f_1)$ $-(f-f_1)$, or $2f_1 = \Delta f$, say.

Let us consider the case where it is required to resolve two bands separated by Γ cm^{-1} and the speed of recording is Σ cm^{-1}/sec. The amplifier must respond to frequencies up to $f_1 = \Sigma/\Gamma$ c/s. The bandwidth of the amplifier must therefore be at least $= 2\Sigma/\Gamma = \Delta f$.

The speed of recording is then given if the bandwidth and resolution are fixed:

$$\Sigma = \frac{\Delta f . \Gamma}{2}$$

The resolution obtainable from an infra-red spectrometer is often limited by the noise level of the detector and not by the optical system; it is necessary to open up the slits to get enough energy to give a good signal/noise ratio in the output. When these conditions apply, further relations may be derived.

The slit width required is proportional to Γ, and the energy is proportional to the square of the slit width; therefore the energy is proportional to Γ^2 and the noise is proportional to $(\Delta f)^{1/2}$. For the signal/noise ratio to be constant, we have

$$\frac{\Gamma^2}{(\Delta f)^{1/2}} = \text{constant}$$

Hence Δf is proportional to Γ^4.

From above

$$\Sigma = \frac{\Delta f . \Gamma}{2}$$

By combining these two expressions, we find

Σ is proportional to Γ^5

Γ is proportional to $\sqrt{(1/S)}$

Γ is proportional to $\sqrt{N}$

if the bandwidth is kept constant.

In the above expressions S = sensitivity of detector in $\mu V/\mu W$ and N = noise of detector in $\mu V/\sqrt{}$(bandwidth of 1 c/s).

These results show that to obtain improved performance it is much more worthwhile, if possible, to use a more sensitive detector than to reduce the bandwidth of the amplifying system; since, if it is required to increase the resolution by reducing the bandwidth and so reducing the noise level, the maximum recording speed possible will be proportional to the fifth power of the separation between bands which it is required to resolve.

THE AMPLIFIER

To make the best use of the detector it must be followed by an amplifier that is capable of amplifying the output signal from the detector to a level suitable to operate some form of recorder, without adding any further noise to the inherent background noise of the detector itself. If it is required to measure very low levels of energy, the amplifier will need to have a narrow pass-band to cut down the noise from the detector. The actual bandwidth which is chosen for any particular application will depend on the balance between the conflicting requirements of high resolution and high speed of response.

REQUIREMENTS IN AMPLIFIERS

The noise level of the amplifier should be appreciably lower than the noise from the detector. This involves careful design of the first stages of the amplifier and choice of suitable components.

The gain of the amplifier should be adequate to reveal the background noise of the detector. It should remain constant over considerable periods of time, and not vary with changing mains voltage or frequency.

When the detector is a bolometer, it is also necessary to provide a polarizing voltage that is very thoroughly smoothed and is constant in magnitude.

When the detector is of low resistance, as with the thermopile and the metal-strip bolometer, it is necessary to use a step-up transformer to raise the level of the signal and noise from the detector above that of the noise in the input stage of the amplifier. It is important to realize that the fundamental signal/noise ratio in the system is determined only by the characteristics of the detector and the bandwidth of the system. If the amplifier is satisfactory, other forms of noise will, at all points in the amplifier, be less than the fundamental detector noise. Provided that these conditions are fulfilled, the actual gain of the amplifier, the use of an input transformer, the type of recorder used and its sensitivity, are purely matters of convenience in achieving desirable amplifier characteristics, and do not affect the fundamental signal/noise ratio.

DESIGN OF AN A.C. AMPLIFIER FOR USE WITH AN INFRA-RED SPECTROMETER

The amplifier to be described is designed for use with a thermistor bolometer of resistance between 2 and 3 megohms. The radiation is interrupted at $16\frac{2}{3}$ c/s by means of a chopper disk driven by a small synchronous motor, before entering the spectrometer.

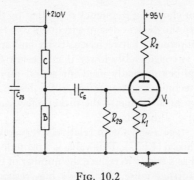

FIG. 10.2

THE INPUT CIRCUIT OF AN A.C. AMPLIFIER
FOR USE WITH AN INFRA-RED SPECTROMETER

B	Bolometer	C_{23}	2 μF
C	Compensator	R_1	2·2 kilohm
V_1	EF37	R_2	100 kilohm
C_6	0·01 μF, mica	R_{29}	10 megohm

(a) Detector Coupling

A polarizing potential of 210 volts is applied to the thermistor bolometer B in series with a compensating element C, which is similar to the bolometer but is screened from the radiation (see Fig. 10.2). As the compensator has the same temperature coefficient as the bolometer, the polarizing voltage across the element does not change with ambient temperature. The polarizing voltage is highly stabilized and very thoroughly smoothed to maintain the detector sensitivity constant and to avoid the introduction to the amplifier input of additional noise or unwanted signals from the power pack. The last stage of smoothing uses a good quality oil-filled paper dielectric 2μF capacitor C_{23}, which has extremely low leakage.

The signal from the bolometer is fed to the input stage of the amplifier by means of a 0·01 μF mica capacitor C_6 and a 10-megohm grid leak R_{29}. Extreme care is necessary to maintain a high standard of insulation resistance in the connections to the bolometer, and only polythene-insulated cable is used. Any defects in the insulation are liable to introduce additional noise. Insulation resistance greater than 10^{10} ohms has been found to be satisfactory. The amplifier may be used with a low-resistance detector, such as a thermopile, by connecting a suitable step-up transformer between the detector and the amplifier input.

(b) Input Stage (V_1)

The maximum chopping frequency is limited by the thermal inertia of the detector. In the present design a frequency of $16\frac{2}{3}$ c/s is chosen, as a reasonable compromise between sensitivity and speed of recording. This frequency is considerably lower than the low-frequency limit of the type of amplifier normally used for sound reproduction, so that rather different techniques are required in the design. At this frequency most of the valve noise is due to the flicker effect, and is much greater than the shot noise of the valve.

For the input stage a valve with relatively very low flicker noise and microphony is chosen (EF37). This valve is a pentode, but in the amplifier is connected as a triode to reduce the number of components which may introduce further noise. A cathode bias resistor of 2·2 kilohms R_1 and an anode load of 100 kilohms R_2 are used with a low h.t. voltage, giving about 40 volts at the valve anode. Under these conditions the grid current is low and the high value of grid leak may be used without difficulty.

The cathode resistor is not bypassed, because an electrolytic capacitor would constitute another possible source of noise; the small amount of negative feedback introduced by the cathode resistor helps to stabilize the gain and does not affect the signal/noise ratio.

Although it is preferable to use a wire-wound resistor for the anode load R_2, to avoid current noise (see chapter seven) it has been found that most high-stability carbon resistors are quite satisfactory from the standpoint of noise, provided that the anode load is not greater than 100 kilohms.

The noise level of the first stage is equivalent to one-quarter of the Johnson noise of the bolometer; this gives a satisfactory margin of safety.

The first valve and the input connections, with the coupling capacitor and grid leak, are enclosed in a separate screening box to reduce pick-up.

(c) Second Stage

Resistance-capacitance coupling is used between the first and second stages, and also between the subsequent stages, the time-constants of the coupling circuits varying between 0·02 sec and 0·22 sec.

The second stage uses a high-gain pentode (EF50) with a 470 kilohm anode load and a 3·3 kilohm cathode resistor. The screen grid is supplied by a 3·3 megohm dropper, decoupled by a 0·1-μF paper capacitor. The cathode resistor is decoupled by a 50-μF electrolytic capacitor.

A plug-in filter circuit, consisting of a parallel-T network, is used to provide negative feedback from anode to cathode in such a way that the stage as a whole behaves as a sharply tuned amplifier.[11]

The noise from this stage is usually negligible in comparison with the input stage, but occasionally it is necessary specially to select the valve. By the output of the second stage, the signal has been amplified enough to be able to insert the gain controls.

(d) Gain Controls

There are two gain controls (1) a stud switch tapping a chain of resistors connected as a potentiometer attenuator, which follows (2) a 500 kilohm wire-wound potentiometer. These two attenuators provide coarse and fine control of the overall gain.

(e) Third Stage

The next stage of amplification is similar to the second stage, except that there is no tuning, and the cathode resistor is not decoupled.

(f) Fourth Stage

The last of the three pentode stages is the same as the second stage with another plug-in filter to provide tuning. The overall frequency response characteristic of the amplifier has an effective bandwidth of about one cycle centered on $16\frac{2}{3}$ c/s.

(g) Fifth and Sixth Stages

The next valve is a double triode (ECC32). One triode section serves as a further voltage-amplifier stage feeding the other section which operates as a phase-splitter.

(h) Signal Rectifier

The rectifier V_6 (see Fig. 10.3) is a double diode (EB34). The two anodes are fed in push-pull from the phase splitter $\frac{1}{2}V_5$, and the cathodes are joined together to a smoothing network of resistors R_{28} and R_{43} and capacitors C_{17-22}, which are arranged to give an output that is equal to the arithmetic mean of the rectified voltage waveform rather than to the peak value of the waveform. This form of smoothing in conjunction with the push-pull rectification reduces interference due to transients. The time-constant of the smoothing circuit may be varied by means of a seven-position stud switch which changes the value of the smoothing capacitor.

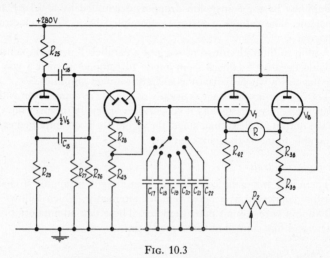

FIG. 10.3

THE SIGNAL RECTIFIER AND OUTPUT STAGE

C_{15}	0·1 μF	R_{27}	470 kilohm
C_{16}	0·1 μF	R_{28}	4·7 megohm
C_{17}	2 μF	R_{38}	1 kilohm
C_{18}	1 μF	R_{39}	390 ohm
C_{19}	0·5 μF	R_{42}	10 kilohm
C_{20}	0·25 μF	R_{43}	3·3 megohm
C_{21}	0·1 μF	P_2	600 ohm
C_{22}	0·05 μF	V_5	ECC32
R_{23}	10 kilohm	V_6	EB34
R_{25}	10 kilohm	$V_{7\,\&\,8}$	L63
R_{26}	470 kilohm	R	Recorder

The amplifier is designed so that an a.c. output of about 60 volts is applied to each of the rectifier anodes for full-scale deflection of the recorder, giving good linearity of rectification down to small signal levels.

(i) Output Stage

One stage of d.c. amplification is required to operate a 2-milliamp moving-coil pen recorder of resistance 2500 ohms. An L63 triode V_7 is used as a cathode follower, with a second similar valve V_8 to obtain a balance at zero input. The recorder is connected between the cathodes of the two valves. Unless the two valves are very badly matched, this stage is very stable and zero drift is negligible

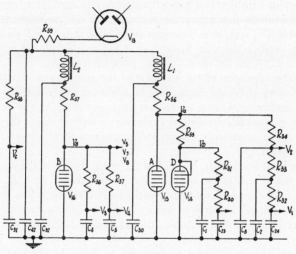

FIG. 10.4

THE POWER PACK, H.T. SUPPLY AND DECOUPLING

C_1	16 μF	R_{32}	100 kilohm
C_2	16 μF	R_{33}	100 kilohm
C_3	16 μF	R_{34}	100 kilohm
C_4	16 μF	R_{36}	220 kilohm
C_5	16 μF	R_{37}	100 kilohm
C_{23}	2 μF	R_{55}	4·7 kilohm
C_{24}	2 μF	R_{56}	2·2 kilohm
C_{30}	16 μF	R_{57}	2·2 kilohm
C_{31}	16 μF	R_{58}	3·3 kilohm
C_{32}	16 μF	R_{59}	220 ohm
C_{42}	16 μF	V_{13}	U52
L_1	25 H	V_{14}	STV280/40 A
L_2	25 H	V_{15}	STV 280/40 A
R_{30}	220 kilohm	V_{16}	STV 280/40 A
R_{31}	100 kilohm		

(j) *Power Pack*

The power pack is built as a separate unit from the amplifier and is contained in a similar type of case (see Fig. 10.4).

The main h.t. supply is obtained from a U52 full-wave rectifier V_{13} which gives a d.c. output of about 450 volts. The reservoir capacitor C_{42} is a 16 μF plain-foil plug-in electrolytic capacitor, and is of generous rating to handle the large ripple current which is present.

Two Stabilovolts—multi-gap gas-discharge tubes—A (V_{15}) and B (V_{16}) are fed from the reservoir capacitor by means of separate chokes L_1 and L_2, smoothing capacitors (C_{30} and C_{32}) and dropping resistors (R_{56} and R_{57}), to give two separate stabilized 280-volt supplies. Stabilovolt A supplies the first two stages through further decoupling networks, while Stabilovolt B supplies the remainder of the amplifier. A third Stabilovolt D (V_{14}), with one gap short-circuited, is fed through a dropping resistor R_{55} from Stabilovolt A to provide a doubly stabilized supply at 210 volts for the bolometer polarizing voltage.

As the voltage gain of the a.c. part of the amplifier is between 10^7 and 10^8, very elaborate decoupling is necessary in the h.t. supply to prevent instability. Owing to the low frequency at which the amplifier operates, normal RC decoupling is not very effective; this is the reason for using the apparently complicated arrangement of three separate Stabilovolt circuits.

It has been found that, because of the sharp tuning of the amplifier, the frequency stability of the a.c. power supply is not good enough to maintain the chopping frequency sufficiently constant, when the synchronous chopper motor was run from the mains. To overcome this difficulty, a simple form of stable resistance-capacitance 50 c/s oscillator (see Fig. 10·5) is incorporated in the power pack, together with a power amplifier and output transformer to drive the chopper motor. A frequency control P_3 is provided to tune the oscillator over a small range, so that the chopping frequency may be adjusted to the centre of the amplifier pass band. The potentiometer P_4 controls the gain of the oscillator valve V_9 by varying the amount of negative feedback. This control is set so that the valve just oscillates.

(k) Layout

Although at low frequencies stray capacitances and the positioning of leads and components are generally much less important than at radio frequencies, some care must be taken with the layout when very high gains are used, and the correct choice of points at which circuits are earthed may often be important for avoiding hum pick-up and instability.

The power consumption of the amplifier and power pack is about 150 watts so that considerable heat is dissipated. The ventilation of the amplifier and power-pack cases must be adequate, and the layout of components must be such that unduly high temperatures are not reached.

All sources of large heat dissipation, such as valves, Stabilovolts, transformers and dropping resistors are mounted above the chassis. Components requiring protection from heat, such as circuit resistors and capacitors and electrolytic capacitors are, as far as possible mounted below the chassis. In the power pack, extra ventilating louvres are provided in the top and bottom of the case to maintain an adequate flow of cooling air.

The resistors and capacitors associated with the valves are mounted on tag boards in accessible positions near the corresponding valve holders. This arrangement gives a neat layout, while all the components may be reached easily for servicing.

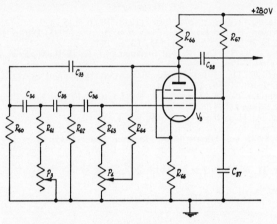

FIG. 10.5

A 50-c/s Oscillator to Drive the Chopper Motor

C_{33}	0·002 μF	R_{63}	1·5 megohm
C_{34}	0·002 μF	R_{64}	470 kilohm
C_{35}	0·002 μF	R_{65}	3·3 kilohm
C_{36}	0·002 μF	R_{66}	470 kilohm
C_{37}	0·1 μF	R_{67}	3·3 megohm
C_{38}	0·0005 μF	P_{3}	500 kilohm
R_{60}	1·5 megohm	P_{4}	20 kilohm
R_{61}	1·5 megohm	V_{9}	EF50
R_{62}	1·5 megohm		

The tuning filters are made up in separate cans which plug into the amplifier. This is very convenient during manufacture, for the components in the filter need to be matched with great accuracy; the filters are made up and tested individually as units before insertion in the amplifier. In use, the filters may be readily changed for others tuned to a different frequency, or with different bandwidths for special applications.

(*l*) *Miscellaneous*

The noise level of the amplifier corresponds to an input voltage of about 0·05 μV, compared with the bolometer noise level of about 0·2 μV.

At full gain setting of the amplifier, the pen recorder gives full-scale deflection for an input to the amplifier of about 1 μV.

If the amplifier and power pack are supplied from a constant-voltage transformer, the maximum variation in recorder reading over a period of several hours is about 2 per cent for the whole system of spectrometer and amplifier.

REFERENCES

1. WILLIAMS, V. Z. *Rev. Sci. Instr.* (1948) **19**, p. 135.
2. ROBERTSON, R. and FOX, J. J. *Proc. Roy. Soc., A* (1928) **120**, p. 128.
3. MOSS, E. B. *J. Sci. Instru.* (1935) **12**, p. 141.
4. CONN. G. K. T., LEE, E. and SUTHERLAND, G. B. B. M. *Proc. Roy. Soc., A.* (1940) **176**, p. 484.
5. LISTON, M. D., QUINN, C. E., SARGEANT, W. E. and SCOTT, G. G. *Rev. Sci. Instr.* (1946) **17**, p. 194.
6. RASSWEILER, G. M., LISTON, M. D., LASH, J. F. and FRY, D. L. *J. Opt. Soc. Amer.* (1947) **37**, 963.
7. PHUND, A. H. *Science* (1929) **69**, p. 71.
8. FIRESTONE, F. A. *Rev. Sci. Instr.* (1932) **3**, p. 163.
9. ROESS, L. C. and DACUS, E. N. *Rev. Sci. Instr.* (1945) **16**, p. 164.
10. DALY, E. F. and SUTHERLAND, G. B. B. M. *Proc. Phys. Soc* (1949) **62**, p. 205.
11. SCOTT, H. H. *Proc. I.R.E.* (1938) **26**, p. 226.

Chapter Eleven

PHOTOELECTRIC DEVICES AND THEIR APPLICATION IN THE VISIBLE AND ULTRA-VIOLET REGIONS

By P. POPPER

In this chapter we shall amplify the information about photo-emissive and photovoltaic cells given in chapter nine, and discuss their application to radiation detection in the visible and ultra-violet regions; it may be noted that photoconductive cells and thermopiles are mostly used for measurements in the infra-red region.

PHOTO-EMISSIVE CELLS

Fundamentals of Electron Emission

Hertz discovered the photo-emissive effect in 1887 when he was experimenting with spark gaps in his research on electromagnetic waves. He noticed that the breakdown length of a spark gap was considerably influenced by ultra-violet radiation. Elster and Geitel, who investigated this phenomenon further, soon found that most metals were sensitive to ultra-violet radiation but that the alkali metals were also sensitive to visible radiation; by enclosing surfaces of these elements in a vacuum they produced in fact the first photo-emissive vacuum cells. These cells had a cathode of an alkali metal which was connected to the negative side of a battery, whilst the anode was connected to the positive side. Negative charges could be transferred from cathode to anode through the vacuum when the cell was illuminated. It was not until J. J. Thomson's discovery of the electron in 1897 that these charge carriers were identified as electrons.

Two basic laws were found to apply to such cells:

(i) The number of electrons emitted per second from the photo-cathode is directly proportional to the incident radiant flux. (The magnitude of the photocurrent collected by the positive anode may thus serve as a measure of light intensity.)

(ii) The energy of the emitted electrons depends on the wavelength of the radiation but is independent of the intensity of the incident radiant flux.

Einstein, using some of the basic concepts of Planck's quantum theory was able in 1905 to explain these experimental findings. He assumed that an electron could absorb energy from a radiation of frequency ν

245

only in the form of quanta of $h\nu$ ergs, where h is Planck's constant and equals $6\cdot6\times10^{-27}$ erg-sec. It was further assumed that an electron had to acquire a minimum energy ϕ in order to escape from the cathode. ϕ, called the work function, is usually expressed in electron-volts (or simply volts) and is characteristic for a particular material. The reader is now referred to the account of the external photo-effect given in chapter nine on p. 205 *et seq.*

Table 11.1 gives ϕ for certain values of λ_0 the threshold wavelength.

TABLE 11.1

λ_0, Å	2000	4000	8000	12 000
ϕ, eV	6·2	3·1	1·5	1·0

The necessary energy for an electron to escape can also be supplied thermally and it is therefore obvious that the work function ϕ is an important characteristic in thermionic emission.

The thermionic current density of the cathode surface is given by Richardson's equation:

$$i = \frac{4\pi mek^2}{h^3}T^2\,\epsilon^{-e\phi\,\cdot\,10^7/kT}$$

where ϵ is the logarithmic constant, e is the electronic charge ($1\cdot6 \times10^{-19}$ coulomb), k is Boltzmann's constant ($1\cdot38\times10^{-16}$ erg/deg. K.), and T is the absolute temperature. Substituting the numerical values reduces the equation to

$$i = 120T^2\epsilon^{-11\cdot600\phi/T}\;\text{amp/cm}^2$$

It is thus obvious that the current emitted thermionically is large for a material with a low work function or a high threshold wavelength.

The thermionic current emitted at room temperature, commonly referred to as the 'dark current', can become a quite appreciable fraction of the photocurrent, particularly in photocells with a threshold wavelength above say 8000 Å.

In practice the following rules should be observed, whenever low intensities of radiation are to be measured:

(i) A photocell with as low a threshold as required by the particular measurement should be used.

(ii) The cathode surface should not be much larger than that required to cover the full aperture of the radiant beam.

(iii) The ambient temperature of the photocell should be kept low; if necessary the cell may be cooled with solid carbon dioxide.

Spectral Response of Vacuum Photocells

The work function of most pure materials lies between 2 and 5 eV. Pure materials are therefore of little use as cathode materials, except for measurements in the ultra-violet region. Details of representative photocells for the ultra-violet region are shown in Table 11.2.

TABLE 11.2*

Cathode material	Spectral range	Wavelength of maximum response
	Å	Å
Zirconium	2000–3150	2340
Thallium	2000–3675	2550
Tantalum	2000–3000	2400
Platinum	below 2000	1700

Such cells must have windows made of quartz or special ultra-violet transmitting glass which should be as thin as possible. The alkali metals have a low work function, e.g. for caesium it equals 1·8 eV. Cells have also been made using composite layers containing caesium which have very much improved efficiencies and higher threshold wavelengths. Of these, the most important photosensitive layers for photocells which are at present commercially available are:

    (i) The silver–oxygen–caesium cathode

    (ii) The antimony–caesium cathode

    (iii) The bismuth–oxygen–silver–caesium cathode

The efficiency of a photosensitive surface is determined by its quantum efficiency,[†] i.e. the ratio (emitted electrons)/(adsorbed quanta). In order that the percentage of radiation absorbed is high the layer must have a low optical reflectivity and transmission.

See Fig. 9.11 for spectral response curves of the three types of cathode.

Table 11.3 shows the most useful wavelength ranges for the three types of cell.

The sensitivity in the ultra-violet region of the Sb–Cs cell is very often impaired by the absorption of the glass envelope. A phosphor applied to the outside of the cell, e.g. magnesium tungstate or silver-activated zinc sulphide, can transform the ultra-violet into visible radiation,

* These details are for the photocells made by the Westinghouse Company of America.

† See also chapter nine p. 214.

R

TABLE 11.3

Surface	Recommended wavelength range
Ag–O–Cs	> 2000 Å
Bi–O–Ag–Cs	6000–7200 Å
Sb–Cs	< 6000 Å

which passes the glass envelope without being absorbed. The phosphor can be applied directly to the glass with a suitable binder and the efficiency of the arrangement may be enhanced by a suitable reflector. [1]

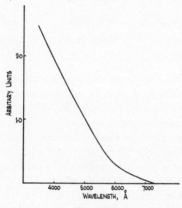

FIG. 11.1

Composite layers with alkali metals other than caesium have been made. The spectral response of the Ag–O–K cell is shown in Fig. 11.1. This cell has been used successfully for accurate photometry, since it can be matched satisfactorily to the response of the human eye using liquid filters. [2]

Electrical Characteristics

The voltage/current relation of a vacuum photo-emissive cell is shown in Fig. 11.2 for different levels of illumination. The current of a vacuum photocell is nearly independent of anode–cathode voltage above a certain voltage. The degree of voltage independence is influenced by the efficiency of the anode as an electron collector. A simple rod-like anode, as used in many photocells, is in this respect not always sufficient, and when complete saturation at low anode voltages is desirable, photocells with a fine wire-mesh anode which completely surrounds the cathode should be used. This type of construction will also prevent charging of the glass walls through secondary emission caused by electrons hitting the glass wall. Cells constructed in this way have been found to have a departure from linearity of response of only a few parts in 10,000 over a range of 10:1 in illumination. For proper operation one should consult the makers' data sheets. Whilst

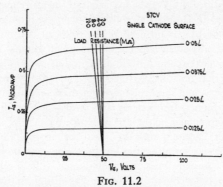

FIG. 11.2

Anode-current/anode-voltage characteristic of a vacuum photocell, with a load line drawn at different voltages to illustrate distortion.

too low an anode voltage may lead to non-linear distortion, too high a voltage may cause ionization of any residual gas and it can damage the rather delicate photosensitive surface.

In general one should use a vacuum photocell with as low an anode voltage as is possible, without running it below the knee of the anode-current/anode-voltage characteristic (Fig. 11.2).

Fatigue effects should cause little difficulty to the spectroscopist, who is usually dealing with only very low intensities of radiation, provided that the following precautions are taken:

(a) The cathode should be illuminated evenly over the sensitive area.

(b) Accidental exposure to intense radiation should be avoided. This will rarely cause permanent damage but may lead to unpleasant drift phenomena persisting for a considerable period.

It has been mentioned above that the intensities of radiation with which one has usually to deal are very low; in fact the highest are usually so small that the detector output currents cannot be measured with the most sensitive galvanometer available, whilst the lowest levels go right down to the limit of detectibility. It is thus clear that the output current of photocells must be amplified by electronic means. There are three ways of amplifying the current available from a photocathode:

(a) Ionization within a gas-filled photocell.

(b) Amplification outside the photocell by means of a highly stable high-gain electronic amplifier.

(c) Amplification through use of multiple secondary electron emission in an electron multiplier.

Of these three possibilities the first is the least satisfactory, and gas-filled photocells are rarely used for accurate measurements, although they are suitable for industrial control purposes. The gain which is normally achieved by gas-filling is of the order of ten, but this amplification is gained only at the expense of very great voltage- and temperature-dependence of the cell's output current. The current through a gas-filled cell is carried not only by electrons but also by the very much heavier positive gas ions, and the inertia of these leads to a serious drop in response at higher frequencies and limits the gas-filled cells to operation at frequencies below 10^4 c/s.

Geiger-Müller counters may be regarded as gas-filled photocells with an infinite gas amplification factor. The emission of a single electron causes complete breakdown of the gas. The discharge is then quenched either by a constituent of the gas filling, or by an external circuit arrangement. It is not intended here to go into the circuits associated with Geiger-Müller counters, but it is worth while to keep in mind that Geiger-Müller tubes can be used as very sensitive detectors of ultra-violet radiations, and for this reason they have been employed in spectrochemical analysis. [3] The amplification methods (b) and (c) are so important that they will be dealt with separately below.

Measurement of Small Photocurrents by means of Valve Amplification

The design of stable high-gain d.c. amplifiers is discussed in chapter five. In this section it is intended to discuss how a photocell is to be connected to such an amplifier and the special considerations which apply.

The photocurrents to be amplified are usually less than 10^{-6} amp and may be as low as 10^{-14} amp. Before a photocell is being used for the measurement of very low light levels it is wise to test the particular cell for its suitability. The insulation resistance of the cell must be very high, and preferably guard rings should be used to separate the photocurrent from the leakage current.

Photocells with top-cap connection are most suitable when high insulation resistance is required. The checking is done by measuring the anode current whilst the cell is in complete darkness. Leakage current can be distinguished from the true dark current, i.e. thermionic emission, by reversal of polarity, but it must be remembered that the surface of the anodes are often somewhat contaminated with the photosensitive material and may have quite a low work function; they will then act as cathodes.

The input voltage to the d.c. amplifier should preferably be about 1 volt. The required input resistor R should therefore be between 10^6 and 10^{14} ohms. It is necessary to estimate the time of response of such a system in conjunction with an input capacitance C of a few picofarads. The time-constant is determined by the product of R and C and ranges thus from a few microseconds to a few hundreds of seconds. The latter is clearly much too long, and in practice one is limited to resistors of values up to a maximum of 10^{11}–10^{12} ohms.

At present it is still difficult to obtain very high resistors with satisfactory stability, although they are being used in increasing numbers for the measurement of very small currents in ionization chambers.

Pyromatic resistors have a large temperature coefficient but a low voltage coefficient, at least for values up to 10^{10} ohms, whilst the glass-sealed resistors have a low temperature coefficient but high voltage coefficient. When the resistors are subjected to only small voltages such as are being considered here, the glass-sealed resistor is to be preferred. It should be noted also that the noise of such high resistors may be many times higher than the theoretically predicted value, particularly at low frequencies.

When very high resistors are connected into the grid circuits of valves, the choice of the valves used and their operating voltages is important. It is usually tacitly assumed that the grid current of a valve is zero, when the grid is biased negatively with respect to the cathode. This is, however, only an approximation, as is shown in Fig. 11.3. Neglecting leakage, the grid current is made up of two parts: the positive grid current and the negative grid current.

The positive grid current is due to collection of electrons by the grid; electrons are emitted with a sufficiently high kinetic energy to reach the grid in spite of its negative potential. Furthermore one must realize that the actual grid-cathode potential may differ from the biasing voltage, because of the differences of contact potential between the various materials employed in the grid circuit.

The negative grid current is due to collection of positive ions by the grid and electron emission from the grid wires. Positive ions may be emitted from the cathode or may be formed by ionization of gas molecules. Thermionic emission of electrons from the grid may occur as the grid wires are heated by radiation from the hot filament; photoemission from the grid may be caused by radiation from the outside of the filament or it may be due to soft X-ray radiation generated at the anode. The negative grid current will therefore increase with the anode current, and as indicated in Fig. 11.3, this characteristic is like an inverted anode-current/grid-voltage characteristic. The resultant grid current (i.e. the sum of positive and negative grid currents), which has a negative peak, is also shown.

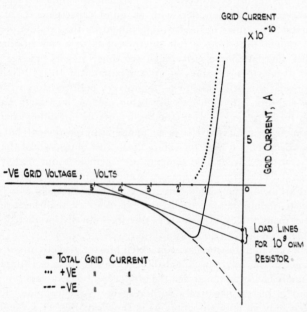

FIG. 11.3
Grid-current characteristic of a valve with negative grid bias.

In Fig. 11.3 two load lines are drawn in the V_g/I_g diagram for a resistor of 10^9 ohm, at $V_g = -4$ volts and $V_g = -5$ volts, to illustrate the effect of a grid current of a few parts of 10^{-9} A. With $V_g = -5$ volts it is shown that the effective grid potential may be either near -4 volts or $-1\cdot2$ volts; with a biasing voltage of -4 volts, the effective grid-cathode control potential is near -1 volt. Clearly changes of the biasing voltage near -4 volts have little effect on the true cathode-grid potential, or in other words the grid loses its control on the anode current. A valve can easily be tested for grid current by shorting a high resistor in the grid circuit and observing the change in anode current, which should be very small.

Valves with low grid current ($< 10^{-13}$ amp) are called electrometer valves. The low grid current is achieved by a special construction which ensures low leakage and also by operation at reduced anode voltage (12 volts) and filament voltage. Positive ions are prevented from reaching the control grid by interposition of a positive space-charge grid. Some standard radio valves can be run under similar conditions as electrometer valves with very much reduced grid current,[4] but then it is usually necessary to select the most suitable valve out of a batch. A circuit using a standard radio valve is shown in Fig. 11.4.

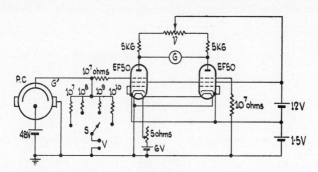

FIG. 11.4

A simple bridge-type valve voltmeter using a selected standard valve.

 PC Photocell;
 G' Guard-ring for use when the photocell has a top-cap anode;
 V Potentiometer for balancing the dark current;
 G Galvanometer.

Whenever one wishes to measure extremely low-intensity radiation, the voltage at the input of the electrometer valve becomes of the order of millivolts rather than volts and one is seriously troubled by drift of the d.c. amplifier. The origin of this drift is mainly to be looked for in the first or second stage of the amplifier and can be due to drift of supply voltages or changes in the emission characteristic of the valve. Bridge circuits compensating for change in h.t. and l.t. voltages are commonly used, and double-electrometer valves are now being produced for such circuits.[5]

A somewhat different method of measuring low intensities of light is particularly attractive for determining the intensity ratio of two fluctuating light sources, or the ratio of intensity of two different lines or bands out of the spectrum from one light source. In this method the photocurrent is made to charge a capacitor *C*, and if the photocell operates for the whole time along the constant-current portion of its characteristic the voltage across the capacitor is a measure of the integrated light output.

$$V = \frac{\int i dt}{C} \text{ or } \frac{it}{C}$$

for a constant light source.

The basic circuit is indicated in Fig. 11.5. The voltage has to be measured with an electrometer-valve voltmeter, since otherwise the capacitor will be discharged during the process of measuring its voltage. The capacitor used must have as little dielectric absorption as possible, and polythene dielectric is the most suitable. The capacitor can be discharged simply by reversing the polarity and illuminating the photocell,

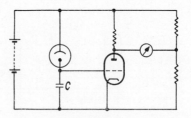

FIG. 11.5
The current-integrating photometer.

when the anode will act as a photosensitive cathode and pass current in the reverse direction. A slight modification, with the same principle, is to charge a capacitor to a given value. When the preset voltage is reached, a trigger circuit discharges the capacitor, and the cycle is then started anew. A mechanical register records the number of discharges in a given time interval.

The Secondary Emission Photoelectron Multiplier

When an electron impinges with sufficiently high energy on a surface it can impart enough of its own energy to several other electrons to allow them to escape. These electrons are called secondary electrons. Electron multiplication by secondary emission can be used to give a much higher output current than gas multiplication in a gas-filled valve and it has a better signal/noise ratio than valve amplification. The materials which have been found most satisfactory for the secondary emission targets, or *dynodes* as they are called, are similar to those used for photo-emission, namely silver–oxygen–caesium and antimony–caesium. Silver–magnesium alloys when suitably activated can also form a good secondary emissive surface—the criterion being a high yield of secondary electrons per primary electron at relative low voltages (about 100 volts).

An electron multiplier which uses a number of multiplying stages can have an output current corresponding to a million electrons for any single primary electron. It is important that all secondary electrons are accelerated towards the succeeding dynode, and this can be achieved by the use of electric or magnetic fields either separately or in combination. Secondary-emission photoelectron multipliers using purely electrostatic focusing are preferable in practice since they do not require external solenoids or permanent magnets.

There are two types with purely electrostatic focusing which have gained considerable practical importance during the last fifteen years. The screen-type multiplier and the multiplier with circular electrostatic focusing.

The screen-type multiplier uses a number of successive fine wire mesh dynodes at increasing potentials. The collector is a high transmission screen in front of the last dynode, which is solid (Fig. 11.6).

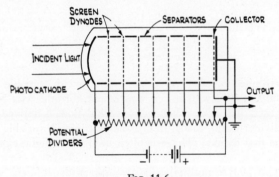

FIG. 11.6
A screen-type photo-multiplier.

The second type of multiplier, exemplified by the R.C.A. 931A[6] is, because of its compactness and stability, very important in spectrophotometry and merits more detailed discussion. The arrangement of the nine dynodes, cathode, and anode is shown in Fig. 11.7. A mica shield prevents 'electron regeneration' from positive ions. The stage gain is about four secondary electrons for one primary electron. The total gain for a nine-stage multiplier is thus 4^9, or about 300,000.

As the secondary-emission yield-factor is very voltage-dependent, we find that the total gain of the electron multiplier is highly sensitive to the voltage used between successive dynodes. In fact an increase of the dynode voltages from 100 to 110 volts almost doubles the total gain. Very stable voltage supplies must therefore be used if the gain is to be constant. If less than 1 per cent fluctuations of the gain are required it is easily shown from the figures just quoted that the power supply must have a stability of at least 5 parts in 10,000.

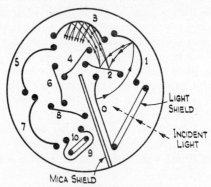

Fig. 11.7

An electron multiplier (RCA 931A) with circular electrostatic focusing.

0 = Photocathode
10 = Anode
1–9 = Dynodes

An electronically stabilized power supply with variable output between 700 and 1000 volts is very convenient, for otherwise batteries have to be used. The correct voltage for each dynode is derived from a potential-divider chain, made up of fixed resistors. A variable adjustment of the first dynode voltage is often used when highest gains are desired.

The R.C.A. 931A multiplier is available with different spectral sensitivities as is indicated in Table 11.4.

TABLE 11.4   VARIANTS OF THE R.C.A. 931A ELECTRON MULTIPLIER

Designation	Surface
931A	Antimony–caesium
IP 21	As 931A but selected for high gain and low dark current
IP 22	Bismuth–caesium
IP 28	As 931A but in ultra-violet transmitting glass envelope

The spectral range of the IP 21 can be considerably extended by the use of phosphors, either applied directly to the multiplier envelope or with an image-convertor tube.

The combination of the nine dynodes and collector can be looked upon as equivalent to the cathode and anode of a photocell. The current–voltage characteristics corresponding to very low-level illumination are shown in Fig. 11.8. It is advisable to check on the saturation of the

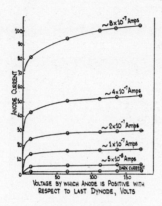

FIG. 11.8
Voltage/current characteristic of the 931A electron multiplier.

anode current when using the multiplier in a radiation-integrating circuit. Fatigue is very small if one keeps below the maximum permissible current (100 μA to 1 mA). Here again one will normally work with very much smaller currents, and precautions should be taken to avoid high illumination. The current of the multiplier in complete darkness is about 0·02 μA. This is due to leakage current plus the true dark current, which is amplified thermionic emission mainly from the photocathode. Thermionic emission can be decreased by cooling (see Fig. 11.9). An oscillogram of the anode current of a refrigerated electron multiplier is shown in Fig. 11.10. The large peaks are due to the current pulse caused by single electrons emitted from the cathode, the smaller peaks may originate from electrons emitted from the first dynode. The lowest levels of radiation can be measured by counting the number of peaks which are greater than a certain value and subtracting the dark current count. This counting method eliminates any difficulties due to leakage current, which is a steady current. The output current of an R.C.A. 931A multiplier is said to be linear within 3 per cent from the lowest level of illumination, as determined by counting of pulses up to the maximum current of 1 mA.

The measurement of the integrated output of fluctuating light sources is often necessary in spectrometry since it is very difficult to keep light emission from arcs, sparks or flames constant. A circuit using a photo-multiplier which fulfils this purpose is shown in Fig. 11.11. The current from the electron multiplier charges a capacitor to a predetermined voltage. This capacitor is also connected across the first valve of a

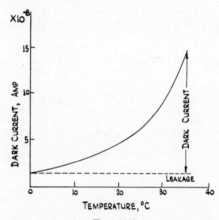

Fig. 11.9

Variation of dark current with temperature for the 931A electron multiplier.

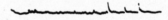

Fig. 11.10

Oscillogram of the anode current of the 931A electron multiplier when cooled with dry ice.

trigger-circuit similar to a Puckle time-base. This first valve is non-conducting until the capacitor is charged to a certain potential (say 50 volts) when the first valve begins to conduct and discharges the capaci-tor. The pulse so obtained is passed via a triode buffer stage (second half of twin-triode) to a scale-of-two counting circuit which at every other pulse operates the mechanical register. The counting rate is controlled by the capacitance of the capacitor used in the integrating circuit. Fig. 11.12 shows the counts/minute against charging current for a capacitor of 100 pF. The counts/minute corresponding to the dark current on this range are about 150.

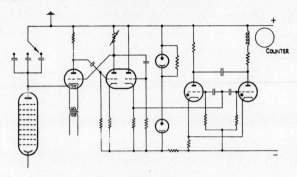

FIG. 11.11

A light integrator using a photomultiplier.
Charging capacitor = 100 pF

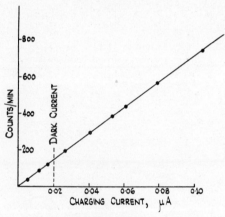

FIG. 11.12

Calibration of the light integrator of Fig. 11.11.

The dark-current count can be compensated by discharging the capacitor at the same rate as the dark current charges it. For satisfactory operation it is desirable that the voltage–current characteristic of the discharge circuit is similar to that of the dynode nine-anode characteristic. A circuit which compensates the dark current using an illuminated photocell is given in Fig. 11.13. The brightness of a small lamp which illuminates a small photocell is adjusted to give zero or a very low counting rate. The conditions which exist when the compensating circuit is derived from a constant-current device (photocell) are shown in Fig. 11.14.

The main advantages of the use of the electron multiplier are:

(*a*) *Convenience*. It is in practice much easier to provide a stabilized power pack and to measure directly the output of the multiplier with

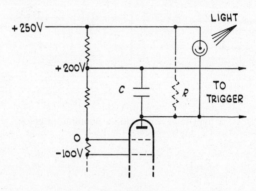

FIG. 11.13
A circuit for dark-current compensation.

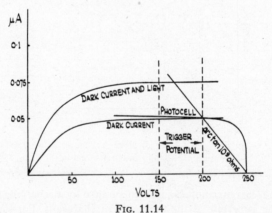

FIG. 11.14
Diagram illustrating the conditions of dark-current compensation.

a galvanometer which corresponds to photo-emissions of 10^{-13} to 10^{-14} amp, than to build a drift-free d.c. amplifier with an electrometer valve input.

(*b*) *Time of response*. The input resistance of an amplifier following the photomultiplier needs to be only R/(gain of multiplier), where R is the input resistance required for the amplifier when a photocell only is used. Light phenomena lasting only microseconds can therefore be observed.

(c) *Signal/noise ratio.* The shot noise of the thermionic emission is amplified in the electron multiplier with very little noise addition. The increased noise is due to the statistical variation in secondary-emission yield for one primary electron. The noise contribution in valve-amplifiers arises mainly from the thermal-agitation noise of the input resistor and is very great when very small currents are being measured.

PHOTOVOLTAIC CELLS

The great advantage of the photovoltaic cells is their convenience. They do not require an external source of power. All that is needed is a suitable current indicator, i.e. microammeter or galvanometer. See also chapter nine, p. 226 *et seq.*

The Spectral Response and Electrical Properties

The cross-section of a selenium barrier-layer photocell, the only type which is commercially available, is shown in Fig. 11.15. An iron

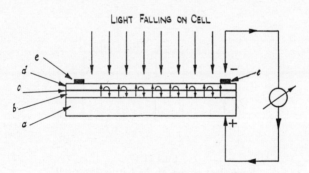

FIG. 11.15
Construction of a selenium barrier-layer cell.
(a) Metal base-plate   (c) Theoretical barrier layer
(b) Selenium layer   (d) Transparent metal layer
(e) Collecting ring
The arrows show the direction of electron flow.

plate forms the positive electrode, and on top of this is a crystalline layer of selenium. The front electrode is a very thin transparent layer of metal applied by evaporation or sputtering.

The spectral response curve of a selenium barrier-layer cell is shown in Fig. 11.16. The peak response is in the green and is very near to the point of maximum spectral sensitivity of the human eye. Because of the extreme fragility of the front electrode, barrier-layer cells are usually protected by a lacquer, and it is this lacquer which normally limits the response in the ultra-violet region. Barrier-layer cells can be

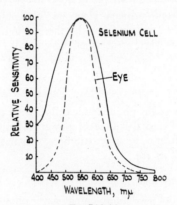

Fig. 11.16
Spectral response of a selenium barrier-layer cell.
- - - - - - Eye   ———— Selenium cell

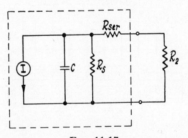

Fig. 11.17
Equivalent circuit of the barrier-layer cell.

used however for measurement of ultra-violet radiation by measuring the light from a phosphor excited by the radiation. A suitable phosphor emitting in the green is zinc beryllium silicate.

The equivalent electrical circuit of a barrier-layer cell is shown in Fig. 11.17, where I represents the equivalent current generator, C and R_{ser} represent internal shunt capacitance and resistance respectively. R_{ser}, the internal series resistance, is mainly in the front electrode. R_2 is the external load resistance. R_{ser} is however a function both of illumination and R_2. The photocurrent is therefore very dependent on load resistance (see Fig. 11.18), and only for very low-load resistances is the photocurrent directly proportional to the illumination. A barrier-layer cell thus works most satisfactorily into a short-circuit.

The current sensitivity is about 300 μA/lumen. The open-circuit voltage is a very non-linear function of illumination, reaching about 0·6 volt for very high illuminations. In fact the open-circuit voltage of a barrier-layer cell is proportional to the logarithm of the illumination. Larger voltages can be reached by connecting a number of small cells in series.

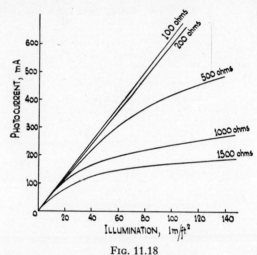

FIG. 11.18
Characteristics of the barrier-layer cell with different load resistors.

Fatigue and temperature dependence of the current increase considerably with high-load resistances. Whenever a barrier-layer cell is to be used in accurate measurements it is thus a great advantage to work into as low a resistance as possible. Fatigue effects are most marked in the red and infra-red regions, and where possible it is advisable to use red absorbing filters to improve the stability of response.

Circuits for use with Barrier-Layer Cells

A circuit in which the barrier-layer cell works under short-circuit conditions is that suggested by Campbell-Freeth and is shown in Fig. 11.19. The method used is referred to as 'current balance'. R_1 is chosen to be large compared with R_2. The magnitude of I_1 is determined from the setting of the potentiometer for which the galvanometer reading is zero. At balance $R_1I_1 = R_2I_2$.

Two barrier-layer photocells are frequently used to indicate equality of two light beams. In this arrangement again it is preferable to use a circuit arrangement where the photocells work under short-circuit rather than open-circuit conditions (Fig. 11.20). The adjustment for equal output of the two cells can be done either with diaphragms or electrically. For this a low shunting resistor rather than a series resistor should be used.

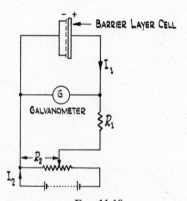

FIG. 11.19
The Campbell-Freeth current balance.

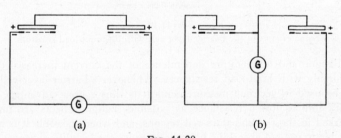

(a)   (b)

FIG. 11.20
Connections of two barrier-layer cells to indicate equality of
illumination.
(a) Open-circuit condition: bad practice   (b) Short-circuit condition: good practice

In absorption spectrometry it is often desirable to read the ratio of two light intensities which are derived from the same source. This reading should also be independent of the intensity of the source. Fig. 11.21 gives a circuit arrangement.

It is easily shown that $I_1/I_2 = x/a$, the value of x will give the ratio I_1/I_2, if a has first been adjusted so that, with $I_1 = I_2$, $x = 1$.

It is not possible to amplify very small output currents of barrier-layer cells in the same way as the currents of photo-emissive cells are amplified, since it is impossible to obtain voltages of the order of 1 volt by passing the current through a large resistor. Amplification of the small output voltages of these cells can be achieved by converting the voltages into alternating voltages before amplification. The techniques here are similar to those employed for measurement of the output of thermocouples or thermopiles and are dealt with in chapter nine.

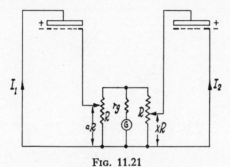

FIG. 11.21

A balanced circuit for direct reading of the ratio of two beams
derived from the same source.

Often, only very small deflections of a galvanometer can be obtained, and these may be amplified using a photoelectric galvanometer amplifier. A simple galvanometer amplifier can be produced by the arrangement of Fig. 11.20(b), in which the light reflected from the primary galvanometer falls on two photocells. The optical layout is such that the current in the secondary galvanometer is zero for zero deflection of the primary galvanometer.

A galvanometer amplifier which uses negative feedback[7] from the twin photocell circuit to the primary galvanometer is shown in Fig. 11.22. Adequate gain to provide for the negative feedback is secured without valve amplification by using a sufficiently intense beam of light. The negative feedback ensures improved stability and linearity. At an overall sensitivity of 15–20 m/μA the instrument is quite stable and zero repetition is within 10^{-10} amp.

Although some methods of amplifying the output of barrier cells have been described it is in general much easier under conditions of low illumination to use photo-emissive cells. The most useful field for barrier-layer cells is in applications where sufficient illumination is available to measure the current directly on a robust ammeter or galvanometer.

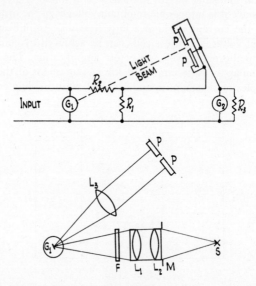

FIG. 11.22

Photo-electric galvanometer amplifier using barrier-layer cells and employing negative feedback.

G_1 = Primary galvometer	M = Mask with rectangular aperture
G_2 = Secondary galvometer	L_1, L_2 = Cemented achromatic doublets
R_1 = Wirewound resistance box	L_3 = Simple convex lens
R_2 = Damping resistance	F = Filter of Calorex glass
S = Lamp	P = Selenium rectifier photocells

APPLICATIONS: DIRECT-READING SPECTROCHEMICAL ANALYSIS

There are numerous applications in spectroscopy where electronic devices are being used with great advantage. A brief list is given below.

> Stabilization of light sources
> Colorimetry
> Spectrophotometry
> Exposure control
> Densitometry
> Flame photometry
> Spectrochemical analysis

It is undoubtedly in the last application that electronics has made the greatest contributions.

The problem in spectrochemical analysis is to record, accurately, the intensity of a number of lines—up to, say, twelve—emitted by the major constituents and the impurities of a substance. For many years the photographic plate has been used exclusively as a recording medium for this purpose. The use of the photographic plate in purely routine application has however been challenged recently by the electron multiplier, which will measure very low light levels directly and instantaneously. The time of an analysis has been reduced to such an extent that it is quite feasible to-day to control the composition of melts of metal. Several different types of such machines, [8, 9, 10] have been built which give the answer directly in percentages immediately after the sparking of the sample.

REFERENCES

1. COLTMAN, J. W. and MARSHALL, F. H. *Nucleonics* (1947) **1**, p. 58.
2. PRESTON, J. S. *Trans. Illum. Eng. Soc.* (1943) **8**, p. 121.
3. DUFFENDACK, D. S. and MORRIS, W. E. *J. Opt. Soc. Amer.* (1948) **32**, p.8.
4. NIELSEN, C. E. *Rev. Sci. Inst.* (1947) **18**, p. 18.
5. PEIRSON, D. H. *Electronic Engineering* (1950) **22**, p. 48.
6. ENGSTROM, R. W. *J. Opt. Soc. Amer.* (1947) **37**, p. 420.
7. PRESTON, J. S. *J. Sci. Inst.* (1948) **23**, p. 173.
8. HASLER, M. F. and DIETERT, H. W. *J. Opt. Soc. Amer.* (1944) **34**, p. 751.
9. SAUNDERSON, J. L., CALDECOURT, V. J. and PETERSON, E. W. *J. Opt. Soc. Amer.* (1945) **35**, p. 681.
10. KESSLER and WOLFE. *J. Opt. Soc. Amer.* (1947) **37**, p. 133.

BIBLIOGRAPHY

MILLMAN and SEELY. *Electronics* (McGraw-Hill, 1941).
ZWORKYN and RAMBERG. *Photoelectricity and its Applications* (John Wiley, 1949).
SOMMER, A. *Photoelectric Cells.* (Methuen, 1946).
PRESTON. Photoelectric Photometers, their Properties, Use and Maintenance. (*Trans. Illum. Eng. Soc.*)

Chapter Twelve

THE PRESENTATION OF INFRA-RED SPECTRA ON THE CATHODE-RAY TUBE

By E. F. Daly

As an introduction to the problem of presenting infra-red spectra on the cathode-ray tube it may be useful to examine theoretically the relationship between resolving power, signal/noise ratio and speed of scanning the spectrum, in a normal spectrometer. This may be carried out in terms of the elementary prism spectrometer illustrated in Fig. 12.1, together with a simplified model of infra-red detector.

The first step consists in obtaining an expression for the power of the radiation beam emerging from the exit slit of the spectrometer.

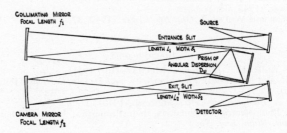

Fig. 12.1
Simplified spectrometer.

Consider a plane radiation source of emissivity ϵ_ν at frequency ν, emitting radiation which is collected in a direction nearly normal to its surface. The power per unit area of the emitting surface within the range of frequencies ν to $\nu + \delta\nu$, and integrated over the hemisphere into which the source radiates, is given by

$$P = \int_{\nu}^{\nu+\delta\nu} E_\nu \, \epsilon_\nu \, d\nu$$

where E_ν is the emitted power of a black body radiator per unit area per unit frequency band about ν.

268

Since the polar diagram for emission from an element of the plane surface is a sphere that is tangent to the surface at the element, the power per unit area per unit solid angle about the normal to the emitting surface will be given by

$$P = \frac{1}{\pi} \int\limits_{\nu}^{\nu+\delta\nu} E_\nu\, \epsilon_\nu\, d\nu$$

It may be simply shown that if radiation of the strength given by this expression is collected by a mirror and focused into an image of the source, the radiation power per unit area of image per unit solid angle will, ignoring reflection losses, be given by the same expression.

A spectrometer entrance slit of length l_1 and width s_1, on which the source image is formed, will pick out an area $l_1 s_1$, and provided that the collimator and prism are fully illuminated, the energy stream accepted by the spectrometer may be calculated. It is given by the expression

$$P = \frac{A s_1 l_1}{f_1^2}\, \frac{1}{\pi} \int\limits_{\nu}^{\nu+\delta\nu} E_\nu\, \epsilon_\nu\, d\nu$$

where

$$E_v = \frac{2\pi\nu^2}{c^2}\, \frac{h\nu}{e^{h\nu/kT}-1}$$

Here f_1 is the focal length of the collimator mirror and A is the effective cross-sectional area of the collimated beam, i.e. the maximum cross-section accepted by the collimator, prism, and the Littrow and camera mirrors together. For simplicity it will be assumed that $\delta\nu$ is a narrow region of the spectrum over which E_ν and ϵ_ν remain constant, so that

$$P = \frac{A s_1 l_1}{f_1^2}\, \frac{1}{\pi} E_\nu\, \epsilon_\nu\, \delta\nu$$

This energy stream accepted by the spectrometer will be dispersed at the exit slit over an area $D_\nu f_2 \delta\nu\, l_1 f_2/f_1$. In this it is assumed that $\delta\nu$ is large compared with a slit width, so that aberration and diffraction may be neglected, or that $\delta\nu$ is comparable with a slit width only when this is sufficiently large for aberration and diffraction to be neglected. Here D_ν is the angular dispersion, assumed constant over the ν to $\nu+\delta\nu$, and f_2 is the focal length of the camera mirror. The power passing the exit slit will then be given by the product of the exit slit area and the power per unit area in the dispersed image of the entrance slit. To simplify the expression, it will be assumed that $s_2/s_1 = l_2/l_1 = f_2/f_1$. Then the power passing the exit slit P_x will be given by

$$P_x = \frac{A s_1^2 l_1 E_\nu \epsilon_\nu}{D_\nu f_1^3 \pi}$$

No account has been taken of losses at mirrors and windows, or by atmospheric absorption, and to cover these an efficiency factor x may be introduced, the power leaving the exit slit and condensed upon the detector receiver being given by $x P_x$.

Now let P_0 be the minimum power which, falling on the detector, will provide some appropriate minimum signal/noise ratio M_0 at the display. To obtain the best resolution, the slits will be closed until the power at the detector $x P_x$ becomes equal to P_0, when the minimum entrance slit width s_0 will be given by

$$s_0^2 = \frac{P_0 \pi D_\nu f_1^3}{x E_\nu \epsilon_\nu A l_1}$$

It is convenient to express spectrometer performance in resolution by means of a quantity Γ, which is defined as the frequency band in wave numbers embraced by one slit width. Then Γ_ν, for the frequency range ν to $\nu + \delta\nu$, and for slit widths at which aberration and diffraction may be neglected, is given by

$$\Gamma_\nu = \frac{s_1}{D_\nu f_1}$$

It has been pointed out by Perry[1] that slit length is normally made as large as is consistent with a reasonable level of aberration, and that in these circumstances the value of l_1 chosen is proportional to the collimator focal length f_1. Putting l_1/f_1 equal to some constant g, we find that

$$\Gamma_\nu = \sqrt{\left/ \left(\frac{P_0 \pi}{x D_\nu A E_\nu \epsilon_\nu g} \right) \right.}$$

It will be noted that in this expression l_1 and f_1 have disappeared and that the quantities which are important in determining the performance of a spectrometer are the angular dispersion of the prism (or grating) and the effective area of the collimated beam (or the area of the prism or grating face).

The second step in this discussion consists in obtaining a value for P_0, the minimum power required at the detector, in terms of known detector parameters. For this purpose a simplified detector model will be used in which it will be assumed that an exponential rise in output voltage occurs when a radiation beam is suddenly applied. This assumption of a single time-constant is appropriate to a number of commonly used thermo-detectors, such as thermocouples and bolo-meters, in which the origin of the time-constant is obviously the lumped thermal capacity of the receiver and the thermal conductance to the heat sink. It must be treated with caution when high radiation chopping frequencies are considered; and the distribution of thermal resistance and capacitance must be taken into account where the heat sink is imperfect and introduces additional time-constants, as in some backed bolometers, or where a thermal differentiating circuit is involved, as in the Golay cell.

On the assumption of a single time-constant τ, the detector output voltage V may be expressed as

$$V = \sigma P(1 - e^{-t/\tau})$$

at time t after a radiation beam of power P is applied, σ being the steady-state sensitivity (volts/watt). In a practical case σ and τ are chosen to fit as closely as possible the initial voltage output rise.

The Johnson noise voltage, appearing within a bandwidth Δf, across a pure resistance R at temperature T is given by

$$\overline{V_n^2} = 4kTR\Delta f$$

where k is Boltzmann's constant (see chapter seven). In a system con-sisting of radiation detector, amplifier and display, it is usually technically possible to make the noise level at the display dependent only on detec-tor noise and on the effective bandwidth of amplifier and display, as when interruption of the radiation beam is employed with rectification and smoothing of the resulting a.c. signal. Thus the observed part of the mean-square voltage fluctuation at the detector may be expressed as

$$\overline{V_n^2} = \mu \Delta f$$

where μ is a parameter characteristic of the detector alone, and Δf is characteristic of the amplifier and display alone. For a thermo-detector in which efficiency is very high, the noise may arise largely from thermal fluctuations in the receiver, in which event μ will decrease for high frequencies. Similarly, if a type of noise such as that arising from the flicker effect is present in the detecting system, the value of μ will increase at very low frequencies. Often in practice, however, the detector efficiency is not so great that the former condition applies, and noise of the latter type does not arise, so that μ may be assumed sensibly constant for a given detector.

With the aid of the simplified detector model described by these three parameters σ, τ and μ, it is possible to calculate the minimum radiation power required to give some arbitrary signal/noise ratio M_0 at the display. The minimum power value arrived at depends on the way in which spectra are being presented. Two principal forms of presentation may be distinguished. One is the chopped-beam system in which the radiation is interrupted at some fixed frequency, so that the detector output is an a.c. signal at this frequency, the amplitude being proportional to the radiation power. For display, a clipping diode, or d.c. restoration circuit, may be used to yield a sinusoidal or pulse signal starting from a constant base line, or rectification and subsequent smoothing may be used, depending on the bandwidth desired. An alternative to this is the video system, in which the radiation beam is interrupted much less frequently than in the chopped-beam system, and modulation of the incident radiation intensity appears as modulation of the tops of the pulses into which the detector output is divided, as in a television video signal.

In a chopped-beam system consisting of radiation pulses separated by gaps of equal duration, and at frequency f, the peak-to-peak height, V_s, of the pulses in the detector output, is given by

$$V_s = \frac{\sigma P_0}{\sqrt{(1 + 4\pi^2 f^2 \tau^2)}} = \frac{\sigma P_0}{\sqrt{(1 + \omega^2 \tau^2)}}$$

If the bandwidth at which the signal is observed is Δf, the r.m.s. noise voltage which must be compared with the signal is given by

$$V_n = \sqrt{(\mu \Delta f)}$$

and the peak-to-peak noise voltage riding on the signal will be,

$$V_p = q\sqrt{(\mu \Delta f)}$$

where q is subject to some arbitrary definition, such as the level above the mean reached by some given fraction of the noise peaks, doubled to allow for peaks above and below the mean. The relations necessary for computing q are set out in papers by Rice. [2] For practical purposes a value of 6–8 may be used. For a minimum acceptable signal/noise ratio M_0 at the display, the beam power P_0 required is given by

$$P_0 = \frac{qM_0}{\sigma}\sqrt{[\mu \Delta f(1 + 4\pi^2 f^2 \tau^2)]}$$

For video presentation the situation is different in that the signal has not a single frequency but a set of Fourier components extending from the pulse repetition frequency f_p up through the series $2f_p$, $3f_p$ ... to some limiting value nf_p, or f_m dependent on the form of the spectrum and the speed with which it is scanned. Similarly, the bandwidth Δf, over which noise is observed must be that required to accommodate the signal components f_p to f_m, i.e. must be approximately equal to f_m. In order to avoid distortion of a video signal by the detector, resulting from a decrease in the response of the detector to higher-frequency signal components, the response characteristic of the amplifier may be modified so that it has a peak at f_m and for any lower frequency f is reduced by the factor

$$\sqrt{[(1+4\pi^2 f^2 \tau^2)/(1+4\pi^2 f_m{}^2 \tau^2)]}$$

On this basis the voltage of the signal at the display, corresponding in waveform to the radiation signal without distortion, is given by

$$V_s = \frac{\sigma P}{\sqrt{(1+4\pi^2 f^2 \tau^2)}}$$

and the r.m.s. noise, integrated over the pass-band, 0 to f_m, will be

$$V_n = \sqrt{\left[\frac{\mu f_m}{3}\left(1+\frac{2}{1+4\pi^2 f_m{}^2 \tau^2}\right)\right]}$$

Then, as before, the radiation power P_0 required to produce an acceptable signal/noise ratio M_0 at the display will be given by

$$P_0 = \frac{qM_0}{\sigma}\sqrt{[\mu f_m(1+\tfrac{4}{3}\pi^2 f_m{}^2 \tau^2)]}$$

It is now necessary to find relationships between scanning speed and resolving power. In a chopped-beam system this might be done by assuming that some arbitrary number α of radiation pulses must occur, while the spectrum traverses one slit width or Γ cm^{-1}. Then the scanning speed Σ in wave numbers per second, may be related to the chopping frequency f as follows:

$$\Sigma = \Gamma\,\frac{f}{\alpha}$$

Alternatively, for a chopped-beam system with rectification and smoothing, or for video presentation, the relationship may be illustrated by Fig. 12.2. If the radiation on the entrance slit of the spectrometer consists of a series of monochromatic lines spaced at intervals of Γ, the pattern of radiation falling on the detector as the spectrum is scanned is as shown in Fig. 12.2(a). Similarly for line spacings of $3\Gamma/2$ and 2Γ the patterns are shown by Figs. 12.2(b) and (c). Now if the rate of scan is Σ cm^{-1} per sec, the frequency of the residual ripple in Fig. 12.2(a) is Σ/Γ c/s, and of the fully resolved ripple in Fig. 12.2(c) is $\Sigma/2\Gamma$ c/s. It may be concluded that the former (Σ/Γ c/s) is the maximum ripple frequency f_m which can appear, and this is also the value of the frequency band Δf, required for reproduction, so that

$$\Sigma = \Gamma f_m = \Gamma \Delta f$$

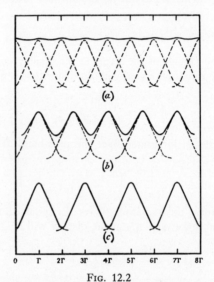

FIG. 12.2

Resolution of a series of equally spaced monochromatic lines:
(a) Γ apart, (b) $3\Gamma/2$ apart, (c) 2Γ apart.

The required relationships between scanning speed Σ, the spectral slitwidth Γ, and signal/noise ratio M_0, may now be summarized as follows:

For chopped-beam presentation:

$$\Gamma_\nu = \sqrt{\left(\frac{P_0 \pi}{x D_\nu A E_\nu \epsilon_\nu g} \right)}$$

$$P_0 = \frac{q M_0}{\sigma} \sqrt{[\mu \Delta f (1 + 4\pi^2 f^2 \tau^2)]}$$

$$\Sigma = \Gamma \Delta f \quad \text{or} \quad \Sigma = \Gamma \frac{f}{\alpha}$$

For video presentation:

$$\Gamma_\nu = \sqrt{\left(\frac{P_0 \pi}{x D_\nu A E_\nu \epsilon_\nu g}\right)}$$

$$P_0 = \frac{q P_0}{\sigma} \sqrt{[\mu f_m (1 + \tfrac{4}{3}\pi^2 f_m^2 \tau^2)]}$$

$$\Sigma = \Gamma f_m$$

For a given detector and spectrometer, the information contained in these equations may conveniently be presented by plotting Γ against Σ, or, for some purposes, Σ or Γ against M_0. Quantitative comparison of the performances of detectors of widely varying characteristics may be made if plots of Γ against Σ are made for them on the basis of a common spectrometer.

When Γ is plotted against Σ on logarithmic scales for some commonly used detectors in a standard prism spectrometer, it is found that the curve consists of four sections, as illustrated by Fig. 12.3(b). The first of these is horizontal, i.e. at constant resolving power, corresponding to the region in which resolution is determined by diffraction and aberration in the optical system rather than by available energy. A second portion—for which the frequency response of the detector is adequate for its task, i.e. $4\pi^2 f^2 \tau^2$ is small compared with unity—has a slope of $1/5$ ($\Gamma^5 \propto \Sigma$). In the third portion the demands made on the detector frequency response are too great, i.e. $4\pi^2 f^2 \tau^2$ is larger than unity, and the slope increases to $3/7$($\Gamma^7 \propto \Sigma^3$). Finally, in thermo-detectors, the lumped thermal constant treatment breaks down and distributed-constant or delay line conditions apply, with a further increase in slope. In photoconductive detectors a similar final steepening of the curve may result if the detector response is limited by the duration of the primary photoelectric process.

Curves (a) and (b) of Fig. 12.3 are plotted for a typical thermo-detector, such as a vacuum thermocouple, having an effective R.M.S.E.N.I. of 10^{-11} watt at $\Delta f = 1$ c/s, and a time-constant of 0.03 sec, used in a lithium fluoride prism spectrometer of conventional arrangement set at 2000 cm^{-1}. The R.M.S.E.N.I. is defined as that radiation power which produced in the detector an output signal voltage equal to the r.m.s. noise voltage, and is given by $q\sqrt{(\mu\Delta f)}/\sigma$. For comparison, curve (c) shows the performance which would be anticipated from a perfect thermo-detector of area $a = 0.004$ cm^2, and with $T = 300°$ K. In such a perfect non-selective detector the signal/noise ratio may be taken to be independent of time constant, since, for a relatively small bandwidth, signal and noise are treated alike by the response characteristic. The value of P_0 is here given by the relation

$$P_0 = qM_0\sqrt{(16\beta kT^{5}a\Delta f)}$$

where β is the Stefan-Boltzmann constant. Other similar curves (d) and (e) in Fig. 12.3, are included for a photoconductive cell, the R.M.S.E.N.I. here being 10^{-12} watt for $\Delta f = 1$ c/s, and the time-constant 100 microseconds.

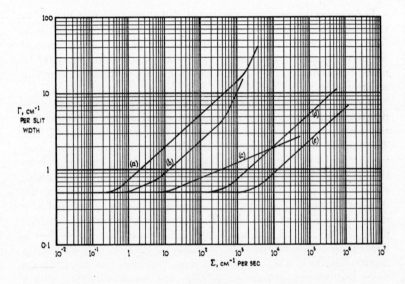

FIG. 12.3

(a) Thermocouple, chopped-beam system. (c) Perfect thermo-detector at 300° K.
(b) Thermocouple, video system. (d) Photoconductive cell, chopped-beam system.
(e) Photoconductive cell, video system.

We have been examining the theoretical basis of fast-scanning spectrometers and we must now consider, in the remainder of this account the various practical problems which arise when a fast-scanning instrument is to be constructed.

There are at present two main types of spectrometer employing cathode-ray-tube presentation. These correspond to the use of standard non-selective or thermo-detectors at room temperature, with scan durations of 10–100 sec; and the use of photoconductive cells either at room temperatures or cooled, with scan durations of 10–100 millisec. In fast-scanning instruments the principal points of difference from standard recording spectrometers concern (i) the provision of special arrangements for scanning a spectrum quickly and for automatically repeating the scan; (ii) wavelength calibration methods suited to fast scanning; and (iii) means of producing a suitable detected signal and applying it to a cathode-ray tube. Discussion of the mechanics and electronics of cathode-ray-tube presentation reduces to a description of methods of making the three modifications mentioned above, for each of the two main types of instrument.

Scanning mechanisms for instruments with 10–100 seconds scan duration may be purely mechanical. In the instrument described by Daly and Sutherland, [3] the table carrying the prism (a 30° back-silvered prism in a Littrow optical arrangement) had attached to it an arm bearing on a suitably shaped cam. This cam was rotated continuously and had on the same shaft a potentiometer which provided the x sweep of the cathode-ray tube. A similar system was used by King, Temple and Thompson. [4] An improved instrument built by Daly and Sutherland [5] employed a Perkin Elmer type 12B spectrometer in which the drive was applied through an electrically controlled gearbox directly to the wavelength drum shaft. By means of magnetic clutches this shaft may be engaged with either a slow countershaft, for scanning, or a countershaft seven times faster, for the flyback. The cathode-ray-tube time base is provided by a continuously rotating potentiometer, driven from a separate motor and variable-speed gearbox; the potentiometer has two contactors on its drive shaft which control the engaging voltages for the magnetic clutches of the spectrometer drive and provide cathode-ray-tube spot suppression during the flyback. The flyback clutch was made to disengage as the spectrometer drum reached some predetermined point, leaving a short dead interval before the start of the next scan, and ensuring that scans start each time from precisely the same wavelength. Another instrument using a Hilger D88 monochromator and having a similar scanning mechanism to that just mentioned has been described by Powell. [6]

In the instrument of Baker and Robb [7] the wavelength drive was provided by a cam which could be driven at various speeds by means of a magnetic clutch against the action of a spring. The cam roller was connected by a push rod and metal tape to the two prism tables of the double monochromator. To execute one scan the cam performed only a fraction of a revolution, and at the end of the scan the cam was declutched and allowed to fall back to its initial position against a stop. A continuously driven potentiometer was used for the cathode-ray-tube sweep, the cam being driven from the same shaft via the clutch.

For instruments having a scan duration of 10–100 millisec the mechanical arrangements mentioned above are too clumsy and some other method must be provided. In the instrument built by Deal, Bradshaw and Matsen[8] for operation in the visible part of the spectrum, a continuously rotating prism is used at speeds of 1800–3600 r.p.m. This is convenient but implies a sacrifice of time, since observations are made during only a small fraction of a prism rotation. In an instrument described by Bullock and Silverman[9] the Littrow mirror of the spectrometer is pivoted, and a lever arm attached to it is driven by the moving coil of a loud-speaker fed from the appropriate frequency, which, in this instance is 40 c/s. More recently Bullock and Silverman[10] have described a spectrometer in which the Littrow mirror is set in vibration by applying to it an alternating torque from a small electric motor, which is driven at the required frequency. Mirror oscillation frequencies of the order of 150 c/s have been achieved. For such a system, in which the mirror vibrates in simple harmonic motion an appreciable sacrifice in time must be made, if a reasonably linear and unidirectional scan is to be selected. The method used in an instrument built recently by Daly[11] consists in fixing a mirror to a robust galvanometer coil which has a stiff strip suspension and a high mechanical resonant frequency but is made critically damped by electrical means. A scanner of this type having a mirror 15×20 mm is introduced into the spectrometer optical system between entrance slit and collimator mirror, and reproduces with reasonable fidelity a sawtooth waveform applied to the galvanometer coil at repetition frequencies between 5 and 25 per second. The frequency response of the coil and mirror combination is approximately flat from 0 to 100 c/s. More recently it has been found possible to construct a scanner using a 40–60 mm Littrow mirror mounted upon a similar galvanometer suspension, and giving good reproduction of applied sawtooth waveforms for repetition frequencies between 5 and 15 c/s. The sawtooth waveform used to operate a scanner of this type may also be used to provide the cathode-ray-tube x sweep, thus ensuring synchronism.

When a scanning device of the type described above is used, its phase and amplitude response characteristics must affect appreciably the relation between the driving voltage applied to it and its actual angular displacement. If the driving voltage is also used for the cathode-ray-tube x sweep, it is desirable to use some means of calibration dependent on the angular position of the scanning mirror. This angular calibration may be carried out quite simply by using an auxiliary light beam reflected from the scanner in addition to the infra-red radiation: an image of an illuminated slit is projected, via the moving mirror, onto a scale having appropriate clear and opaque portions, and behind this is a photocell. The output of this photocell is used to provide calibration marks. When this is done it is necessary to ensure only sufficiently good linearity in scan and cathode-ray-tube sweep for easy interpolation between calibration marks and for the avoidance of any obvious variation in writing speed along the trace.

An alternative system may be used in which the cathode-ray-tube sweep itself is generated by the angular movement of the scanner. By using a slit image, formed, after reflection by the scanner mirror, on a wedge-shaped aperture in front of a photocell, a signal linearly related to the angular deflection of the mirror may be obtained. Provided that the photoelectric system is distortionless, effects arising from deficiencies in the mechanical response of the scanner may be avoided, but it may still be desirable to have an auxiliary system providing calibration marks.

For spectrometers having a scan duration of 10–100 sec the video system of presenting spectra might be used, but, since a suitable a.c. amplifier would be extremely clumsy, a d.c. amplifier would be required, with consequent liability to drift during a scan or between successive scans. Most instruments of this speed therefore employ chopped-beam presentation with or without rectification and smoothing. In such arrangements the deviation from standard a.c. amplifier and rectification practice may be very small. A standard self-balancing potentiometer recorder may have a bandwidth of 0·1 or 0·2 c/s, whereas the bandwidth necessary for the reproduction of reasonable detail in scans of 10–100 sec duration maybe 1–10 c/s. This must be the minimum bandwidth both of the a.c. amplifier about the chopping frequency, and of the post-detector smoothing circuits. If rectification and subsequent smoothing of the chopping frequency signal are employed, an adequate interval, say a factor of 10, should be allowed between the chopping frequency and the maximum frequency passed by the smoothing circuits, so that the residual ripple may be reduced to a low value without especially elaborate filtering. When efforts are being made to secure very good smoothing of the a.c. ripple the possibility of phase distortion by the filtering networks should be taken into account, since distortion arising here may result in quite reproducible but very misleading spectra.

A device which to some extent avoids the filtering problem is the use of a clipping detector, or d.c. restoration diode, in place of normal detection, and the presentation of the a.c. signal on the cathode-ray tube. The time-constant of the clipping circuit should be appropriate to the highest frequency which would have to be passed by the normal rectifying and smoothing circuit, and must be a factor of 10 longer than the length of a chopped radiation pulse if excessive clipping is not to occur.

When scan durations of 10 to 100 sec are used, cathode-ray tubes

T

having afterglow or long-persistence screens are suitable. By working in a darkened room it is possible to observe simultaneously the traces of a small number of consecutive scans, a useful feature if comparisons between spectra are to be made.

For faster scans of 10–100 millisec duration both video and chopped-beam systems of presentation become feasible, with the use of normal electronic techniques. The video method will be considered first.

At a scan repetition frequency of 10 per second, almost the slowest rate at which a reasonably steady picture may be maintained on a cathode-ray tube, the frequency spectrum of the video pulses may extend from the fundamental 10 c/s up to, or beyond, its tenth harmonic at 100 c/s. It is thus necessary to design a detector-amplifier combination, the frequency response of which as regards both amplitude and phase is flat over at least the range 10 c/s–100 c/s. This does not present very great difficulties at the higher-frequency end of the band, since falling off in detector response may be partly compensated by the introduction of anode loads resonant at some frequency above the upper limit of the pass-band, but it necessitates the use of rather long time-constant inter-stage couplings if phase distortion at the lower end of the pass-band is to be avoided. If, as is so in some applications, appreciable distortion of the spectrum may be tolerated, a normal resistance-coupled audio-frequency amplifier is suitable.

It is desirable that some form of shutter be introduced into the radiation beam during the flyback period in order that an energy zero level may be established. In the final stage of amplification before the cathode-ray tube a d.c. restoration or clipping diode may be used to set this energy zero to some constant level on the tube. The height of the trace above this level is then proportional at any point to the infra-red energy stream at the corresponding wavelength.

It will be appreciated that, in suggesting an amplifier response covering the tenth harmonic of the scan repetition frequency, we assume that the ratio of time spent in the linear part of the scan to time occupied by the flyback and disturbances arising from it is quite large, e.g. four or five. Thus eight or nine absorption bands might be distinguished on a scan if the width of each band corresponds to one cycle of the tenth harmonic. If, however, the ratio of linear scan time to the unused interval between scans is smaller, fewer cycles of the tenth harmonic may be accommodated on each scan and less information will be obtained for a given noise bandwidth or signal/noise ratio. When operation at scanning speeds much higher than 10 c/s is considered it is found that the mechanical difficulties of obtaining an adequate linear section of scan during each cycle increase rapidly. The decrease in efficiency described above must be compensated by a rapid increase in the high-frequency limit of the response of the amplifier-detector combination, if the quality of the spectra presented is not to deteriorate.

For chopped-beam presentation with scan durations in the 10–100 millisec range, the electronic problem of the design of the amplifier is simplified, although more attention must be paid to rectification and smoothing if this is employed. An amplifier broadly tuned to the radiation chopping frequency and having a bandwidth appropriate to the highest Fourier component of the spectrum modulation is necessary, and is not difficult to construct. Chopping of the radiation, at first sight a very easy operation, must be carried out with care. When a chopping disk with a number of teeth is used, high accuracy must be achieved in the form of the teeth and the centring of the disk, if modulation at the frequency of rotation of the disk is not to be introduced. It appears likely that a shutter of the vibrating-reed type or an oscillating mirror would provide a more precise chopping mechanism which could not introduce modulation at frequencies lower than that required.

The chopping frequency will be largely determined by the time-constant of the detector used and will normally be as high as possible. If an a.c., or rectified but unfiltered, signal is displayed on the cathode-ray tube it is not profitable to make an element of the scan corresponding to one cycle occupy an interval on the tube much smaller than the spot diameter. On this basis a scan would preferably consist of 100 or 200 cycles at the chopping frequency. Thus one arrives, with a 100-millisec scan, at an interruption frequency of 1000–2000 c/s, which is of the same order as the optimum value for a lead-sulphide photoconductive cell. In rectifying and smoothing a signal at this frequency the same problems arise as have already been discussed in connection with slower-scanning systems, and the same expedient of using d.c. restoration is possible.

It may be of some interest to inquire into the limits of high-speed scanning of spectra. If a resonant mirror system were used for scanning there is no doubt that a mirror of 15×20 mm could be driven in simple harmonic motion at 1000 c/s to the amplitude of a few degrees necessary when the scanner is situated between spectrometer slit and collimator. Thus a repetition frequency of 1000 c/s and an effective linear scan duration of 200 microsec are practicable. Time-constants of the order of 10–20 microsec have been reported for some lead-sulphide and lead-selenide photoconductive cells (though not those of highest sensitivity) and it would therefore be possible to obtain spectra embracing a useful amount of detail within the duration of a 200-microsec scan. An amplifier bandwidth of 100 kc/s would be required, but this would involve no more than a threefold or fourfold increase in noise level above that of an instrument already mentioned, [11] which has been found adequate for work with liquid samples. It would be desirable to use only video presentation, and it should be possible to observe transient phenomena, such as chemical reactions, of the order of 10-millisec duration.

A final topic which may be discussed here is that of double-beam spectroscopy with fast-scanning presentation. As with standard recording infra-red spectrometers two modes of double-beam operation are possible. The first is the time-sharing system in which two similar optical channels are used, with switching of the radiation between them and observation of the switched radiation signal by a single monochromator and detector. The second involves video presentation of the spectra with either simultaneous operation of two optical channels and two detectors, or switching of the radiation between two optical channels for alternate scans, with the use of some storage mechanism to retain the spectrum of one scan for comparison with the subsequent scan.

It appears, from the earlier part of this discussion, that the time-sharing or chopped-beam system is advantageous at low and intermediate scan repetition frequencies, and that the video system with storage of information between one scan and the next is likely to prove more satisfactory at very high scan repetition frequencies. The use of two separate detector-amplifier systems which must be precisely matched in spectral response and in electrical phase and amplitude frequency response, remains a difficult technical problem even after the application of negative radiation feedback to the detector-amplifier channels. The required storage of information between scans may be achieved very simply by providing some distinguishing coding for the scans from alternative optical channels and presenting both on a cathode-ray tube that has a screen with an appropriate decay time, i.e. an interval of several scans. If, however, an objective and instrumental comparison of successive scans is required, a storage device such as a supersonic delay line might be used at the higher scan repetition frequencies, but only at the cost of considerable complication in the electronic and display part of the instrument. Thus, for simplicity in comparing spectra at high signal/noise ratios the advantage appears to lie with the time-sharing system.

An instrument using the time-sharing system, having a scan repetition frequency between 5 and 25 c/s, and a chopping or beam switching frequency of 2000 c/s, has been described by Daly. [11] Chopping is carried out by means of a rotating disk on which are formed two images of the Nernst glower source (see Fig. 12.4), the separation of the images being the same as the width of each tooth or gap of the disk.

The beams are recombined by an optical mixer at the spectrometer entrance slit. A Littrow arrangement, with off-axis paraboloidal collimator mirror, is used in the spectrometer, the scanning mirror being a 15×20 mm mirror mounted on a robust galvanometer coil and located

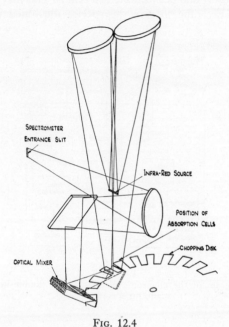

FIG. 12.4

Pre-slit optical system of double-beam fast scanning spectrometer.

at a point approximately one-fifth of the distance from slit to collimator. A magnetically operated shutter is interposed between the optical mixer and the entrance slit during each flyback.

A lead-sulphide cell detector is used, the output signal of which consists of video pulses on which is superimposed a 2-kc/s ripple corresponding to the optical switching between beams of differing power. This signal is modulated on a 200-kc/s carrier, the bandwidth up to this point being 2 c/s–10 kc/s, and the carrier amplitude set to zero at the zero-energy gaps between scans. The modulated carrier signal is then fed through an automatic-gain-controlled amplifier in which the gain-control voltage is filtered by a circuit that attenuates the 2-kc/s ripple but allows Fourier components of the signal corresponding to absorption bands to pass, within the range 2–200 c/s. The carrier leaves the a.g.c. amplifier at constant peak height, and, so long as the reference beam is stronger than the sample beam, the amplifier performs the function of standardizing the reference beam. From the carrier output, by rectification and smoothing, a 2-kc/s ripple component may be recovered which is proportional to the percentage difference in absorption between the two beams. This may be presented on a cathode-ray tube to give the spectra illustrated in Fig. 12.5.

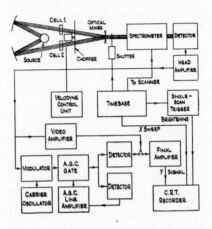

FIG. 12.6

Block diagram of the electronic circuits of the double-beam fast-scanning spectrometer.

A block diagram of the instrument is shown in Fig. 12.6, and waveforms for various parts of the circuit appear in Fig. 12.7. Fig. 12.7(a) represents the video pulses coming from the detector, (b) the modulated carrier, (c) the gain control voltage, (d) the carrier leaving the a.g.c. amplifier, (e) the rectified and smoothed signal, and (f) the filtered 2-kc/s ripple signal as displayed on the cathode-ray tube.

In work on chemical reactions, it is desirable that absorption occurring in both beams, e.g. that of the solvent, should not appear in the final spectrum, but that small changes in percentage absorption should be readily detectable. This implies that a good signal/noise ratio should be maintained in the difference spectrum. In the spectrometer described, a limiting error of 2 per cent of the transmission of the reference beam arises from imperfections in dimensions of the order of 10μ in the chopping disk, giving change-over disturbances varying from one tooth to the next; it arises also from imperfections in the absorption cells and optical mixer, which prevents the attainment at the entrance slit and at

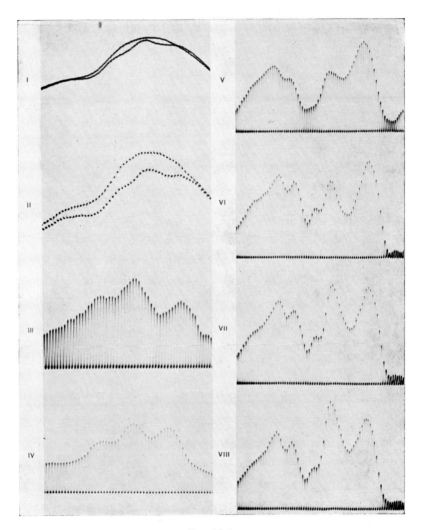

Fig. 12.5.

I. Video traces for water and a mixture of water plus 10 per cent acetone (successive exposures).
II. Video trace showing switching between water and water plus 10 per cent acetone.
III. Percentage absorption of acetone at 10 per cent concentration in water (5 per cent peak absorption).
IV. Percentage absorption of pure acetone (50 per cent peak absorption).
V. Percentage absorption difference between (i) 20 per cent N methyl morpholine, 20 per cent dibenzyl phosphite and 60 per cent ethyl alcohol; and (ii) 40 per cent carbon tetrachloride and 60 per cent ethyl alcohol.
VI–VIII. Percentage absorption difference between (i) 20 per cent N methyl morpholine, 20 per cent dibenzyl phosphite, 20 per cent carbon tetrachloride and 40 per cent ethyl alcohol; and (ii) 60 per cent carbon tetrachloride and 40 per cent ethyl alcohol, at 230, 1,020 and 1,930 seconds after start of reaction.

All scans are of 40 m. sec. duration, I–IV covering the range $1 \cdot 5\,2\mu$ and V–VIII the range 2–$2 \cdot 5\mu$, with longer wave-lengths on left.

[*facing p.* 284

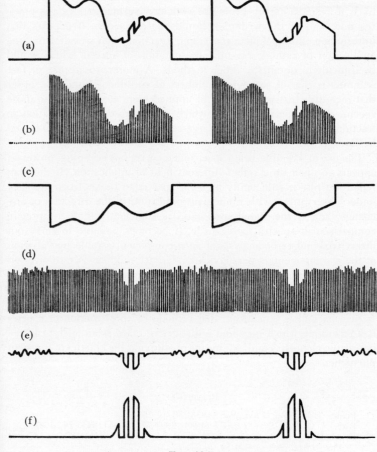

FIG. 12.7

Waveforms in a fast scanning double-beam system.

(a)	Video pulses from detector.	(d)	Carrier leaving an a.g.c. amplifier.
(b)	Modulated carrier.	(e)	Rectified and smoothed signal.
(c)	A.G.C. voltage.	(f)	Filtered 2-kc/s ripple signal.

the collimator of distributions of light which are the same for both optical channels. More recent work offers a reasonable hope of overcoming these difficulties and reaching the signal/noise ratio set by the detector and the amplifier bandwidth.

It may be asked in what sphere fast-scanning spectrometers are likely to be most useful. From the work of Silverman[9, 10] on gas-phase reaction, and of the writer on liquid-phase reaction, it appears that information on the kinetics of rapid reactions may result from the application of cathode-ray-tube presentation of spectra which would be difficult to obtain by other methods. A more prosaic use of fast scanning is that of surveying numbers of specimens rapidly in order that recording instruments may be applied more economically to those specimens or spectral regions which are interesting. Application to fractionation and the control of large-scale reaction has been mentioned by Powell.[6]

The use of a double-beam spectrometer with fast scanning, however, appears to open up a rather different field of application. If the scan repetition rate is sufficiently high for spectra to be kept continuously under observation, with immediate indication of the direction of any change, and if the signal/noise ratio is sufficiently high for precise comparison of spectra to be made, it becomes possible to carry out direct trial-and-error analysis of an n-component sample by variation of the n components separately in a reference mixture. Alternatively it becomes possible to observe very small changes in the spectrum of a sample with changes in its physical condition by first balancing the spectra of two such samples and then altering the conditions of one. It may be said in conclusion that cathode ray presentation of spectra is a technique which may find a distinctive place as an analytical tool in organic chemistry and as a means of studying the kinetics of transient phenomena.

REFERENCES

1. PERRY, J. W. *Proc. Phys. Soc.* (1938) **50**, p. 265.
2. RICE, S. O. *Bell. Syst. Tech. J.* (1944) **23**, p. 282 and (1945) **24**, p. 46.
3. DALY, E. F. and SUTHERLAND, G. B. B. M. *Nature* (1946) **157**, p. 547 and *Proc. Phys. Soc.* (1947) **59**, p. 77.
4. KING, J., TEMPLE, R. B. and THOMPSON, H. W. *Nature* (1946) **158**, p. 196.
5. DALY, E. F. Thesis, Cambridge University (1947).
6. POWELL, H. (editor) 'Symposium on spectroscopic methods in hydrocarbon research', Institute of Petroleum (1950) p. 28.
7. BAKER, E. B. and ROBB, C. D. *Rev. Sci. Inst.* (1943) **14**, p. 362.
8. DEAL, W. E., BRADSHAW, W. and MATSEN, F. A. *J. Chem. Phys.* (1948) **16**, p. 638.
9. BULLOCK, B. W. and SILVERMAN, S. *J. Opt. Soc. Amer.* (1949) **39**, p. 200.
10. BULLOCK, B. W. and SILVERMAN, S. *J. Opt. Soc. Amer.* (1950) **40**, p. 608.
11. DALY, E. F. *Nature* (1950) **166**, p. 1072.

Chapter Thirteen

SOME OPTICAL PROBLEMS

By A. M. Taylor

The quality and intensity of the image in a spectrograph or of the light emerging from the slit of a monochromator are matters of vital interest for spectroscopists. Evaluation of these quantities is frequently a matter of some complexity in practice although fundamentally simple in theory. The principles of photometry, of diffraction and of polarization, as well as of geometrical optics, are those governing the formation of the final image, and it will be convenient to discuss the problem from the point of view of each one of these in turn.

Illumination of an Image formed by an Optical System

The illumination in the spectrum produced by a spectrograph or monochromator is determined by the principles governing the formation of images by any optical system. If luminous flux F, measured in microwatts, is defined as light energy per second, the illumination E, of an element of area δa is given by $E = \delta F / \delta a$; the luminous intensity I of a source is given by $I = \delta F / \delta \omega$, where $\delta \omega$ is the element of solid angle subtended at the source by the element of area δa. The luminance B of a source when viewed at an angle α is defined as

$$B = \frac{\delta I}{\cos \alpha \, \delta s} = \frac{\delta F}{\cos \alpha \, \delta s \, \delta \omega}$$

where δs is the element of area of the source, and B is measured in microwatts per unit area per unit solid angle; the cosine term is the expression of Lambert's law.

Now as was first shown by Robert Smith in his 'Compleat System of Optics',* the brightness of an image is related simply to that of the object. The relationship may be derived from Fig. 13.1.

P_1 and P_2 are entrance and exit pupils, (images of the aperture stop D formed by the relevant portions of the optical system). Consider the flux through a small element of area δa situated in the

---

* Cambridge, 1738, Book 2, Chapter 5, pp. 255–261.

entrance pupil and distant r from an element of area δs_1 in the source; then by Lambert's cosine law, with r and δa as shown,

$$\delta F_1 = B_1 \cos \alpha \, \delta s_1 \, \delta \omega$$

where $\delta \omega = \delta a / r^2$. As $\delta a = 2\pi r \sin \alpha \times r \, \delta a$, it follows that

$$\delta F_1 = 2\pi B_1 \delta s_1 \sin \alpha \cos \alpha \, \delta \alpha$$

and on integration

$$F_1 = \int \delta F_1 = 2\pi B_1 \delta s_1 \int_0^{\theta_1} \sin \alpha \cos \alpha \, \delta \alpha = \pi B_1 \delta s_1 \sin^2 \theta_1 \quad (13.1)$$

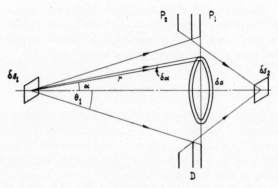

FIG. 13.1

By exactly similar considerations we obtain an expression for the flux F_2 passing through an element of area δs_2 situated in the image; it is

$$F_2 = \pi B_2 \, \delta s_2 \sin^2 \theta_2 \quad (13.2)$$

As there will be certain losses in the optical system due to absorption and to reflection at the surfaces, we may write $F_2 = kF_1$, where $k < 1$. It follows, therefore, that

$$kB_1 = B_2 \frac{\delta s_2 \sin^2 \theta_2}{\delta s_1 \sin^2 \theta_1}$$

If the optical system is Gaussian then Lagrange's law holds, i.e.

$$\mu_1 h_1 \sin \theta_1 = \mu_2 h_2 \sin \theta_2$$

where h_1 and h_2 are linear dimensions of object and image, and μ_1 and μ_2 are the refractive indices in the object and image spaces respectively.

If the system is free from the aberration of coma $h_2/h_1 = $ constant independent of α, (Abbe's sine condition), whence

$$\frac{\delta s_1}{\delta s_2} = \left(\frac{h_1}{h_2}\right)^2$$

and if object and image are both in air, $\mu_1 = \mu_2$; it follows that $\delta s_1 \sin^2 \theta_1 = \delta s_2 \sin^2 \theta_2$ and therefore $kB_1 = B_2$. Thus the brightness of the final image is less than the brightness of the source by only a factor k, which, though necessarily less than unity, may not differ greatly from it. It follows from this important theorem that, so long as the aperture of the condensing lens used to fill the collimator slit is sufficiently great to fill the collimator lens, the maximum of light enters the system.

In practice we may image the source of light either on the entrance slit of the system (Fig. 13.2) or upon the collimator lens (Fig. 13.3);

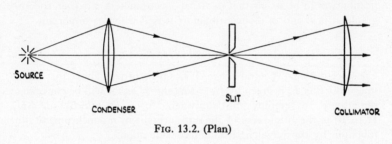

FIG. 13.2. (Plan)

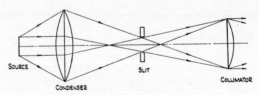

FIG. 13.3. (Elevation)

in the first arrangement we obtain point-to-point correspondence, in the second we obtain uniform illumination of the slit. It should be noted that in the second arrangement the source must be large enough for its image to fill the collimator lens.

The theorem just proved may be applied to the condensing lens which is used to image the source upon the entrance slit, but if the source is of finite depth in the third dimension then δs_1 is not restricted to a plane. It may be seen, however, that δs_2 need not coincide with the entrance slit; all that is necessary is that δs_2 should subtend at the collimator slit an angle larger than the condenser lens, which itself must be large enough for the collimator lens to be filled with light. Nielsen[1] has discussed the problem particularly with regard to the use of a capillary discharge tube as a source, and concludes that it is necessary to choose an optimum size, position and focal length of the lens which is used as a condenser.

LIGHT GATHERING POWER OF SPECTROGRAPHS AND MONOCHROMATORS

Our concern is with the spectrum formed in the focal plane of the final lens (or mirror) system, but on the method of detection of this spectrum depends whether it is the brightness B, illumination E, or total flux F, which is of importance. For detection by the eye the significant quantity is B, by a photographic plate it is E, and by a photocell, bolometer or thermo-element it is F. Another way of classification would be to say that in visual spectrometers it is B, in spectrographs it is E and in monochromators it is F which is important.

LINE SPECTRA

Consider the final spectral image. It has been proved above that in this image the flux F_2 is given by $F_2 = \pi B_2 \sin^2 \theta_2 \, \delta s_2$; it will be convenient sometimes to employ the equivalent form $F_2 = k\pi B_1 \sin^2 \theta_1 \delta s_1$. Here B_1 is the brightness of the entrance slit in monochromatic illumination by the wavelength under consideration.

Now illumination in this final image is given by

$$E_2(\text{monochromatic}) = \frac{\text{Flux}}{\text{Area}} = \frac{k\pi B_1 \sin^2 \theta_1 \, \delta s_1}{h_2 \, \delta x_2}$$

where h_2 is the height of the spectral image and δx_2 its width. As the spectral line is the image of the entrance slit, we have

$$\frac{h_2}{h_1} = \frac{f_2}{f_1} = \frac{\delta x_2}{\delta x_1} \text{ and } \delta s_1 = h_1 \delta x_1$$

where δx_1 is the width of the entrance slit and h_1 is its height; f_1 and f_2 are the focal lengths of collimator and telescope (or camera) lenses. It follows that

$$E_2(\text{monochromatic}) = \frac{k\pi B_1 \sin^2 \theta_1 f_1^2 \, \delta s_1}{f_2^2 h_1 \, \delta x_1}$$

$$= \frac{k\pi B_1 \sin^2 \theta_1 f_1^2}{f_2^2} \tag{13.3}$$

Thus the illumination in the spectral image is independent of the width of the entrance slit and increases, other things being equal, as the square of f_1/f_2.

CONTINUOUS SPECTRA

For continuous spectra the argument outlined holds for any infinitely narrow spectral range, but there is, however, another factor which must be considered. With varying dispersion in the system there will be a varying amount of overlapping of the monochromatic spectral images of the slit. Each wavelength gives rise to a single image of the slit, and these images overlap, producing some spectral impurity, and at the same time an increase in the apparent brightness.

Suppose we have a continuous spectrum formed by illumination with white light of an entrance slit of width δx_1 (which for the moment is to be thought of as vanishingly small). Consider an area of the spectrum extending over a wavelength range $\delta\lambda$, i.e. over a linear range δx_2, which equals $f_2(d\beta/d\lambda)\delta\lambda$, where $d\beta/d\lambda$ is the angular dispersion. Then, as before,

$$E_2 = \text{Flux/Area} = \frac{k\pi B_1 \sin^2\theta_1 \, \delta s_1}{h_2 f_2 (d\beta/d\lambda)\delta\lambda}$$

Now, however, B_1 must be expressed as a function of λ and of $\delta\lambda$, i.e. $B_1 = B_\lambda \, \delta\lambda$. As the area of the entrance slit is given by $\delta s_1 = h_1 \, \delta x_1$ we have

$$E_2(\text{continuous}) = \frac{k\pi B_\lambda \sin^2\theta_1 f_1 \, \delta x_1}{f_2{}^2(d\beta/d\lambda)} \tag{13.4}$$

Thus the apparent illumination of the continuous spectrum is proportional to the entrance-slit width and inversely as the angular dispersion in the instrument. The equation may also be written

$$E_2(\text{continuous}) = \frac{k\pi B_\lambda \sin^2\theta_1 f_1{}^2 \, \delta x_2}{f_2{}^3(d\beta/d\lambda)}$$

$$= \frac{k\pi B_\lambda \, \delta\lambda \sin^2\theta_1 f_1{}^2}{f_2{}^2}$$

which compares with eqn. (13.3) for the illumination in a line spectrum; it may be remembered that B_1 for monochromatic light is comparable with $B_\lambda \, d\lambda$ for a continuous spectrum. However eqn. (13.4) is convenient because it shows clearly how the apparent illumination depends upon entrance slit width and upon angular dispersion.

It is more usual in treating this subject to have the equations expressed in the form

$$E_2(\text{monochromatic}) = k\pi B_1 \sin^2 \theta_2 \tag{13.5}$$

and

$$E_2(\text{continuous}) = \frac{k\pi B_\lambda \sin^2 \theta_2 \, \delta x_1}{f_1(d\beta/d\lambda)} \tag{13.6}$$

and these equations may quickly be obtained by means of the substitution $\sin^2 \theta_1 \, \delta s_1 = \sin^2 \theta_2 \, \delta s_2$. They show that if E_2 is to be large it is important to make the angle θ_2 as large as practicable, i.e. the ratio of d_2/f_2 (the numerical aperture of the camera or telescope lens) should be large.

Spectrographs

For photographic recording of the spectrum it is E_2, the image intensity, which is important; this is because the density of the photographic record is proportional to $\log(E_2 t)$, where t is the time of exposure. It will be seen from eqn. (13.3) that for photography of weak spectra with a fixed value of the entrant cone of light, it is an advantage to make the ratio f_1/f_2 as large as possible, i.e. to have a long-focus collimator and a short-focus camera lens.

Two factors may be distinguished: speed, and ability to distinguish a line from the continuous background. From eqn. (13.5) speed depends only upon $\sin^2 \theta_2$, i.e. on the numerical aperture of the camera lens.

If eqn. (13.3) is divided by eqn. (13.4) the ratio is obtained

$$\frac{E_2(\text{monochromatic})}{E_2(\text{continuous})} = \frac{f_1}{\delta x_1} \left(\frac{d\beta}{d\lambda} \right) \frac{B_1}{B_\lambda}$$

Clearly this ratio is a measure of the ability to distinguish a monochromatic line from the continuous background; it increases with the angular dispersion and with $f_1/\delta x_1$. This is to be expected, because spectral purity increases with just these two factors.

It follows that spectrographs for the study of Raman lines should have a short-focus camera lens, a long-focus collimator lens and high dispersion. The latter is usually obtained by the use of a train of prisms. The collimator lens is normally of fairly large focal length, because the conditions of illumination by Raman scattering generally do not permit a very wide angle cone of light to be admitted to the entrance slit.

There are many advantages in using a collimator lens of long focus combined with a camera lens of short focus. It is easy to fill with light a collimator lens of small angular aperture. For a given spectral purity, i.e. a fixed value of $f_1/\delta x_1$, the longer f_1 the larger δx_1. It follows that with a long-focus collimator lens the entrance slit may be comparatively crude and coarse, which implies economy in manufacture and ruggedness in use. The longer the focus of a collimator lens, of a given diameter, the simpler it is to correct for spherical aberration and coma. The longer the focus of the collimator lens, the smaller the aperture of the condenser lens which is needed to fill the collimator with light.

MONOCHROMATORS

In modern practice, spectra are often directly recorded by photo-electric means; the instrument used is a monochromator and it is the total flux F_2 emerging from the exit slit which is of importance; (this assumes all flux to fall upon the sensitive element of the detector). The total flux F_2 emerging from the exit slit is given by

$$F_2 = E_2 \times \text{area} = E_2 \, h_2 \, \delta x_2$$

For line spectra we have from eqn. (13.3)

$$F_2(\text{monochromatic}) = \frac{k\pi B_1 \sin^2 \theta_1 f_1^2}{f_2^2} h_2 \, \delta x_2 \qquad (13.7)$$

As the spectral line is the conjugate image of the entrance slit, then, so long as the exit slit is large enough to accommodate this image, $\delta x_2 = \delta x_1 \, (f_2/f_1)$. It follows that

$$F_2(\text{monochromatic}) = k\pi B_1 \sin^2 \theta_1 \, h_1 \, \delta x_1 \qquad (13.8)$$

For continuous spectra we have

$$F_2(\text{continuous}) = \frac{k\pi B_\lambda \sin^2 \theta_1 f_1 \, \delta x_1}{f_2^2 (d\beta/d\lambda)} h_2 \, \delta x_2$$

$$= \frac{k\pi B_\lambda \sin^2 \theta_1 \, h_1 \, \delta x_1 \, \delta x_2}{f_2 (d\beta/d\lambda)} \qquad (13.9)$$

In working with a monochromator it is generally the practice to use entrance and exit slit widths which are related as conjugate images:

$$\delta x_2 = \delta x_1 \frac{f_2}{f_1}$$

If this is so

$$F_2(\text{continuous}) = \frac{k\pi B_\lambda \sin^2 \theta_1 \, h_1 \, \delta x_1^2}{f_1 (d\beta/d\lambda)} \qquad (13.10)$$

It will be noted that under these conditions of use the total emergent flux is proportional to the square of the slit width, and this is in contrast to line spectra, where the total emergent flux is proportional to the first power of the slit width.

As before, the ability to distinguish a line spectrum from a continuous background may be judged from the ratio obtained by division of eqn. (13.8) by eqn. (13.10)

$$\frac{F_2(\text{monochromatic})}{F_2(\text{continuous})} = \frac{f_1}{\delta x_1} \left(\frac{d\beta}{d\lambda}\right) \frac{B_1}{B_\lambda}$$

It is therefore an advantage to use a monochromator which gives a high spectral purity, i.e. which has a large value of $f_1/\delta x_1$ and of $d\beta/d\lambda$. It is advantageous to work with narrow slit widths, the narrower the better, so long as the photoelectric signal/noise ratio is large enough.

The separation of a Raman line from the continuous background follows, in this case, a law different from that in the photographic case. A photocell gives a response linearly proportional to the incident light flux. A photographic negative has an optical density proportional to the logarithm of the exposure. It is therefore impossible to detect by photography a weak line superimposed on a strong background, whereas so long as the increased signal due to the weak line is distinctly greater than the unavoidable but unwanted 'noise', the line may, with suitable electrical circuits, be detected by photoelectric means.

CORRECTIONS TO BE APPLIED OVER THE SPECTRAL RANGE

It is sometimes stated that in systems uncorrected for chromatic error the illumination in the spectral image changes throughout the spectrum; the magnitude of this change depends on the circumstances of design. Suppose the lenses of the collimator and the camera to be of the same material, and the system, as in some monochromators, to be always maintained in correct adjustment for collimated light incident upon the prism, i.e. the collimator and telescope are individually focused as the wavelength is altered. As both f_1 and f_2 are proportional to $(\mu - 1)$, where μ is the refractive index of the material, it is clear that the influence of refractive index vanishes in the term f_1/f_2 but not in the terms $\sin^2 \theta_1$ or $\sin^2 \theta_2$. The value of E_2, and also of F_2, must therefore be subject to a variation with wavelength. If, as in spectrographs, the collimator is in correct adjustment for one wavelength only, the overall magnification alters through the spectrum, and the effect upon $\sin^2 \theta_2$ of a variation in μ is enhanced. While calculation of this effect is quite simple it requires detailed knowledge of the design of the instrument.

Sawyer quotes the case of a quartz lens used in a spectrograph at wavelengths 2265 Å and 3961 Å, and he states that the illumination alters, from this cause alone, in the ratio of 1·23 : 1.

It follows from what has been said, that, in continuous spectra, the light-gathering power of the system appears to be greater in regions of low dispersion. In fact, a correction proportional to the reciprocal of $d\beta/d\lambda$ must be applied. For a prism of angle A used at minimum deviation

$$\frac{d\beta}{d\mu} = \frac{2\sin(A/2)}{\sqrt{[1-\mu^2\sin^2(A/2)]}}$$

as may be seen by differentiating the expression for the deviation. For a 60° prism this reduces to

$$\frac{d\beta}{d\mu} = \frac{2}{\sqrt{(4-\mu^2)}}$$

Now μ for any substance may be expressed approximately by a Hartmann formula of the form, $(\mu-\mu_0)(\lambda-\lambda_0) = c$, where μ_0, λ_0 and c are constants. Therefore, by differentiation,

$$\frac{d\mu}{d\lambda} = \frac{-c}{(\lambda-\lambda_0)^2}$$

whence

$$\frac{d\beta}{d\lambda} = \frac{d\beta}{d\mu}\cdot\frac{d\mu}{d\lambda} = \frac{-2c}{(\lambda-\lambda_0)^2\sqrt{(4-\mu^2)}}$$

For a 60° prism of flint glass typical constants may be $\lambda_0 = 2034\cdot6$, $c = 146\cdot23$, $\mu_0 = 1\cdot617$, so that at a wavelength of 4358 Å, e.g.

$$\frac{d\beta}{d\lambda} = 4\cdot99\times10^{-5}\ \text{rad/Å}$$

CURVATURE OF SPECTRAL LINES

It is a matter of common observation that spectral lines are curved. The light coming from the entrance slit is collimated before passing through the prism; this does not, however, mean that the light consists of a single parallel beam but of an infinite set of parallel beams, each originating at one point of the slit. It is only from the point at the centre of the slit that the light traverses the prism in the plane normal to the refracting faces. For all other parallel beams, the light is inclined to this plane and the prism therefore is of effectively greater angle. This results in a greater deviation of the light from the top and bottom of the slit, with the result that the spectral image is curved.

U

Kayser[2] treats this in detail, and Hartinger[3] gives the following expression for r, the radius of curvature of the spectral line formed by a 60° prism at minimum deviation:

$$r = \frac{f_2 \mu \sqrt{(4-\mu^2)}}{2(\mu^2-1)}$$

More complicated expressions may be derived giving r as a function of the angle of incidence, for any arbitrary path through a prism of any angle.

In designing a monochromator either the exit or the entrance slit should be appropriately curved, for otherwise there will result a great decrease in spectral purity and in consequent resolution.

TRANSMISSION OF LIGHT THROUGH THE PRISM

Light falling on the prism surfaces suffers a loss by reflection and this loss follows the well-known expressions for reflection first given by Fresnel. In Fig. 13.4, if the light is incident at an angle θ_1, the refracted angle θ_2 is given by Snell's law

$$\mu_1 \sin \theta_1 = \mu_2 \sin \theta_2$$

Fresnel's equations for reflection differ according as the electric vector of the incident light is in, or perpendicular to, the plane of incidence, and this is denoted by the subscripts p and s respectively. The expressions are

$$I_{3s} = I_{1s} \frac{\sin^2(\theta_2-\theta_1)}{\sin^2(\theta_2+\theta_1)} \tag{13.11}$$

$$I_{3p} = I_{1p} \frac{\tan^2(\theta_1-\theta_2)}{\tan^2(\theta_1+\theta_2)} \tag{13.12}$$

where I is the luminous intensity.

It will be noted from their symmetry that the reflection loss on incidence θ_1 at the interface between medium μ_1 and medium μ_2 is the same as the reflection loss at an angle of incidence θ_2 at an interface between medium μ_2 and medium μ_1. In Fig. 13.5 these equations are plotted graphically; it will be noted that at all angles of incidence other than 0° or 90° the curve for reflection of the s component lies above that of the p component. Moreover at an angle of incidence known as the Brewster angle the reflection of the p component falls to zero.

As a rule, the light incident on a prism is unpolarized, but the effect of incidence on the prism faces at angles differing from normal results in different reflection losses for the rays polarized in the two possible directions parallel and perpendicular to the plane of incidence. As a result the light after transmission is partially linearly polarized.

Pickering[4] calculated the loss of light by reflection and gave tables of the results. It will be realized that if a train of prisms is used, as the light passes through surface after surface, it becomes progressively more and

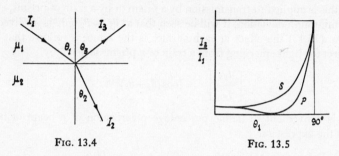

FIG. 13.4   FIG. 13.5

more linearly polarized. When the light has become completely polarized, then, if the prism angles are such that the incidence is at the Brewsterian angle, there ensues no further loss by reflection no matter how long the train of prisms. This explains the variation of transmission as the number of prisms and their refractive indices and angles are altered; it is discussed in Baly's 'Spectroscopy', Vol. 1 pp. 68–71, where a selection of relevant tables is to be found. At minimum deviation the angle of incidence equals the Brewsterian angle for prisms of $67°22'$, when $\mu = 1 \cdot 5$; $64°0'$, when $\mu = 1 \cdot 6$; and $60°56'$, when $\mu = 1 \cdot 7$. As the refractive indices of commonly used glasses centre around $1 \cdot 7$, this explains the usual choice of a prism angle of $60°$.

POLARIZATION PRODUCED BY PRISM INSTRUMENTS

As has been mentioned, passage through any refracting surface at abnormal angles of incidence results in partial linear polarization of the light. Calculation of the magnitude of this effect is useful and instructive; the effect is often unknown or ignored—at times with surprising consequences.

The transmitted intensity I_2 may be obtained by consideration of the principle of conservation of energy, from which it follows that

$$I_1 = I_2 + I_3 \text{ (Fig. 13.4)}$$

therefore

$$I_2 = I_1 \left(1 - \frac{I_3}{I_1} \right)$$

We may now consider the ratio of the energy transmitted by the two components polarized in the s and p directions. From Fresnel's reflection equations it may quickly be shown that

$$\frac{I_{2s}}{I_{2p}} = \cos^2(\theta_1 - \theta_2) \qquad (13.13)$$

If this is applied to transmission by a prism or by a train of prisms, each at minimum deviation, it will be seen that as $\theta_1 \sim \theta_2$ only is involved in eqn. (13.13) the effect at each surface is the same; it follows that the effect for light emerging from a train of n prisms is given by

$$\left[\frac{I_{2s}}{I_{2p}}\right]_n = [\cos(\theta_1 - \theta_2)]^{4n}$$

It is convenient to define percentage polarization of a beam of light by the expression

$$\text{Percentage polarization} = 100\frac{I_p - I_s}{I_p + I_s} = 100\frac{1 - I_s/I_p}{1 + I_s/I_p}$$

For example, for a single prism of 60° and light of a wavelength for which the refractive index of the prism is 1·63, the angle of incidence at minimum deviation is 54°35′, so that

$$(\theta_1 - \theta_2) = 24°35' \text{ and } \cos^4 = 24°35' = 0·6838$$

thus

percentage polarization $= 100 \times 0·3162/1·6838 = 18·8$ per cent

and is such that the emergent light is partially plane polarized, with the electric vector parallel to the plane of incidence. For a refractive index of 1·7, the percentage polarization will be greater, and for a train of prisms it will be so great that the light is very strongly polarized indeed. In a spectrograph, where the photographic plate is inclined steeply to the direction of the light, there will be a further marked effect. This will result in making it difficult to record spectra of incident light which is polarized with the electric vector parallel to the entrance slit. The difficulty is important in Raman spectroscopy.

Not only does this effect result in instruments with several prisms being almost opaque to light polarized with the electric vector parallel to the entrance slit, but in a monochromator used with unpolarized incident light the light emerging from the exit slit may be very strongly polarized. As detecting elements may have very marked anisotropy towards the plane of polarization, this may have serious consequences, e.g. a photocell in which the light falls obliquely on the photocathode is much more sensitive to light polarized with the electric vector in the plane of incidence on the photocathode, than it is to light polarized with the electric vector at right-angles to this. Marked differences in response will be obtained if the relative orientation of the photocell and monochromator are altered.

In instruments with crystalline quartz lenses or prisms, there will be additional complications due to rotation of the plane of polarization by each component. It is not possible to generalize about the effects; each case must be considered individually. Instances where this effect has produced fringes in the spectrum have been reported by Ellis and Kaplan,[5] by Barer[6] and by Gibson and Balcolm.[7]

Approximate compensation of the effect of polarization produced by the instrument may, if necessary, e.g. in spectrophotometric comparison of two polarized beams, be achieved by the use of a second set of reflecting surfaces. This appears to have been first done by Hüfner[8] in the design of his spectrophotometer, in this the dividing rhomb and the prism were of the same glass and the angle of incidence on the rhomb was the same as that on the prism, the planes of incidence on the rhomb and the prism being rotated through a right-angle with respect to one another. Another example of its use was given by Durfee and Taylor[9] in which approximate compensation was achieved by using a plane parallel plate of the same refractive index as the prism. This was inserted in the collimated beam, in such a position that the angles of incidence on the plate and on the prism were the same, and so placed that the planes of incidence on the plate and on the prism were mutually perpendicular. Here the compensation is not exact because multiple reflections occur within the plate. Though these give coherent beams, which add by amplitudes, for a comparatively thick plate the phases of these beams are sufficiently random for summation by intensities to be correct. In these circumstances it may be shown that, as a result, transmission of the s component is about 3 per cent greater than simple calculation would give. To use the example above, a plane parallel plate of refractive index 1·63 so placed that the angle of incidence upon it is 54°35′ would produce a partial polarization of about 17·4 per cent. A slight increase in the angle of tilt of the plate is sufficient to increase the partial polarization so that it exactly equals that produced by the prism. Adjustment by trial and error is better than by calculation.

CRITICAL SLIT WIDTH

Spectrographs

In the spectroscopy of line sources the question of the optimum value of the entrance slit is important. Many writers have considered this problem and it will be convenient to review briefly some of these discussions.

Schuster[10] considered a slit of width δx_1 at the focus of a collimator lens of focal length f_1 and of diameter a_1. The camera lens which forms the image is of at least equal diameter. From consideration of simple diffraction theory the spectral image of an infinitely narrow slit in monochromatic light has an angular half width α, where $\alpha = \lambda/a_1$. If the slit is now widened to δx_1, then according to geometrical optics the angular width of the image is increased by $\delta x_1/f_1$; the total angular width of the image is now given by

$$\left(\frac{\delta x_1}{f_1} + \frac{\lambda}{a_1} \right)$$

If the dispersion is $d\beta/d\lambda$ and $\delta\lambda$ is the spectral range corresponding to this angular width, then

$$\delta\lambda = \left(\frac{\delta x_1}{f_1} + \frac{\lambda}{a_1} \right) \frac{d\lambda}{d\beta}$$

If we denote the resolving power by $P = \lambda/\delta\lambda$, where $\delta\lambda$ is now the least resolvable difference in wavelength, we have

$$P = \frac{\lambda(d\beta/d\lambda)}{(\delta x_1/f_1) + (\lambda/a_1)}$$

$P \to a_1(d\beta/d\lambda)$ as the slit width $\delta x_1 \to 0$, and $P \to (\lambda f_1/\delta x_1)(d\beta/d\lambda)$ when δx_1 becomes large. If now Rayleigh's criterion for the perfection of optical images is adopted, namely that so long as the extreme path difference between the edges of the slit to any point on the lens aperture does not exceed $\lambda/8$ the perfection of the optical image is unimpaired, it follows that the critical slit width is given by $\delta x_1 \not> \lambda f_1/4a_1$. Schuster calls this value of the slit width the 'normal slit width'. Wadsworth has criticized this conclusion and has pointed out that critical definition in the image was still attained when the slit width exceeded the value given by Schuster.

Van Cittert[11] gave an exhaustive treatment of the subject on rather different lines; he discussed the problem from the point of view of the various modes of illumination of the entrance slit. Two modes in particular may be distinguished, the coherent and the non-coherent. For example, the illumination of the slit is non-coherent if, as in Fig. 13.2 the source is imaged upon the slit, i.e. each point in the slit is effectively a separate and independent source; if a small and distant source is used without any condenser lens the illumination is coherent. Van Cittert uses the quantity $\pi a_1 \delta x_1/2\lambda f_1$ as a parameter and finds that when this parameter $= \pi/2$, i.e. when $\delta x_1 = \lambda f_1/a_1$, the intensity at the mid-point of the image, when the illumination is noncoherent, is a maximum. This is to be compared with Schuster's conclusion that at $\delta x_1 = 2\lambda f_1/a_1$ the intensity is 0·9 of the maximum possible from an infinitely wide slit, and that the spectral purity has fallen to only one-half the maximum possible from an infinitely narrow slit. Van Cittert finds, for illumination of the slit in the coherent mode, that there is a maximum of intensity at the centre of the spectral image for a slit width

$$\delta x_1 = \frac{2\lambda f_1}{a_1}$$

As a practical guide, it may be noted that this width is sufficient just to fill the collimator lens with the central maximum of the diffraction pattern. A simple rule for setting the slit width is then as follows:

> With a normal source of illumination such as an arc or a Pointolite lamp, a wide slit, and with no condensing lens in place, the observer looks into the camera lens. The slit width is now decreased until the characteristic Fraunhofer diffraction pattern appears. The narrowing of the slit is continued until the two first dark bands bounding the central maximum separate and just reach the edge of the lens mount. The slit then has the critical width $2\lambda f_1/a_1$.

A careful experimental examination of the problem has been made by Stockbarger and Burns,[12] and their work confirmed that when the slit width has this critical value the best resolution is obtained.

Measurements on the intensity of spectral lines should be made under conditions such that the contour of the spectral image is flat-topped. This implies the use of a fairly wide entrance slit, which, however, must be no wider than necessary if a serious loss of resolving power is to be avoided. Stockbarger and Burns say that a slit width of four times the critical value, together with a condensing lens of numerical aperture one-half that of the collimator lens, is the one nearest to giving spectral lines with a flat-topped intensity distribution. It is interesting to note that Schuster states that a slit of critical width, combined with a condensing lens of double the numerical aperture of the collimator, gives maximum intensity in the image. For measurements of intensity to be reliable this would be most undesirable, and it is important to realize that, for line spectroscopy with slit widths of this order of magnitude, the aperture of the condensing lens is important.

When use is made of a monochromator system, the entrance-slit width must exceed the equivalent exit-slit width if flat-topped contours are to be obtained from the spectral response curve of the detector.

CORRECTIONS FOR FINITE SLIT WIDTHS

The end of experimental observations of spectral energy distribution is to obtain a graph representing the spectral energy $E(\lambda)$ at any wavelength as a function of the wavelength λ. In practice it is necessary to work with finite slit widths. Although with line spectra the critical slit widths discussed in the previous section may sometimes be achieved, with absorption spectra, particularly in regions of low energy, both entrance and exit slits have usually to be very much wider. In consequence we obtain from the experiment, not $E(\lambda)\delta\lambda$, but a quantity

$$\int_0^\infty W(\lambda)d\lambda$$

where $W(\lambda)$ is a function depending on a number of instrumental and experimental factors.

A great many writers have discussed the problem, and partial solutions have been offered by many, notably Rayleigh,[13] Runge,[14] Paschen[15] and Slater.[16] The latter treats the subject somewhat as follows. The spectrometer is supposed to be illuminated with light of a definite wavelength range; the pass-band of the instrument extends from λ to $\lambda+\Delta\lambda$. Let $\phi(\lambda)$ be the observed experimental distribution of energy incident upon the detector; then

$$\phi(\lambda) = \int_\lambda^{\lambda+\Delta\lambda} W(\lambda)\, d\lambda$$

This expression assumes that there is no scattered light of wavelength outside the pass-band reaching the detector. Suppose that $W(\lambda)$ may, over the wavelength range considered, be expressed as a power series of only a few terms. Within the narrow pass-band $\Delta\lambda$ we may neglect all but the first two of these terms, so that within this range $W(\lambda)$ may be represented by a parabola. Denote this by $W_0(\lambda)$ and let it pass through the points $W(\lambda_0)$, $W(\lambda_0+\Delta\lambda/2)$ and $W(\lambda_0-\Delta\lambda/2)$, all of which, it should be noted, lie upon the true curve. Then $\phi_0(\lambda)$ is the average value of $W(\lambda)$ over the range, and is given approximately by substitution of $W_0(\lambda)$ for the true $W(\lambda)$. Hence

$$\phi(\lambda_0) = \frac{1}{\Delta\lambda} \int_{\lambda-(\Delta\lambda/2)}^{\lambda+(\Delta\lambda/2)} W_0(\lambda)\, d\lambda$$

The following simple rule may be deduced. Plot the experimental curve of $\phi(\lambda)$ against λ', take two points thereon separated by the pass-band width $\Delta\lambda$, and join them by a straight line. Draw the vertical ordinate λ_0 half-way between these two points, and measure on it the intercept between the curve and the straight line. One-third of this intercept subtracted from the $\phi(\lambda)$ curve gives a point lying on the true $W(\lambda)$ curve. If the curve $W(\lambda)$ may be identified with the curve $E(\lambda)$, i.e. if variation in spectral sensitivity of the detector may be neglected, then the result gives the desired solution. It must be recalled that a number of possible sources of error have been from the outset omitted in this discussion.

CORRECTION FOR ESTIMATING TRUE LINE SHAPE

Boillet[17] has given a method for finding the shape of spectral lines from experimental observations.

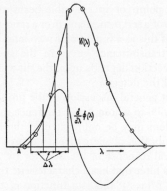

Fig. 13.6

The experimental curve $\phi(\lambda)$ is measured and $d\phi(\lambda)/d\lambda$ is plotted against λ. This curve is divided into segments by vertical ordinates $\Delta\lambda$ apart, by starting with the point A for which $\lambda = \lambda_1$, and $d\phi(\lambda)/d\lambda = 0$, as shown in Fig. 13.6. The coordinates of points lying on the true curve $W(\lambda)$ are then

$$\lambda = \lambda_1 + (n - \tfrac{1}{2})\Delta\lambda \text{ and } W(\lambda) = \sum^{n} \frac{d}{d\lambda}\phi(\lambda_n)$$

It may be noted that the maximum value of $W(\lambda)$ does not necessarily occur at the wavelength λ_m for which $\phi(\lambda)$ is a maximum, but lies between $(\lambda_m + \Delta\lambda/2)$ and $(\lambda_m - \Delta\lambda/2)$. A simplification ensues if the slit width is greater than the line width, i.e. the flat-topped condition referred to earlier; the maximum of $W(\lambda)$ now lies half-way between the two points of inflexion of the curve of $\phi(\lambda)$.

As in the previous discussion, it should be noted that the resulting curve, believed to represent the true course of $W(\lambda)$, is not necessarily to be identified with $E(\lambda)$. Such identification implies a neglect of instrumental factors, and justification for this must be sought within the framework of the individual experiment.

SPECTROPHOTOMETRY

Spectrophotometry is concerned with the measurement of the spectral transmittance or spectral reflectance of the substance under investigation. Continuous radiation is used, and a monochromator selects a narrow range of wavelengths from this radiation; the response of the detector to this selected radiation, with and without the presence of the sample, is determined. Comparison of these two values is obtained either manually point by point, or in a double-beam automatic recording intrument, by means of a servo-mechanism or a ratio-recorder. The curve showing the result of this as a function of wavelength does not however represent the true transmittance curve of the specimen, and needs correction. This correction depends upon the slit widths, the source, the monochromator and the detector.

A recent and most general discussion of the problem has been given by Hardy & Young,[18] to whose paper reference must be made for full details. Their problem may be enunciated in the following way.

The spectral distribution of energy from a source may be denoted by $E(\lambda)$, and the spectral response of the detector by $S(\lambda)$. A monochromator is a band-pass filter that has a characteristic transmittance, which may be denoted by $M(y, \lambda)$; this is a function of the drum setting y, and of the wavelength λ of the radiation considered. The actual response of the detector at any wavelength setting is given by

$$\int_0^\infty E(\lambda) S(\lambda) M(y, \lambda) \, d\lambda = \int_0^\infty W(\lambda) \, d\lambda$$

If now an absorbing material be inserted in the path of the radiation, and the spectral transmittance is denoted by $t(\lambda)$, we have $T(y)$, the ratio of the response with and without the absorbing material for a particular setting of the wavelength drum, given by

$$T(y) = \frac{\displaystyle\int_0^\infty W(\lambda) t(\lambda) \, d\lambda}{\displaystyle\int_0^\infty W(\lambda) \, d\lambda} \qquad (13.14)$$

The problem is to find $t(\lambda)$, given a set of experimental values of $T(y)$ for different values of y.

Hardy & Young conclude that the solution is

$$t(y) = T(y) - \sum_{n=1}^{\infty} a_n \frac{d^n T(y)}{dy^n}$$

where the a's are functions of y. If the instrument is calibrated by the use of a line source and very narrow slits it may be assumed that $y \equiv \lambda$ and hence $t(\lambda) \equiv t(y)$.

Now Van den Akker[19] attacked the problem experimentally. He postulated that a filter of an approximately linear characteristic $t(\lambda) = a + b\lambda$ was available. On substituting this in eqn. (13.14), we obtain

$$T(\lambda) = a + b \; \frac{\displaystyle\int_0^\infty W(\lambda)\,\lambda\,d\lambda}{\displaystyle\int_0^\infty W(\lambda)\,d\lambda}$$

There is an effective wavelength

$$\lambda_e = \frac{\displaystyle\int_0^\infty W(\lambda)\,\lambda\,d\lambda}{\displaystyle\int_0^\infty W(\lambda)\,d\lambda}$$

which gives, for measurement in continuous radiation, the same value of $T(\lambda_e)$ as that obtained by measurement with monochromatic light of wavelength λ. The usual experimental method of using this result is to obtain $T(\lambda)$ in monochromatic light, and then by trial and error to find λ_e such that the same value is obtained for $T(\lambda_e)$. The difference $\lambda - \lambda_e$ is the correction to be applied when the instrument is used with continuous radiation. This is, in fact, the first term a_1 in the equation derived by Hardy & Young. Second-order correction terms are discussed by them, and their magnitude can, if necessary, be derived from measurements of transmittance of two samples of different thickness. For details of these calculations, which look more formidable than they are, reference may be made to the original paper.[20]

AUTOMATIC CORRECTION FOR SLIT WIDTH

Hardy and Young suggest that a straight edge of proper slope, placed across the top of one of the slits of the monochromator, would cause the effective wavelength of the pass-band to be that given by the drum reading (i.e. the value which it would in fact have if the bilateral slits were narrowed to their limit). The slope of this straight edge may be adjusted to reduce the calibration error to zero. A cam may be cut to maintain this slope automatically correct throughout the spectrum.

REFERENCES

1. NIELSEN, J. R. *J. Opt. Soc. Amer.* (1930) **20**, p. 701.
2. KAYSER, H. 'Handbuch der Spektroskopie' (S. Hirzel, Leipzig, 1900), Vol. 1, p. 319, *et. seq.*
3. HARTINGER, H. 'Handbuch der Physik' (Julius Springer, Berlin, 1927) **18**, p. 236.
4. PICKERING, E. C. *Phil. Mag.* (1868) **4**, pp. 36, 39.
5. ELLIS, J. W., and KAPLAM, J. *J. Opt. Soc. Amer.* (1935) **25**, p. 357 and (1937) **27**, p. 94.
6. BARER, R. *J. Sci. Instrum.* (1949) **26**, p. 325.
7. GILSON, K. S. and BALCOLM, M. M. *J. Opt. Soc. Amer.* (1947) **37**, p. 593.
8. HUFNER, G. *Z. Phys. Chem.* (1889) **1B**, p. 562.; MARTIN, L. C. 'Optical measuring Instruments' (Blackie, 1924) p. 223.
9. DURFEE, D. and TAYLOR, A. M. *J. Opt. Soc. Amer.* (1933) **23**, p. 263.
10. SCHUSTER, A. *Astrophys. J.* (1905) **21**, p. 197.
11. VAN CITTERT, P. H. *Z. Phys.* (1930) **65**, p. 547 and (1931) **69**, p. 298.
12. STOCKBARGER, D. C. and BURNS, L. *J. Opt. Soc. Amer.* (1933) **23**, p. 379.
13. Lord RAYLEIGH. *Phil. Mag.* (1871) **42**, p. 441.
14. RUNGE, C. *Z. Maths* (1897) **42**, p. 205.
15. PASCHEN, F. *Wied. Ann.* (1897) **60**, p. 712.
16. SLATER, J. C. *Phys. Rev.* (1923) **25**, p. 783.
17. BOILLET, P. *Rev. opt. (Theor. Instrum.)* (1945) **24**, p. 85.
18. HARDY, A. C. and YOUNG, F. M. *J. Opt. Soc. Amer.* (1949) **39**, p. 265.
19. VAN DEN AKKER, J. A. *J. Opt. Soc. Amer.* (1943) **33**, p. 257.
20. HARDY, A. C. and YOUNG, F. M. *loc. cit.*, p. 269.

BIBLIOGRAPHY

BALY, E. C. C. 'Spectroscopy' (Longmans Green & Co. London, 1924).
CANDLER, C. 'Practical Spectroscopy' (Hilger & Watts, London, 1949).
HARRISON, C. R., LORD, R. C. and LOOFBOUROW, J. R. 'Practical Spectroscopy' (Blackie, London, 1948).
LOTHIAN, G. F. 'Absorption Spectrophotometry' (Hilger & Watts, London, Second Edition 1958).
SAWYER, R. A. 'Experimental Spectroscopy' (Chapman & Hall, London, 1945).

Chapter Fourteen

POLARIZED-BEAM TECHNIQUES IN INFRA-RED SPECTROMETRY

By A. Elliott

Introduction

It is now more than fifty years since Merritt [1] showed that the absorption coefficient of a crystalline material may depend on the direction of the electric vector of the absorbed beam. Although examples of this phenomenon (known as *dichroism* or sometimes as *pleochroism*) are to be found in the older literature, [2] it is only fairly recently that results have been obtained which add much to our knowledge of molecular structure. This may be attributed in part to lack of a convenient and efficient technique for producing polarized radiation over a wide range of wavelengths, and to the fact that polarized-beam techniques are particularly suited to the study of organic compounds containing co-valent linkages of which the infra-red spectra are much better understood now than formerly. A third factor is that polarized radiation is proving of use in the field of high polymers, itself of relatively recent growth. Since the technique of infra-red spectroscopy is now being developed and extended fairly rapidly, it is natural that such developments should allow the use of techniques long familiar in the visible region of the spectrum. As will be shown later, it is now possible, in suitable cases, to determine approximately the directions of various covalent linkages in a molecule by means of polarized infra-red radiation.

We now consider the various methods available for producing a plane polarized beam of infra-red radiation.

Production of Plane Polarized Radiation

(a) Double Refraction

The double refraction of calcite may be used from the visible region to a wavelength of about 2μ, enabling a number of overtone and combination bands to be observed with polarized radiation. Ellis and his co-workers have made many such observations. Longer wavelengths, in the region where the fundamental vibrations occur, cannot be observed because of the absorption of calcite. It may be noted that none of the crystals commonly used for windows in the infra-red region (alkali halides, thallium halides, fluorite, etc.) are doubly refracting.

(b) Dichroism

Dichroic filters, such as Polaroid, are now much used in the visible region. They consist of highly oriented molecular structures which absorb strongly the component of radiation falling on them that makes an appropriate angle with the molecular axes. The other component is transmitted and this transmitted radiation is therefore plane polarized. Such polarizers may consist of oriented crystal layers, but the current types of Polaroid consist of oriented high polymers. The polarizing properties of Polaroid do not extend far enough into the infra-red region to interest spectroscopists, but Blake, Makas and West[3] in a communication from the Polaroid laboratories have referred to a heat-treated oriented polymer film containing iodine, which is said to have useful polarizing properties in the region from $0.75-2.8\mu$. Such a polarizer would cover the region of overtones and combination bands, but is inadequate for most fundamental bands.

(c) Reflection from Dielectric

One of the oldest methods of producing plane polarized light is to reflect a beam of natural light from a flat surface of a dielectric (e.g. glass) at the Brewster or polarizing angle θ, where $\tan \theta = n$. The reflected beam is completely plane polarized. The same method can be used in the infra-red region if a transparent dielectric is used. The intensity of the beam reflected at the polarizing angle increases with the refractive index of the polarizing angle; hence it is an advantage to use a material of high refractive index. Pfund[4] has used selenium ($n = 2.54$) which can be used from the visible region to wavelengths 15μ at least, and possibly further. This enables many of the most important fundamental vibrations to be observed.

The reflection polarizer produces high polarization, but the intensity of the reflected beam (see Fig. 14.1) from selenium is only about 25 per cent of the incident beam, and hence half of the intensity of the polarized component is lost. In infra-red spectroscopy this is a serious loss. A further disadvantage of the reflection polarizer is that the direction of the beam is changed by reflection. The beam may be brought back to its original direction by means of two more reflections (from metallic mirrors), but the arrangement is clumsy and takes up much space. Further, if the polarizer is removed from the beam, the length of the optical path is changed. It will be seen from Fig. 14.1 that the E vector of the reflected beam is normal to the plane of incidence.

(d) Transmission Polarizer

The property of a dielectric to reflect polarized radiation at the Brewster angle can be used to make a polarizer in which the transmitted beam is used. Since the beam transmitted by a single surface contains a considerable component with the E vector normal to the plane of incidence, it is necessary to employ a number of reflecting surfaces to

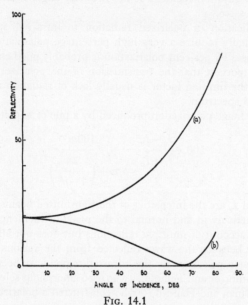

Fig. 14.1

Reflection from a dielectric (selenium). (*J. Opt. Soc. of Amer.*)

$n = 2.54$
(a) Electric vector perpendicular to plane of incidence.
(b) Electric vector parallel to plane of incidence.

make the transmitted beam sufficiently polarized. This device has long been known as the 'pile of plates' or the 'poor man's nicol prism', and such piles of glass plates were at one time used when a wide beam of polarized light was required.

It should be noted that if the radiation falls at the Brewster angle on each surface of a pile of plates (and this of course means that a parallel beam must be used), the number of plates can be increased without limit and provided that the surfaces are clean and the plates transparent, there is no loss of intensity in the beam whose E vector is in the plane of incidence. With an increasing number of plates, the transmitted beam becomes more perfectly plane polarized.

In practice, the surfaces cannot be expected to remain clean, and it is therefore a great advantage if, by employing a dielectric of high refractive index, the number of plates required to produce the necessary polarization can be kept small. It would be inconvenient if a polarizer could not be used in a converging or diverging beam, and this provides a second reason for keeping the number of plates small, since the loss of radiation for rays not incident at the Brewster angle would otherwise become excessive.

The application of polarized radiation to infra-red spectroscopy does not usually require a very high percentage polarization, and for many purposes 95 per cent polarization is probably good enough. It is, however, important that the transmission of the polarizer should be high, since the limiting factor is usually lack of radiation intensity in the infra-red spectrum.

The percentage polarization produced by a pile of m plates is

$$100 \times \frac{I_\pi - I_\sigma}{I_\pi + I_\sigma} = \frac{100m}{m + \left(\dfrac{2n}{1-n^2}\right)^2} \tag{14.1}$$

where I_π and I_σ are the intensities of the transmitted beams with the E vector respectively in and normal to the plane of incidence. Formula (14.1) takes account of multiple reflections but does not allow for any interference between the waves reflected from the various surfaces. [5]

Transmission polarizers for the infra-red region have been described by Elliott, Ambrose and Temple, [6] who used amorphous selenium films, and by Newman and Halford, [7] who constructed a polarizer of silver-chloride sheet.

The selenium polarizer employs films of amorphous selenium which are formed by evaporating the element *in vacuo* on a temporary backing of, for instance, cellulose nitrate, which is later dissolved off. The various stages are shown in Fig. 14.2. The film on its base is fastened to one edge of a brass foil support by means of a protein glue such as Lepage's, the selenium-coated side being attached to the metal. The film is then trimmed to the same size as the frame, by using a razor blade, and stuck down to the frame in several places with a weak solution of cellulose nitrate in amyl acetate, and allowed to dry. It is next held vertically in a vessel containing acetone, the glued edge being uppermost. The base and cellulose nitrate cement are dissolved away, leaving the selenium film attached to the frame by its upper edge only. The frame is withdrawn from the acetone, and it will be found that surface-tension forces have stretched it neatly over the frame, to which it adheres on drying.

To make a polarizer, five or six mounted films are set up in a holder so that radiation falls on them at an angle of 65°. The films are fragile, but such polarizers are quite serviceable. The life is prolonged by protecting them from extremes of temperature. The films used are very thin (approximately 3μ thick; in this thickness the colour of a single film is similar to that of a Wratten 89 filter).

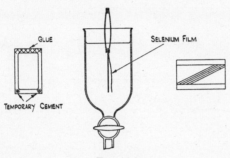

Fig. 14.2

Stages in the manufacture of a selenium polarizer.

The performance of such polarizers is very good. With five films, the transmission is about 47 per cent and the percentage polarization better than 94 per cent in the wavelength region $2-14\mu$. With six films, the corresponding figures are 43 per cent and 98 per cent. It is a great advantage of the selenium polarizer that the films are so thin that they are practically without effect on the optical path and do not displace the beam traversing them.

The silver-chloride polarizer is more robust, but is less efficient than selenium on account of the lower refractive index. The performance quoted for a pile of six sheets is 91 per cent for the percentage polarization, 52 per cent transmission at a wavelength of 8μ and 40 per cent transmission at a wavelength of 3μ.

It may be noted that, with complete polarization, no interference fringes can be produced as a result of reflections at the surfaces of the polarizing plates, for the polarized transmitted beam is not capable of being reflected at the polarizing angle. Interference fringes may be produced in an imperfect polarizer. The effect is shown in Fig. 14.3, which shows interference fringes produced by a single plate. When, however, a pile of plates instead of a single plate is interposed in the beam, the fringes are much reduced. It may happen, however, if the plates are very uniform in thickness that interference effects persist to an undesirable extent, and it is advisable to make up a pile from plates of three different thicknesses, so chosen that the interference peaks do not coincide.[8] The behaviour of polarizers consisting of thin plates has been discussed by Conn and Eaton.[9]

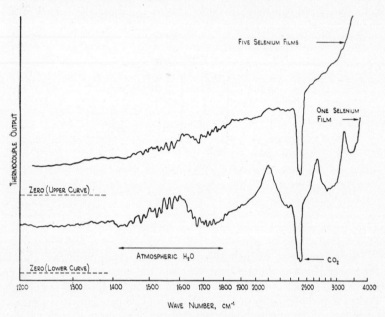

FIG. 14.3
Interference fringes in spectra. (*J. Opt. Soc. Amer.*)

PREPARATION OF ORIENTED SPECIMENS

The preparation of suitably thin, oriented specimens constitutes the greatest difficulty in the use of polarized radiation. It is often necessary to develop a new technique for each material. The following notes give some methods which have proved useful.

(a) Crystals

Single crystals provide ideally oriented specimens, but are often too thick when grown to form plates of convenient size. The use of a reflecting microscope (see below) to form an enlarged image of the specimen on the slit is a help, since it enables smaller crystals to be used. Crystal layers in which a number of crystals have a common direction of orientation are often useful. These may be grown, with some materials, from the melt. This may be done by melting the material between plates of rock salt, etc., and allowing it to cool slowly, if necessary under a weight. The material may be melted on the surface of a rock-salt plate and allowed to cool under the influence of a temperature gradient. [10] It is usually necessary to prepare many specimens and select the most suitable.

When the material does not readily melt, a crystal layer may sometimes be grown from solution. The supporting plate (which must of course be insoluble in the solution) is placed nearly horizontal, partly immersed in the solution, which is allowed to evaporate slowly. In this way a crystalline layer is formed at the drying edge on the upper surface of the supporting plate.

(b) High Polymers

It is often possible to produce considerable orientation in a high polymer by mechanical methods such as stretching a sheet or fibre of the material. This process is frequently assisted by first swelling the material slightly in a suitable swelling agent. Steam is often efficaceous. The material may be mounted in a small rack so that the amount of stretching can be regulated.

Some materials will not stretch in this way without breaking, and it is sometimes possible to cast the material on a base such as rubber or polythene film, which may then be stretched. The support given to the material in this way may allow orientation to be produced. It is generally advisable to employ a swelling agent with such materials.

Perhaps the most generally successful method is extending between the rolls of a small jeweller's rolling mill. If thin films are required, it is generally necessary to cast the film on a support and to roll out support and film together. For support, metals such as lead or cadmium may be used, when the film must of course be stripped from the support. If, however, silver chloride sheet is used, stripping is unnecessary, since silver chloride is transparent to about 12μ. If the polymer softens on heating, it may be useful to heat the rolls by a blast of hot air before rolling the material. It should be noted that rolling and stretching may not produce the same kind of orientation (see below).

(c) Fibrous Materials

Many fibres are too thick for infra-red spectroscopy. Fibres which are not too thick may be mounted side by side to make a larger specimen by a technique which has been described by Holliday. [11] It cannot be expected, of course, that quantitative results can be obtained from such an arrangement, since the thickness is not uniform.

Thicker fibres and a number of natural, oriented structures may be sectioned on a microtome. For examination in a polarized beam such sections will generally be cut parallel to the fibre axis. Soft materials may be cut by the usual techniques, using the standard types of knife supplied with the microtome. It is very difficult to cut very thin sections of hard fibrous material in this way, however. For this purpose I have found it much better to employ a knife sharpened to an angle of 90° and mounted as in Fig. 14.4. It does not appear necessary to do

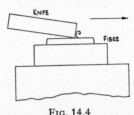

FIG. 14.4
Microtome knife for hard fibres.

any stropping for such a knife, honing on a very fine stone being sufficient. I have, at the suggestion of Dr E. M. Crook, used beryllium-copper for the knife, but it is quite possible that tool steel would be satisfactory.

(d) Mounting of Specimens

Specimens should preferably be mounted on some form of holder so that they may be easily positioned in the spectrometer. Often it is desirable to immerse the specimen in a medium of similar refractive index to reduce scatter; this is usually the case with specimens cut with the 90° knife described in the preceding paragraph. Unfortunately the choice of media is very limited. The most useful are the following:

	Approximate refractive index
Liquid paraffin	1·48
Carbon tetrachloride	1·46
Carbon tetrachloride (10 ml)+Carbon tetrabromide (18 g)	1·53
Carbon disulphide	1·63
Hexachlorobutadiene	1·554

The transparency of the usual solvents for infra-red spectroscopy is discussed by Torkington and Thompson.[12] For the 3μ region specimens may be mounted between glass microscope cover slips.

SPECTROMETER ARRANGEMENT

Magnification

The problem of producing suitable specimens is considerably eased if a magnifying system is used, since it is much easier to make small oriented specimens than large ones. Provided that the aperture of the magnifying system is large enough to fill the collimator mirror of the spectrometer, there is no loss of light grasp involved in this procedure. The angle of the cone of radiation incident on the specimen must be increased in order to satisfy this condition, however, and dichroic effects may be reduced if this angle is made very large. For producing a small magnification ($2\frac{1}{2}$) a simple arrangement of parabolic

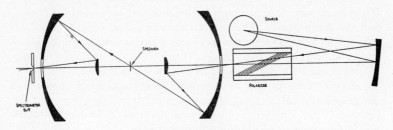

Fig. 14.5
Concentric mirror magnifying system

mirrors may be employed.[13] For higher magnification, some form of reflecting microscope is more suitable.[14, 15, 16, 17] The magnification which can be employed is in any event low, and a reflecting microscope of the concentric spherical surface type is adequate. The general arrangement is given in Fig. 14.5, which shows the magnifying system used by Elliott and Ambrose for their work on the dichroism of single protein crystals.

Whatever design is employed, it is very desirable to have the reflecting microscope made on a large scale to obtain adequate room for the special cells and specimen holders which may be needed. It is also important that the size of the radiation cone which it delivers to the spectrometer should be matched to the collimator aperture.

Position of Polarizer

The effect of a spectrometer on the state of polarization of a radiation beam passing through it is discussed in chapter thirteen. It requires that consideration should be given to the position of the polarizer if dichroism is to be measured accurately.

The ideal arrangement is to have unpolarized radiation on the specimen, followed immediately by the polarizer, the radiation transmitted by the polarizer then falling on the spectrometer slit. With such an arrangement the spectrometer must affect the radiation, when the specimen is in or out of the beam, in the same way, and measured densities will not be affected by polarization in the spectrometer. An equally good arrangement would be to send the radiation through the spectrometer, polarizer and specimen in that order, and then to receive it on a receiver which did not affect its state of polarization. This arrangement has the further advantage that the specimen receives far less radiation than in the first arrangement, and is not so liable to be affected by heating.

When using a reflecting microscope or other magnifying arrangement, it may be impossible to find room for the polarizer between the specimen and the spectrometer. The best arrangement then is to polarize the radiation before it falls on the specimen, if necesssary using a spherical mirror to form an auxiliary image. It may be noted that, as Professor Taylor pointed out in discussion, so long as observations are made with the electric vector parallel to or perpendicular to the spectrometer slit, the polarization of the spectrometer does not introduce errors and the position of the polarizer is relatively unimportant. Such conditions are met in the examination of fibrous high polymers.

Measurement of Absorption

For several reasons, the most convenient function for representing the absorption is the *optical density*, $(d = \log_{10} I_0/I)$ where I_0 and I are the radiation intensities incident on and transmitted by the specimen, respectively. Densities are additive; hence if an absorption band is superposed on an absorbing background, the density of the background may be subtracted to obtain the density of the absorption band.

In order to eliminate absorption by water vapour, changes in intensity resulting from interference bands, etc., it is necessary to measure the radiation at a number of wavelengths, with the specimen removed from the beam. This may be done by one of the various double-beam systems, or simply by moving the specimen in and out of the beam at short time intervals (e.g. 2 sec) by an automatic rocking arrangement. This method is simple and allows the attainment of the maximum accuracy of which the instrument is capable. If the specimen is mounted in an immersion medium between windows, the movement of the rocking mechanism may be arranged to allow the radiation beam to traverse the blank part of the cell in the 'specimen out' position. This eliminates errors from reflection at the window surfaces.

If possible, a wavelength should be found where the specimen does not absorb, and the density should be measured at this point, so that it may be subtracted from other measured densities. This procedure must of course be done for each position of the polarizer, since if radiation does not fall normally on the specimen, reflection losses will depend on the direction of the electric vector.

The labour of measuring up a spectral record is greatly reduced by using an extensible rule, which may be made from a uniform strip of rubber. A natural or light coloured rubber may be ruled with Indian ink. The scale is arranged as shown in Fig. 14.6, running from 0 to

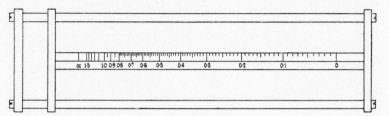

FIG. 14.6
Extensible rubber rule for measuring optical density.

infinity. The scale reading S at any point must be equal to $\log I_0/I$. The scale should be ruled when stretched to its maximum extension, to minimize errors of ruling.

A method of using a reflecting microscope in conjunction with a double-beam spectrometer has been suggested by Blout and Abbate[18] and more recently Ford, Price, Seeds and Wilkinson[19] have described a microspectrometer with an oscillating specimen stage in which the percentage transmission is recorded directly.

Interpretation of Results

The change in molecular state which occurs when a quantum of infra-red radiation is absorbed is accompanied by a change in dipole moment of the molecule. The probability of the quantum transition, and hence the intensity of the absorption band, depends on the rate at which the dipole moment varies with the normal coordinate for the particular normal mode corresponding to the band in question. In principle, the *transition moment*, whose square is proportional to the probability of transition and hence to the absorption intensity, may be calculated by quantum-mechanical methods.[20] All that can in practice be done with polyatomic molecules, however, is to predict from the symmetry of a molecule, by such methods, whether the components of the transition moment along suitably chosen rectangular axes are finite or zero.

When a molecule is irradiated by plane polarized radiation, the intensity of an absorption band depends on the angle between the electric vector of the radiation and the transition moment (which is also a vector). If this angle is θ, the absorption coefficient per molecule is proportional to $\cos^2 \theta$. The direction of the electric vector which gives the maximum absorption coefficient (which is proportional to optical density) gives therefore the direction of the transition moment.

Polarized radiation has hitherto been used chiefly where the transition moment is related (at least qualitatively) in a simple and obvious manner to the direction of a chemical valency bond. Those vibrations of a polyatomic molecule which involve chiefly the motion of light univalent atoms are of this type. We may give as examples the characteristic CH, NH, and OH frequencies. In stretching modes of these groups, the change in dipole moment is approximately along the valency bond, though if hydrogen bonding is present there may be some deviation from this direction. Similarly, in a deformation mode the transition moment in these groups is approximately normal to the valency bond. If there is more than one such group (CH, NH, etc.) in a molecule the *resultant* transition moment for each normal mode of the molecule involving such groups must be found. As an example, in a CH_2 group we have two frequencies which involve stretching of the CH bond. These motions and the corresponding transition moments are shown in Fig. 14.7. The complexity of the situation rapidly increases with an increase in the number of atoms. With linear high polymers, however, it has been suggested (Kellner[21]) that the spectrum consists essentially of the bands which would be given by one of the repeating units of which the polymer is built. The subject of normal modes in linear high polymers has recently been investigated in detail and the relation between the modes of the isolated chain and of chains in the crystalline parts of the polymer is now understood.[22-25] In some cases there may be no simple or close relation between the direction of transition moment and the valency bonds in a chemical group. Fraser and Price have shown that this may be expected in some of the vibration modes of the peptide group and this has been found to be the case in some model compounds.[26,8,27]

In a crystalline arrangement of molecules the interpretation of polarized spectra is complicated by the fact that in general a plane-polarized wave passing through the crystal becomes elliptically polarized. However, there are certain directions of the electric vector for which the plane-polarized character of the wave is maintained, and these should be chosen where possible.[28] It seems likely that in oriented preparations of high polymers containing micro-crystalline regions, the material behaves as if it has cylindrical symmetry if a fibre, and orthorhombic symmetry if a film. It is therefore possible to examine such materials in polarized radiation without complications arising from the plane-polarized wave becoming elliptically polarized. To do this, the direction of the electric vector of the incident beam should be restricted to parallel or perpendicular to the fibre axis. In the case of the film, this vector should be along one of the pseudo-orthorhombic axes.

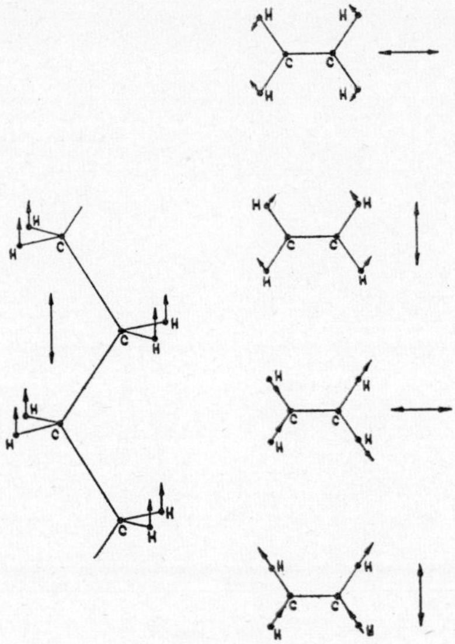

FIG. 14.7
CH$_2$ modes in a long-chain paraffin. The direction of transition moment is indicated by an arrow.

DICHROISM AND MOLECULAR STRUCTURE IN HIGH POLYMERS

(*a*) *Fibre Orientation*

In oriented fibres, the long-chain molecules of which the fibre is composed are arranged more or less along the direction of the fibre. Molecules are to be found in all possible orientations around the fibre axis, however, and the fibre as a whole has axial symmetry. The actual molecular pattern is of course very complicated; in many polymers there are crystalline micelles in which the regularity of arrangement may be quite high, surrounded by less orderly regions and some regions in which the molecules are in a random state. The same molecule may pass through several regions of crystalline micelles.

The vibration modes which give rise to characteristic frequencies often have transition moments that are either *along* the fibre axis (parallel modes) or *at right angles* to it (perpendicular modes). Figs. 14.8–14.10 give some examples. It will be realized that, with fibrous orientation, the dichroism of the symmetric and antisymmetric CH_2 modes should be identical in a fully extended hydrocarbon chain.

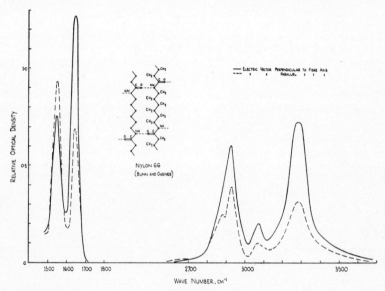

FIG. 14.8

Spectrum of nylon 66

Note—'perpendicular' dichroism of C = 0, C—H and N—H stretching frequencies at 1640, 2900 and 3300 cm⁻¹, respectively. The N—H deformation mode at 1560 cm⁻¹ is parallel.

As an example of the use of polarized radiation in the study of molecular structure, the evidence of chain folding in polypeptides and proteins provided by this method may be mentioned.[29, 30] A straight (fully extended) polypeptide chain has the N–H and C = 0 groups of the peptide at right angles to the chain direction; hence the bands characteristic of these groups should have dichroism similar to that of nylon (Fig. 14.8). Astbury has shown that the X-ray diffraction spacings observed with feather keratin (β keratin) indicate an extended chain, whereas with porcupine quill (α keratin) the spacings indicate some kind of fold. Fig. 14.9 shows that the dichroism of the

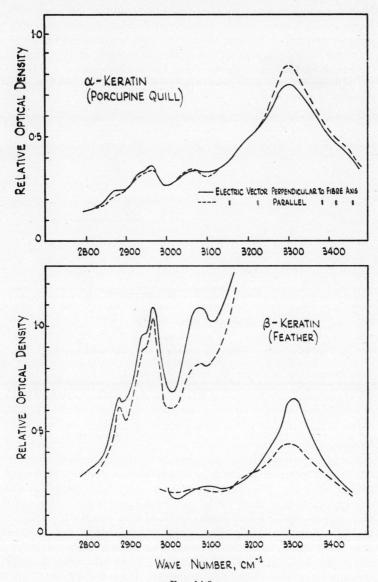

FIG. 14.9

Fibrous proteins. (*Nature*)

Note that the N—H stretching mode at 3300 cm^{-1} is 'perpendicular' in the β-keratin, which has an extended chain, but 'parallel' in the folded configuration of α-keratin.

N–H stretching mode in porcupine quill is *parallel* in character, indicating a folded chain. Similar results may be found in synthetic polypeptides prepared in suitable ways.[31,32] These are shown in Fig. 14.10.

It may be mentioned that the transition moment of the carbonyl band at about 1660 cm^{-1} (shown in Fig. 14.10) is now known to make an angle of about 17° to the C = O valency bond, being inclined towards the CN bond.[26,8,27]

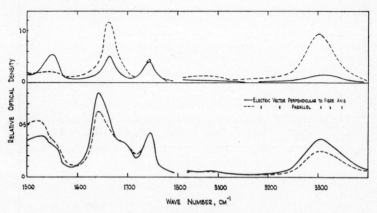

FIG. 14.10

Spectra of poly-γ-methyl-L-glutamate DL phenylalanine 1 : 1.
(Royal Society)

Upper spectrum: polymer cast from *m*-cresol and oriented.
Lower spectrum: polymer cast from formic acid before orientation. Note that dichroism of lower spectrum is similar to that of nylon, showing the polypeptide to be in an extended configuration. The peptide bands of the upper spectrum show reversal of the dichroism as a consequence of chain folding.

Other examples of the use of polarized radiation may be found in references 33–38.

For some purposes it is convenient to represent the state of orientation of a polymer in terms of a hypothetical 'average' molecule (which, of course, like the 'average man', does not exist). Hermans and Platzek[39] have made use of such a concept. For our purposes, we may suppose the actual molecules replaced by a number of (straight) molecules arranged so as to form a cone of semi-angle θ with the fibre axis. If θ is chosen so that this assembly has the same infra-red dichroism as the actual fibre, then θ is an angle which is a measure of the 'average' orientation of the fibre molecules. It has been shown[39] that for *parallel* bands

$$\frac{\log I_0/I_\pi}{\log I_0/I_\sigma} = 2\cot^2\theta$$

Here $\log I_0/I_\pi$ and $\log I_0/I_\sigma$ are the densities of a band measured with the electric vector of the radiation parallel and perpendicular to the fibre axis, respectively. Their ratio is known as the *dichroic ratio*.

For perpendicular bands the dichroic ratio is equal to

$$2 \sin^2 \theta/(2-\sin^2 \theta).$$

With many fibrous materials it is found that the dichroic ratios are low, much lower than would be expected from the orientation of the crystalline portion, as determined from X-ray measurements. This result appears to be a direct consequence of the large amount of amorphous material present Fraser[40] has proposed a model for an oriented polymer consisting of a fraction f of perfectly oriented material, the remainder $1-f$ being completely unoriented. If the transition moment in the oriented part makes an angle α with the fibre axis, then the dichroic ratio is

$$\frac{\log I_0/I_\pi}{\log I_0/I_\sigma} = \frac{f \cos^2 \alpha + \frac{1}{3}(1-f)}{\frac{1}{2}f \sin^2 \alpha + \frac{1}{3}(1-f)}$$

This model has been discussed and extended, and graphs have been published to facilitate its use.[41,42]

A few cases have been reported of bands showing very high dichroism in a spectrum where for the other bands the dichroism is low.[34,35,36] The explanation suggested by Vallance Jones and Sutherland is that these bands derive their intensity chiefly from the crystalline rather than from the amorphous regions. This view is supported by results which they have obtained in an examination of stretched rubber by means of polarized infra-red radiation. Crystalline bands are now known in many polymer spectra, and are often recognized by the high dichroism which they show.

(b) Double Orientation in High Polymers

In suitable cases, greater orientation than that produced in fibres may be obtained. This is particularly the case in rolled sheets of high polymers which have a layer structure. Bunn and Garner[43] have observed such orientation in rolled nylon sheets, which have different refractive indices in each of three mutually perpendicular directions. These directions are: (1) the direction of rolling, (2) perpendicular to the direction of rolling and in the plane of the sheet, and (3) perpendicular to the sheet. This means that certain planes (for instance, the plane containing a layer of nylon molecules all hydrogen-bonded to neighbouring molecules in the layer) are all more or less parallel to one another. The degree of order is however less than that in a crystal, for in the polymer some crystalline regions may be arranged at 180° to

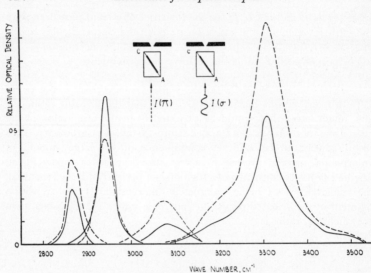

Fig. 14.11

Double orientation in nylon 66. (Royal Society.)

Direction of chain axis (CA), radiation and electric vector shown with reference to spectrometer slit on inserts. The spectra corresponding to π and σ are drawn in broken and full lines respectively.

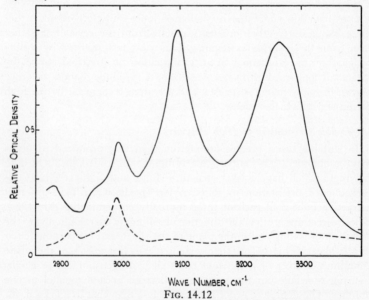

Fig. 14.12

Spectrum of acetyl glycine ethyl ester $CH_3.CO.NH.CO\ OC_2H_5$ with electric vector in each of two mutually perpendicular directions.

Note almost complete disappearance of some bands in one direction of E the electric vector.

other crystalline regions. Bunn and Garner refer to this type of orientation as 'double orientation'.

The use of polarized radiation for doubly oriented polymers should give more information than can be obtained from fibres or sheets which have only fibrous orientation. This requires that radiation should be sent through the oriented sheet in directions other than normal to the sheet. It is not satisfactory merely to tilt the specimen with respect to the incident beam, for refraction at the polymer surface would limit the transmitted beam to angles of refraction within the critical angle, and the reflection losses at the surface would be considerable. The

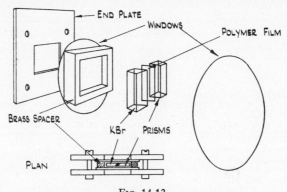

FIG. 14.13
Specimen with radiation at oblique incidence.
(Royal Society)

specimen may, if considerations of solubility and swelling allow, be mounted in a small cell containing carbon tetrachloride[13] arranged so that the angle of incidence may be varied. An alternative method is to mount the specimen between two prisms of rock salt or other transparent material[44] as shown in Fig. 14.13. Optical contact is made between specimen and prisms with a suitable immersion medium. This method may be used for a polymer with the radiation making a small angle to the chain axis, and was used to obtain the spectrum of doubly oriented nylon 66 sheet shown in Fig. 14.11. The different dichroic character of the two CH_2 frequencies is very apparent. This, combined with the dichroism of the N–H band, may be taken as confirmation of Bunn and Garner's layer structure[43], and of the current interpretation of CH_2 frequencies. Tilting the specimen in the way described may, however, introduce errors into the dichroic measurement because the E vector will not always be vibrating in such a direction that the transmitted beam retains its plane polarized character.

CONCLUSION

It will be seen that a polarizing device can easily be fitted to an existing spectrometer to enable measurements to be made with plane polarized radiation, and that this need not involve any readjustment of the optical parts. Such measurements can be of great assistance in problems of molecular structure or in studying the physical configurations which flexible molecules may take up.

Although the examples given refer chiefly to high polymers, there is no doubt that valuable information could be obtained from an examination of simple compounds in the crystalline state. Fig. 14.12 shows the high dichroism which may be obtained in such compounds. The interpretation of crystalline spectra observed with polarized radiation, can however be very complicated in crystals of low symmetry.

REFERENCES

1. MERRITT, E. *Wied. Ann.* (1895) **55**, p. 49.
2. SCHAEFFER, C. and MATOSSI, F. 'Das Ultrarote Spektrum' (Berlin, 1930) Chap. 5.
3. BLAKE, R. P., MAKAS, A. S., and WEST, C. D. *J. Opt. Soc. Amer.* (1949) **39**, p. 1054.
4. PFUND, A. H. *Johns Hopkins Univers. Circ.* (1906) **4**, p. 13.
5. PROVOSTARE, M.F., de la and DESAINS, P. *Ann. Chim. Phys.* (1850) **30**, p. 159.
6. ELLIOTT, A., AMBROSE, E. J., and TEMPLE, R. B. *J. Opt. Soc. Amer.* (1948) **38**, p. 212.
7. NEWMAN, R. and HALFORD, R. S. *Rev. Sci. Inst.* (1948) **19**, p. 270.
8. ABBOTT, N. B. and ELLIOTT, A., *Proc. Roy. Soc. A.* (1956) **234**, p. 247.
9. CONN, G. K. T. and EATON, G. K., *J. Opt. Soc. Amer.* (1954) **44**, p. 553.
10. MANN, J. and THOMPSON, H. W. *Proc. Roy. Soc. A.* **192**, p. 489.
11. HOLLIDAY, P. *Nature* (1949) **163**, p. 602.
12. TORKINGTON, P. and THOMPSON, H. W. *Trans. Far. Soc.* (1945) **41**, p. 184.
13. ELLIOTT, A., AMBROSE, E. J., and TEMPLE, R. B. *J. Sci. Inst.* (1950) **27**, p. 21.
14. COATES, V. J., OFFNER, A and SEIGLER, E. H., *J. Opt. Soc. Amer.* (1953) **43**, p. 984.
15. FRASER, R. D. B., *Disc. Faraday Soc.* (1950) **9**, p. 378.
16. BLUNT, E. R., BIRD, G. R. and GREY, D. S. *J. Opt. Soc. Amer.* (1950) **40**, p. 304.
17. NORRIS, H. P., *J. Sci. Inst.* (1954) **31**, p. 284.
18. BLOUT, E. K. and ABBATE, M. J., *J. Opt. Soc. Amer.* (1955) **45**, p. 1028.
19. FORD, M. A., PRICE, W. C., SEEDS, W. E. and WILKINSON, G. R., *J. Opt. Soc. Amer.* (1958) **48**, p. 249.
20. HERZBERG, G. *Infra-red and Raman Spectra, New York* (1945).
21. KELLNER, L. *Nature* (1949) **163**, p. 877.
22. TOBIN, M. C. *J. Chem. Phys.* (1955) **23**, p. 891.
23. LIANG, C. Y., KRIMM, S. and SUTHERLAND, G. B. B. M., *J. Chem. Phys.* (1956) **25**, p. 543.
24. KRIMM, S., LIANG, C. Y. and SUTHERLAND, G. M. M. B., *J. Chem. Phys.* (1956) **25**, p. 549.
25. NIELSON, J. R. and WOOLLETT, A. H., *J. Chem. Phys.* (1957) **26**, p. 1391.
26. FRASER, R. D. P. and PRICE, W. C., *Nature* (1952) **170**, p. 490.
27. SANDEMAN, I., *Proc. Roy. Soc. A.* (1955) **232**, p. 105.

28. NEWMAN, R. and HALFORD, R. S., *J. Chem. Phys.* (1950) **18**, p. 1276.
29. AMBROSE, E. J., ELLIOTT, A., and TEMPLE, R. B. *Nature* (1949) **163**, p. 859.
30. AMBROSE, E. J. and ELLIOTT, A. *Proc. Roy. Soc.* A. (1951) **206,** 206.
31. BAMFORD, C. H., HANBY, W. E., and HAPPEY, F. *Proc. Roy. Soc., A.* (1951) **205**, p. 30.
32. AMBROSE, E. J. and ELLIOTT, A. *Proc. Roy. Soc., A.* (1951) **205**, p. 47.
33. HALVERSEN, F. and FRANCEL, R. J. *J. Chem. Phys.* (1949) **17**, p. 694.
34. SUTHERLAND, G. B. B. M. and VALLANCE JONES, A. *Trans. Far. Soc.*
35. GLATT, L., WEBBER, D. S., SEAMAN, C. and ELLIS, J. W. *J. Chem. Phys.* (1950) **18**, p. 413.
36. ELLIOTT, A., AMBROSE, E. J. and TEMPLE, R. B. *J. Chem. Phys.* (1948) **16**, p. 877.
37. CROOKES, D. A. *Nature* (1947) **160**, p. 17.
38. DARMON, S. E. and RUDALL, K. M. *Trans. Far. Soc.*
39. HERMANNS, P. H. and PLATZEK, P. *Kolloid Zeits* (1939) **88**, p. 68.
40. FRAZER, R. D. B., *J. Chem. Phys.* (1953) **21**, p. 1511.
41. BAMFORD, C. H., ELLIOTT, A. and HANBY, W. E. *Synthetic Polypeptides* (1956, Academic Press, New York), p. 409.
42. BEER, M., *Proc. Roy Soc. A.* (1956) **236**, p. 136.
43. BUNN, C. W. and GARNER, E. V. *Proc. Roy. Soc., A.* (1947) **189**, p. 39.
44. AMBROSE, E. J., ELLIOTT, A., and TEMPLE, R. B. *Proc. Roy. Soc., A.* (1949) **199**, p. 183.

INDEX

329